VNR Illustrated Guide to
POWER TOOLS

Rudolf F. Graf and
George J. Whalen

VNR **VAN NOSTRAND REINHOLD COMPANY**
New York Cincinnati Toronto London Melbourne

Copyright © 1978 by Graf-Whalen Corporation
Library of Congress Catalog Card Number 77-25869
ISBN 0-442-22801-5

Printed in United States of America
Designed by Loudan Enterprise
Unless otherwise indicated, line drawings rendered by
Michael Hernandez.

Published in 1978 by Van Nostrand Reinhold Company
A division of Litton Educational Publishing, Inc.
135 West 50th Street, New York, NY 10020, U.S.A.

Van Nostrand Reinhold Limited
1410 Birchmount Road
Scarborough, Ontario M1P 2E7, Canada

Van Nostrand Reinhold Australia Pty. Ltd.
17 Queen Street
Mitcham, Victoria 3132, Australia

Van Nostrand Reinhold Company Limited
Molly Millars Lane
Wokingham, Berkshire, England

16 15 14 13 12 11 10 9 8 7 6 5 4 3 2 1

Library of Congress Cataloging in Publication Data
Graf, Rudolf F.
    VNR illustrated guide to power tools.

    Includes Index.
    1. Power tools—Handbooks, manuals, etc.
I. Whalen, George J., joint author. II. Title.
TJ1195.G67   621.9   77-25869
ISBN 0-442-22801-5

Contents

Acknowledgments

Allis Chalmers Corp., Milwaukee, Wisconsin

Ambitech Industries, Inc., Westwood, New Jersey

Amerind-MacKissic, Inc., Parker Ford, Pennsylvania

Ariens Company, Brillion, Wisconsin

Bernzomatic Corporation, Rochester, New York

Black & Decker Mfg. Co., Towson, Maryland

Burgess Vibrocrafters, Inc., Grayslake, Illinois

Deere & Company, Moline, Illinois

Disston, Inc., Pittsburgh, Pennsylvania

Douglas Division, The Scott & Fetzer Company, Bronson, Michigan

Dremel Manufacturing, Div. of Emerson Electric Co., Racine, Wisconsin

Electro Engineering Products Co., Inc., Chicago, Illinois

Electromagnetic Industries, Inc., Subsidiary of Square D Co., Clearwater, Florida

Flotec, Inc., Norwalk, California

Gilson Brothers Company, Plymouth, Wisconsin

Homelite, Division of Textron, Inc., Charlotte, North Carolina

H. D. Hudson Manufacturing Company, Chicago, Illinois

Jacobsen Manufacturing Company, Racine, Wisconsin

Lambert Corporation, Dayton, Ohio

Leviton Manufacturing Company, Inc., Little Neck, New York

Little Giant Corp., Oklahoma City, Oklahoma

Maxi-Vac Manufacturing Company, Palatine, Illinois

McGraw-Edison Co., Portable Appliance and Tool Group, Columbia, Missouri

McGraw-Edison Co., Portable Electric Tools Division, Geneva, Illinois

McCulloch Corporation, Los Angeles, California

Millers Falls, an Ingersol Rand Tool Company, Greenfield, Massachusetts

Miracle Instrument Co., Palisades Park, New Jersey

Montgomery Ward, Chicago, Illinois

Pass & Seymour, Inc., Syracuse, New York

Radio Shack, Div. of Tandy Corp., Fort Worth, Texas

Rockwell International Power Tool Division, Memphis, Tennessee

Simer Pump Company, Minneapolis, Minnesota

Simplicity Manufacturing Company, Inc., Port Washington, Wisconsin

Skil Corporation, Chicago, Illinois

Square D Company, Lexington, Kentucky

Stanley Power Tools, Div. of the Stanley Works, New Britain, Connecticut

The Toro Company, Consumer Products Div., Minneapolis, Minnesota

Triway Manufacturing, Inc., Winch Division, Marysville, Washington

Ungar, Division of Eldon Industries, Inc., Compton, California

USM Corporation, Consumer Products Div., Reading, Pennsylvania

Wahl Clipper Corporation, Sterling, Illinois

Weed Eaters, Inc., Houston, Texas

Weller-Xcelite Electronics Div., The Cooper Group, Apex, North Carolina

Preface

A revolution is often regarded as finished when it has only just begun. History books describe the Industrial Revolution as something that happened between 1750 and 1850. But that was just the beginning. Man, previously limited by crude hand tools and implements powered by his own muscle or that of animals, then began discovering that other kinds of energy could power his tools—first falling water . . . then steam . . . then gasoline . . . and, finally, electricity. The successful harnessing of power sources to tools began the revolution that continues today.

What revolution? Why, the explosive growth of powered tools for the home, shop, lawn, and garden! Never before has such a fascinating array of gas- and electric-powered tools been available to the homeowner, do-it-yourselfer, gardener, and craftsman. Pick up a magazine . . . thumb through a catalog . . . browse in a hardware or garden shop. For just about every task you can think of, there's a power tool to help you do it!

Have you found yourself drawn toward buying a power tool, but do you lack the know-how necessary to handle it confidently and keep it in shape? Are you curious about the way it works, whether it's worth the price in terms of what it can do for you? Or, do you, like so many of us, already own a fair number of under-used tools that lie idle for long periods? Chances are you bought each for just *one* kind of job. Wouldn't you like to know how every one of your tool investments can pay you back again and again by easing your work in home, shop, and garden jobs?

The answers you're looking for are in this book. In its pages you'll find everything you want and need to know about every up-to-date convenience that's come our way thanks to the power tool revolution. Spend a few minutes skimming its contents. Concise, fact-filled text is backed up by easy-to-understand photos and drawings for each tool. In just minutes you can become familiar with a tool's basic parts, inner workings, and major uses. Then go on to the "how-to" details—the secrets that help make you an expert in knowledge of the tool's strengths. Captions covering important "extras" are scattered throughout the text—all designed to round out your power tool know-how.

Every detail in this book has been gathered from power tool experts—the people behind the continuing power tool revolution, whose engineering talent and problem-solving ability is placing so many different and useful devices within easy reach of our waiting hands.

We are indebted to our many friends throughout the industry for sharing with us the hundreds of inside tips that often don't appear in the instruction booklets.

After reading through this book, we're sure you'll agree that there's no job that can defy the right power tool in the hands of a knowledgeable user!

Rudolf F. Graf & George J. Whalen
New Rochelle, New York

1

Portable Electric Drills

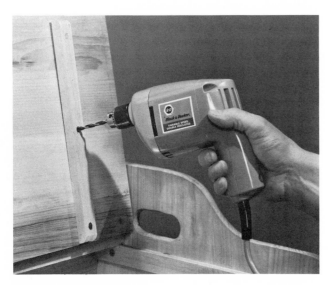

Figure 1-1. Portable electric drill. Photograph courtesy of Black and Decker Mfg. Co.

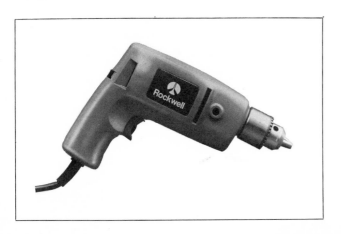

The need to make holes in things is as old as mankind; and that need is growing, judging by the fast pace of portable electric-drill sales. Modern drills can tackle wood, metal, concrete, and masonry with equal ease. In addition, they serve as portable drive units for rotary accessories, such as grinding wheels, wire brushes, sanding discs, buffing wheels, saws, screwdrivers, and even paint stirrers!

WHAT'S AVAILABLE

Drills come in three common sizes, according to chuck capacity—1/4 inch, 3/8 inch, and 1/2 inch. This simply means that the chuck (the drill part that holds the shank) can accommodate bits and accessories with up to that diameter shank. Generally, chuck capacity is a good measure of drill power: 1/4-inch drills tend to be light duty, 3/8-inch means a medium-duty drill, and 1/2-inch types are workhorses.

One-Quarter-Inch Drills

A standard for general work around the home and shop, the 1/4-inch drill is compact and lightweight. It's good for drilling sheet metal, plastic, wood, and other materials, as long as they're not too thick or too hard (few can handle more than 1/4-inch-thick mild steel or 1/2-inch-thick hardwood without overheating). Most have only a single-stage reduction-gear set, so the chuck spins at high speed (2,000 rpm and more). Usually powered by a 1/7-horsepower motor, the drill lacks the *torque* (twisting power at the chuck) and stamina of huskier models, but is a capable, comfortable performer when used within its limitations.

Figure 1-2. Light, fast, easy to use, the 1/4-inch drill is the first tool to reach for when you need a compact, but versatile, boring tool. Photograph courtesy of Power Tool Division, Rockwell International.

Three-Eighth-Inch Drills

This is a good all-around choice for a first drill. Most feature 1/2-horsepower motors and *two* stages of reduction gearing between motor shaft and chuck. This means much more torque, which lets you bear down on the drill with little change in speed. Slower than the 1/4-inch drill, most 3/8-inch types have a top speed of 1,000 rpm. This means easier hole starting (the drill won't tend to "walk") and better biting in thick, hard materials. As a rule, 3/8-inch drills handle more attachments than their 1/4-inch cousins and can perform most of the jobs a quarter-incher does. About the only jobs that might require a 1/4-inch drill's higher speed are finishing-sanding jobs and buffing jobs. So, if you have to choose between power and speed, choose *power*. It might take a bit longer to get through some jobs and the results may not be quite so smooth as with a high-speed 1/4-inch drill, but the slower-speed 3/8-inch drill is far less apt to burn out in your hands if you hit an unexpected knot.

One-Half-Inch Drills

Generally used by service tradesmen, the high torque and slow speed of the 1/2-inch drill (usually about 600 rpm, tops) makes drilling large holes in wood or metal quite effortless. Definitely for brute jobs, such as drilling pipe holes through studs and making large anchor holes in masonry, the half-incher works hard and well for a living; but it can be clumsy and muscle-bound when you need a drill with a lighter touch and a smoother finish. Choose this hefty performer if all your jobs are big ones or if you can afford to round out its capabilities with a 1/4-inch or 3/8-inch drill.

HOW THEY WORK

Power is applied through the trigger switch or speed control to a universal (series-wound) motor, easily identified by its copper-sectioned commutator and two carbon brushes. The motor shaft spins on bearings, turning an impeller fan that blows cool air over the motor windings. The tip of the same shaft is a small pinion gear that meshes with a large-diameter compound spur gear that turns more slowly. The output half of the compound gear engages a large-diameter gear on the end of a shaft that turns the Jacobs chuck. This two-stage, reduction-gear drive trades speed for torque—the high-speed, low-torque input of the motor is thus converted to a high-torque chuck output, at a tenfold lower speed.

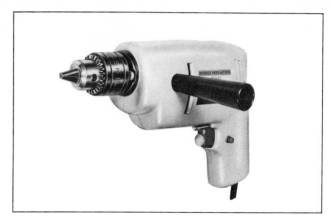

Figure 1-3. SKIL MODEL 457 DOUBLE INSULATED ADJUSTABLE DRIVE-R-DRILL®. The medium-weight contender in the power drill field, the 3/8-inch drill runs at lower speed than lightweights, but delivers more forceful turning power to cut through thicker, harder materials. Photograph courtesy of Skil Corporation.

Figure 1-4. SKILL MODEL 600 EXTRA-TOOL®. Top of the line in size, weight, and torque, the 1/2-inch drill delivers real power to the workpiece for smooth going in the toughest materials. This model features drilling, hammering, and chisel functions, as well. Photograph courtesy of Skil Corporation.

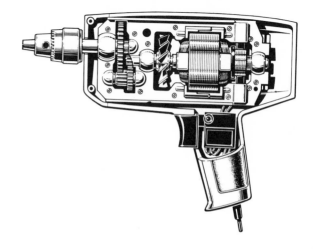

Figure 1-5. Internal construction of a modern electric drill. Technical artwork prepared by Peter Trojan.

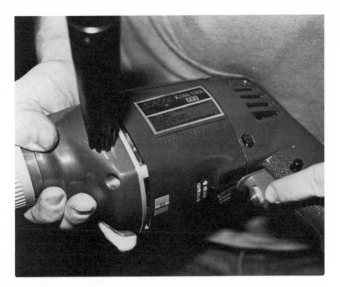

Figure 1-6. Variable-speed trigger control is an electronic device that tailors speed of the drill to the pressure your finger applies. The silver knob is a stop that lets you preset top speed. A locking button on the handle holds trigger in the "on" position to relieve finger strain. A flip lever in front of the trigger control allows you to drive the drill chuck in a forward direction or in reverse, to back a jammed bit out of a tight hole. GRAF-WHALEN photograph.

Figure 1-7. A nonconductive housing and built-in insulators that keep the drill's metal parts safely isolated from the motor add up to *double insulation*, a safety feature now offered in most modern drills. GRAF-WHALEN photograph.

IMPORTANT FEATURES TO LOOK FOR
Variable-Speed Trigger Control
Available on all size drills, this electronic power controller replaces the drill's ON/OFF switch. The speed you get depends upon how far back you pull the trigger. In most, a knob lets you preset the trigger, so you don't have to rely on finger pressure. This simplifies hole starts and lets you drill at low or high speeds without robbing torque.

Reversible-Drive Switch
Ever jam a drill bit in a thick stud? With a drill equipped with reversible drive, just flip a switch, squeeze the trigger, and the chuck turns in reverse, backing the bit out of the hole with ease. It's very handy for backing out screws, too.

Double Insulation
This places a nonconductive plastic housing between you and the drill's electric motor *and* isolates the motor from the metal chuck by use of a nonmetallic part in the drive system. Result? The power gets to the motor, but there's no way it can get to you (unless you open up the housing and touch things you shouldn't!).

TIPS ON USING YOUR DRILL ACCESSORIES
Twist Drills
"Drill bits" available today will cut holes from .0135 inch to 1 inch in diameter. Of course, the shank size of a larger bit must match the chuck capacity of your drill (bits are available with shanks turned down to 1/4 inch or 3/8 inch), but it is the hole diameter and material hardness that determine your chances of drilling success. A large bit in a light-duty drill may stall the motor if the going gets tough. Here the "torquier" output of larger drills is a definite advantage, and a 1/2-inch bit with a 1/4-inch shank is decidedly more potent in a drill of 1/2-inch chuck capacity than in a 1/4-inch drill.

Twist drills come in three types—*carbon steel* for soft materials like wood or plastic, *high-speed steel* for soft materials *and* metals, and *carbide-tipped* for concrete and masonry drilling. Most bits come with a "split-point" tip. These start their own holes without walking around on the work. Good practice, however, is to drill a small "pilot" hole before tackling a large-diameter hole. The larger bit then simply follows the path blazed by the smaller bit, and drilling time is greatly reduced.

When bits grow dull replace them, unless you can afford a bit sharpener, which grinds new cutting surfaces on the twist drill at the critical angle required for clean drilling. See chapter 3 for more information about drill-bit sharpeners.

Figure 1-8. Wood-boring bits and twist drills are the basic cutting pieces used in today's drills. For additional details, see chapter 3 on drill-bit sharpeners. GRAF-WHALEN photograph.

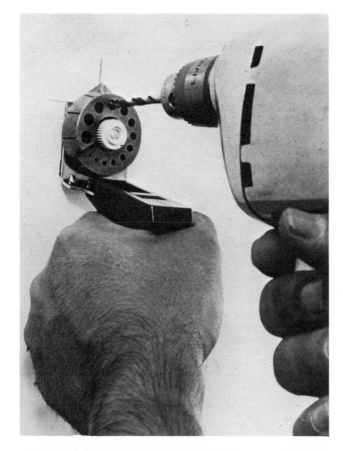

Figure 1-9. A drill guide is a handy accessory when you must keep the bit perfectly straight. The guide is simply a rotary cylinder that is bored with clearance holes for most common twist-drill sizes, secured to a pistol-grip holder. This simple, but effective, accessory can make every hole you drill straight and true. GRAF-WHALEN photograph.

Wire Wheels

Handy for removing rust, scale, and for rough-polishing metal, the drill-powered wire wheel can be hand-held or stand-mounted. Eye protection should be used with this accessory.

Sandpaper Discs

A rubber disc with a central shank and attaching screw that can hold a sandpaper disc converts your drill into a *rotary sander*. Ideal for furniture stripping and general sanding, this handy accessory accommodates sandpaper and emery discs of any texture and abrasion.

Figure 1-10. The drill-driven wire brush gobbles up rust and scale on wrought iron, leaving the surface ready for finishing in just a matter of minutes. Photograph courtesy of Black & Decker Mfg. Co.

Figure 1-11. Some drills like this SKIL XTRA-TOOL® have "built-in" accessory features. A rotary ring allows you to select normal drill (or screwdriver-bit) drive, a combination action of drilling plus sharp hammerlike blows (ideal for penetrating tough masonry), or a hammer-and-chisel action. GRAF-WHALEN photograph.

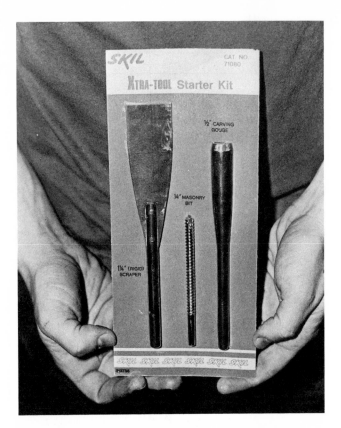

Grinding Wheels

Need a tool to sharpen scissors, hedge clippers, knives, and pruning forks? The Carborundum® wheel with a central shank mounted on a horizontal drill stand makes a very nice bench grinder out of your drill. Eye protection is essential and high speeds should be avoided.

Buffing Wheels

Hard felt, wool, and pile buffing wheels extend your drill's usefulness by bringing out the sheen on metal and painted surfaces. A lamb's wool pad slips over the hard rubber disc used in sanding and makes your drill an ideal arm saver when waxing your car to a diamond-hard finish. Chrome, silver, and newly painted surfaces buff up to pleasing brilliance with just a few passes of a pile wheel.

Figure 1-12. Accessories for the XTRA-TOOL® include a scraper that easily removes paint and scale, a masonry bit, and a carving gouge for grooving work. These expand the basic capability of the tool beyond its useful drilling versatility. GRAF-WHALEN photograph.

Figure 1-13 a, b, and c. With proper bit selection and careful speed control, the modern drill can handle tile, glass, and masonry or brick-drilling jobs. Photographs courtesy of Skil Corporation.

a

b

c

  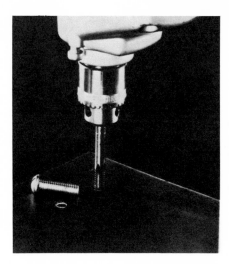

a   b

Figure 1-14 a, b, and c. For metal-drilling and -tapping, a well-balanced
drill with electronic speed control is your very best choice. Photographs
courtesy of Skil Corporation.

Figure 1-15. For drilling in tight spots and around corners, consider
this right-angle drive head. It takes the place of the standard drill
chuck and lets you reach into spots that would be impossible to reach
with an ordinary drill. GRAF-WHALEN photograph.

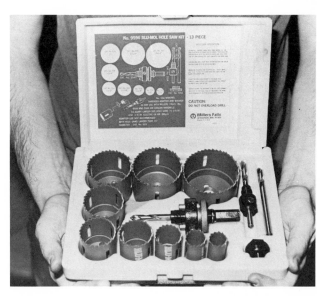

Figure 1-16. Hole saws make circle-cutting almost a pleasure. The
center drill holder accepts screw-on blades, and your electric drill
supplies the force to cut a perfect circle every time. GRAF-WHALEN
photograph.

Circular and Jigsaws

If you're paneling the playroom or cutting the pieces for your wife's new sewing center, these accessories make worthwhile additions to your tool arsenal. The circular saw is useful for straight-cutting or ripping in wood up to 3/8 inch thick. Cutting is a two-handed operation, with the drill handle upright and at a right angle to the cut. With the jigsaw accessory, cuts can be made along curves, into sharp angles, and around complex scroll-work.

TIPS AND TECHNIQUES FOR USING YOUR DRILL

First and foremost: *Match the drill and accessory to the job!* Be aware of your drill's capabilities and limitations. A 1/4-inch drill is failure prone in tasks requiring repeated drilling of deep holes in hard materials or where you have to "lean" on the drill to bite into the work. Any job that causes the drill to labor will surely cause it to heat up.

Figure 1-17. A "flying chuck key" can cause injury if the key is accidentally left in the drill chuck when power is applied. This danger can be eliminated through the use of a new type of safety self-ejecting key made by Miracle Instrument Company, 248 Broad Avenue, Palisades Park, New Jersey 07650. The new Miracle key features a patented, spring-loaded ejection device, which prevents the key from remaining in position after the chuck has been tightened and pressure on the key has been released. This is a worthwhile safety addition to the accessories you use with your electric drill. Photograph courtesy of Miracle Instrument Company.

Take this as a sign that your drill isn't equipped for such hard work. Excessive heating can ruin a drill or subject you to hazards from jerky operation.

Also, just because a bit or accessory shank fits the chuck of your drill, don't automatically assume that it's right for any job that comes along. Accessory manufacturers try for the widest market and don't always consider that their part may come between the weakest drill and the toughest job. A drill that stalls in driving an accessory is probably not up to the job. You may be better off in buying a larger drill to upgrade your work capacity than in chancing the risk of ruining your *only* drill!

Firm support is essential in any drilling or accessory task. Most 3/8-inch and 1/2-inch drills offer screw-in side handles so you can augment the pistol-grip hold of one hand with the steadying grip of the other. Two hands are better than one in most drilling operations, and just as important is the need to clamp down the piece being drilled, or worked, if both your hands are occupied. Remember that a 3/8-inch or 1/2-inch drill has enough torque to whip the workpiece about if it snags or to violently twist the tool out of your hands. Sheet metal that "grabs" on the drill bit can become a deadly, whirling knife. Solid clamp support of the workpiece and a firm grip on the drill are your best insurance against trouble.

Holes in wood and metal can be made with the same twist drills. In thick stock there is considerable friction, and the wood waste does not easily pass up the drill flutes. Carbon drills may overheat unless pulled out frequently to clear chips from the flutes.

To start a hole accurately, make an indentation with a punch or even an ordinary nail. However, the drill may drift from a hard section to a softer or run along a grain line in the wood. Where hole location is critical, it's a good idea to lay it out with cross lines, punch marking the intersection, and then to inspect the depression made by the drill before it has fully entered. The cross marks will show up any shift, even though the drill has obliterated the original punch mark.

Take it easy when using tungsten-carbide drill bits. The tips of these extra-hard bits can shatter. Don't ram the drill into the hole like a chisel. This only chips the cutting edge and beats up the drill's bearings. Just keep steady pressure on the drill and pause frequently to clear concrete or masonry chips from the hole. An occasional water flush will remove debris from the hole and leave a lubricating water film on the hole surfaces.

2

Bench-Top Drill Presses

Hand-held drills have decided limitations where hole size, shape, and position tolerances are tight. Human hands and arms are pretty poor supports for a drill. There's no way to tell if the bit is exactly perpendicular to the workpiece, so some holes that start straight wind up at an angle through the workpiece. In sheet metal, this

Figure 2-1. Bench-top drill press. GRAF-WHALEN photograph.

may only mean a slightly oval hole that will still accept a fastener; but, where the workpiece is thick, a slanting hole won't pass the fastener or will ruin the alignment accuracy of the joined parts. What's more, when hand-drilling on tough surfaces, it's easy for the bit to "creep" or "walk" from the intended hole position. This results in a marred surface and, probably, a hole where you didn't want it. Finally, there's the problem of the small work-piece. You need three hands to accurately drill a small piece with even moderate accuracy. In most cases, the two-handed results are less than satisfactory. Where drilling accuracy is a real requirement, you should consider a drill press.

WHAT'S AVAILABLE

Drill presses come in a varied range of sizes and capabilities that includes at its extremes the exquisite (but costly), stand-up, professional models used in high-precision factory work, as well as the models meant for bench-top use by people who need accuracy in drilling at an affordable price. The popular bench-top versions all consist of a heavy metal base (or *table*), with a vertically rising *column* (usually a heavy-walled, smooth tube), on which the *drill head* is supported. The head mounts a motor and drive system that turns a *chuck*, which accepts the bit (or other accessory). The head is arranged so that it can be adjusted in height on the column and so that it can be moved side to side, as needed, while remaining per-pendicular to the workpiece. The drill head also contains a *depth gauge*—two adjustable nuts which set the limit of up-down travel of the head when the *feed adjustment* lever is operated. This latter adjustment is usually a lever on the side of the head. When pressed, it moves the drill head down, so that the bit engages the workpiece on the table at a perfect right angle. Pressing the feed lever pro-vides the pressure needed for the rotating bit to enter and bore a smooth, round hole in the workpiece to the depth preset on the depth gauge. When the lever is released, the head rises through spring tension, backing the bit out of the workpiece hole, smoothly and accurately.

At all times, the bit is maintained perpendicular to the workpiece by the fixed relationship of the column and the table. This means that the drilled hole will be precisely straight, round, and true in all dimensions and that the hole position is the same as the point at which the bit first engaged the work, without "walking" or "creeping."

In some more-costly bench-top models, the motor sits astride the rear of the head, driving the chuck through a belt-and-pulley system. To vary speed in such a system, the belt is slipped from one step to another on a cone pulley fitted to the motor shaft. (Large-diameter step gives high speed; small-diameter step gives slow speed.) Other models use a built-in motor with electronic speed control. In these, the power to the motor is variable and precisely regulated, so that drill speed can be selected by a dial, instead of by mechanically shifting a drive belt on a pulley. This latter type is mechanically simpler and more convenient in the home workshop, where ease of operation and light-to-moderate drilling demands are the usual case.

IMPORTANT FEATURES TO LOOK FOR
Rugged Construction
To realize the accuracy possible from the use of a drill press there must be enough substance in its parts to stand up to rough use—a natural consequence of its operation. Look for a heavy, cast or forged table (base), milled flat and arranged to securely accept the column. The column should be a thick-walled tube which cannot be easily deformed, nor should its fit in the base be dependent on a fastener to take up "slack" and maintain alignment accuracy. The drill head should be high-impact plastic or metal construction, with a solid mechanical support for the chuck. This will ensure that the bit position remains true, even when the head is subjected to deforming pressure, as the bit engages the workpiece.

Three-Point Chuck
A three-point chuck is optimum for maintaining concentricity of the bit. Two-piece chucks may allow the bit to be positioned off center with consequent misalignment of the hole. A positive method of chuck-key storage with safety interlocking is a decided safety plus. This will prevent drill start-up with the chuck key in the chuck—a situation which can lead to serious injury.

Ease of Adjustment
It should be possible to make all adjustments without tools. Also, speed of drilling that is set by a dial, rather than a belt-and-pulley adjustment, is a favorable point.

Security of Mounting
Three, or preferably, four bench-top mounting feet on the drill-press base will ensure a rigid support for the tool with improved accuracy. Heavy bolts secure these feet to the bench surface.

Smoothness of Operation
It should be possible to make all adjustments without unnecessarily strong-arming the drill press.

Repeatability of Settings
It should be possible for you to drill duplicated holes with comparative ease. All adjustments should allow you to re-establish conditions without undue effort, so that holes can be drilled without making each an individual setup job.

TIPS FOR USING YOUR DRILL PRESS
Drill Bit and Speed Selection
The drill press can accommodate a range of accessories like those used in portable drills (see figure 1-12). For actual drilling operations, a bit that is of appropriate size and hardness for boring into the workpiece material should be selected. Similarly, the motor speed should be preset so that heating at the cutting edge is held to a minimum. For cutting soft materials (aluminum, brass, copper, etc.), small twist drill-bits (to 1/4 inch) can be run at a speed of 5,000 rpm; however, larger holes (to 1/2 inch) demand reduced speed in the vicinity of 2,000 rpm because of their greater frictional surface area. Harder materials (cast iron, mild steel, hard steel, etc.) require slower cutting speeds. With twist drills of up to 1/4 inch, speeds of 700 to 1,200 rpm may be appropriate. However, larger holes (up to 1/2 inch) require really slow cutting speeds of 350 to 600 rpm. What's more, it may be advisable to use a cutting fluid (such as soluble oil or mineral oil) to carry away heat and to lubricate the surface between drill bit and workpiece.

Wood-boring bits cut best in the range of 1,000 to 1,500 rpm. However, twist drills used for wood-drilling can be run at 5,000 rpm (up to 1/4-inch holes), 3,000 rpm (up to 1/2-inch holes), and between 2,000 rpm and 500 rpm for holes progressing in size from 1/2-inch to greater than 1-inch diameter.

The selected drill bit should be inspected before installing it in the chuck to be sure that its shank is not burred or deformed. (If it is, it will not run true and the hole will be misshapened.) With power off, insert the drill bit into the chuck and hand tighten the chuck, while turning the bit slightly in the chuck jaws to be sure it centers up. Snug the chuck with the chuck key. (Be sure to remove the key from the chuck!) Apply power for an instant, and check that the bit is spinning straight and true in the chuck. Turn power off.

Sizing to the Work

Adjust the drill head to the size of the workpiece and the location of the hole. (In some models, the drill table can be raised or lowered for this purpose. With others, the head is adjusted on the column.) If a scrap backup piece is being placed below the workpiece, be sure to take this into consideration when sizing to the work.

Depth of Cut

To set the maximum downward travel of the bit's cutting edge, place the workpiece behind the bit and pull the feed lever downward, lowering the bit. Now, adjust the two nuts in the drill head until the maximum downward travel equals the desired depth of cut in the workpiece. When the feed lever is next pulled, the rotating bit will be stopped at this depth in the workpiece. (You may also want to set depth of cut for the bit's penetration beyond the workpiece, so as not to risk striking the metal table surface by drilling through the backup board.)

Motor Speed

Select an appropriate speed before commencing drilling. (In models having electronic speed control, you may want to note the reference dial-number settings at which best results are obtained in cutting different materials.)

Clamping the Work

You should immobilize the workpiece with clamps, just on the chance that the drill bit will bind and whip the work violently around. Small workpieces can be held in a special vise that fits to the grooves of the table.

Feeding

With power on and the speed selected, activate the feed adjustment lever to bring the bit into contact with the workpiece at the point marked for drilling. Note the "feel" of the bit as it cuts, and do not apply excess pressure to the feed lever, as its mechanical advantage may be great enough to snap a small bit against the work. The finest

Figure 2-2. The bit should be fitted to the chuck with care to ensure that it is centered before the chuck is tightened. GRAF-WHALEN photograph.

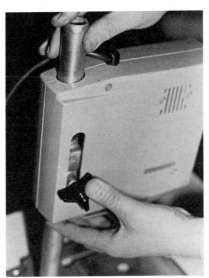

Figure 2-3. Drill head position on the column is manually adjusted and locked with a clamp knob. GRAF-WHALEN photograph.

Figure 2-4. Depth-of-cut adjustment is set by two opposing nuts. These determine how far down the spinning bit can travel when feed lever is pulled down. GRAF-WHALEN photograph.

holes are made where the bit does the cutting, backed by the least possible effort of your arm. Smooth feed, easy back-out, and a sturdily secured workpiece will produce accurate hole-cutting to fine tolerances.

RULES FOR SAFE USE

As in all cutting operations, eye protection should be worn whenever the drill press is used. Similarly, your hands should always be well clear of the path of the bit, so as to prevent injury should a bit shatter under pressure. Be sure that the chuck key is removed from the chuck before applying power! (The Shopmate model illustrated includes an ingenious chuck-storage interlock that won't let you turn power on until the key is safely stowed in a niche aside the drill head.)

DRILL PRESS MAINTENANCE

The maintenance steps which apply to the bench-top drill press are similar in scope to those for the portable electric drill. (See chapter 1.) Keep the press free of dust and cutting chips, and be sure that the motor gets adequate ventilation. In belt-driven models, periodically inspect the belt for signs of wear and fraying that could lead to early failure.

Figure 2-5. The clever mechanical interlock in this Shopmate drill press requires that you safely stow the chuck key in a recessed space or the power switch won't turn on. The key can't be removed while power is switched on either. With this feature, you run no risk of injury from a thrown chuck key that has been carelessly left in the chuck. GRAF-WHALEN photograph.

3

Drill-Bit Sharpeners

There's nothing worse than a collection of dull drill bits. You may have paid a bundle for them and they may have given you good service, but without their cutting edge, they're useless. You know this, but somehow you can't bring yourself to throw them away either. Chances are you're better off making an investment in a drill-bit sharpener—an electrically powered tool for your workbench that can put a keen cutting edge on any twist drill-bit from 1/8 to 3/8 inch, other than carbide-tipped bits. Like a pencil sharpener, it can point up the bit you need and restore its cutting edge in just seconds. And that means you'll drill clean, exact holes, with less wear and tear on your drills, your nerves, and your home projects. It also means that you can save money on bits you won't have to buy, because you'll be recycling the bits you've invested in.

Some people may argue that they can dress up a dull drill bit on a bench grinder, and so they don't need a sharpener. To an extent, that's true. With patience and a nearly superhuman steadiness of hand, you *can* shape up a bit, given lots of time. But a sharpener gives top results in just a few seconds—every time. And so, it's best to save your grinder for other tasks, while using a sharpener to keen up bits when you really need help in a hurry—in the middle of a project.

The modern twist drill-bit is a precision cutting tool that can cut through both wood and metal. Commencing from the *shank* (the smooth-surfaced end that is clamped by the drill's chuck), the bit is cut in an ascending spiral that terminates in a point formed by two precisely angled, chisel-edged surfaces. The spiral cut is called the *flute*, and its ascending rise is called the *helix angle*. The point formed by the two chisel-edged ends of the flute is at the exact center of the bit and is essential to good starting on a hard surface, without "walking." The actual cutting is done by the sharpened *cutting lips* of the chisel surfaces, as the drill bit cuts into the work. The *chip* removed from the workpiece rises into the *web* of the flute and is carried backward, toward the drill, as the flute penetrates into the workpiece. Thus, the bit combines the essentials for centering up the hole, efficiently cutting material and carrying material up and out of the hole, so that it does not interfere with the cutting action.

Figure 3-1. Drill-bit sharpener. Photograph **courtesy of** Black & Decker Mfg. Co.

17

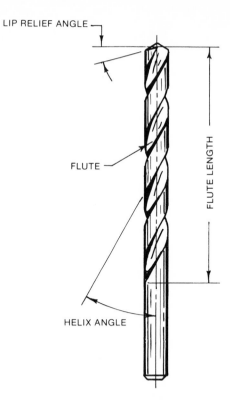

LIP RELIEF ANGLE

FLUTE

FLUTE LENGTH

HELIX ANGLE

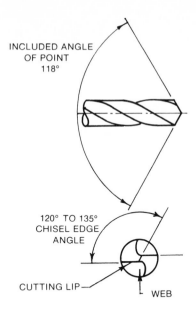

INCLUDED ANGLE
OF POINT
118°

120° TO 135°
CHISEL EDGE
ANGLE

CUTTING LIP

WEB

Figure 3-2. A primary requirement for drilling accurately sized holes is that there be minimal difference between the tip heights of the two flutes. Variations in the two lip heights will alter the centrality of the point, which will produce eccentric drilling.

When a bit goes dull, the point wears down and the chisel edges lose their keenness. This causes the bit to spin in the workpiece, without cutting, or to walk from the desired hole location, marring the surface of the workpiece. To regain effective cutting action, the *lip-relief angle* of the cutting edge must be restored, while the cutting lips are given a new, sharp edge. This is the function of the drill-bit sharpener.

HOW THEY WORK

The bit sharpener consists of an abrasive grinding wheel that is precisely shaped to grind the tip of the drill bit at a fixed angle (usually 118 degrees). The wheel is rotated by an electric motor within a housing topped by a head. The head has a series of predrilled clearance holes of small to large diameter, positioned in a circle that is sized to correspond with the grinding-edge bevel of the abrasive wheel below. By inserting a bit through the appropriate-size hole, turning it so that its chisel edge falls on the wheel, and applying power, it is possible to quickly grind the bit to the required angle and sharpness. By turning off power and rotating the bit 180 degrees, the action can be repeated to grind the opposite bit face. In this way, point, edges, and lip relief of the bit are promptly restored.

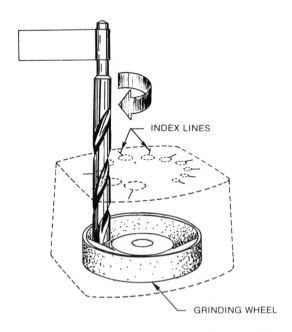

INDEX LINES

GRINDING WHEEL

Figure 3-3. The grinding wheel face is angled to match that of drill end. Wheel refaces one cutting lip at a time.

TIPS FOR USING YOUR DRILL-BIT SHARPENER

It takes far more time to tell how to use the sharpener than it does to actually use it. To begin, affix a piece of tape to the shank end of the dull bit to form a flag. (Once the point end of the bit is inserted into the sharpener, the flag will serve to tell you which way the bit is oriented.) Turn the adjustment knob of the sharpener to a vertical position. Next, insert the bit in the sharpener's head into the smallest hole in which it will fit. Push the bit downward and rotate it until the bit's chisel edge seats against the grinding wheel surface. While maintaining slight downward pressure on the bit, depress the power switch of the sharpener (hold for 2 seconds with small bits, 3 to 4 seconds for large bits). Release the power switch. Lift the bit and turn it within the head until the flag lies 180 degrees opposite its former position. Lower the bit and feel for the seating position of the bit's second chisel edge against the grinding wheel. Press down slightly and apply power for the same time as earlier to sharpen this second edge. Remove power and withdraw the sharpened bit. It should now have two well-defined chisel edges with a centered point. The metal surface should be silvery in color without any blue tint. If the tip is bluish, the grinding wheel has overheated it and the tip's cutting edge is "soft." You should repeat the sharpening operation, applying less downward pressure on the bit. Also, try quenching the bit in a water bath immediately after sharpening each edge.

If, on inspection, the bit's point is off center, chances are you've ground one chisel edge more than the other. Correct this by resharpening for equal chisel surfaces.

Small bits require few repetitions of the sharpening cycle. Larger bits require more work. As the bit shapes up, however, inspect it to be sure that the cutting edge of each chisel surface is riding slightly above the trailing edge, at an angle between 45 and 60 degrees. If the angle is too low or too high, the bit will cut poorly. To offset this problem, reset the adjusting knob counterclockwise by 1/8 inch, if cutting edge is too far above trailing edge; make a similar clockwise adjustment if cutting edge is too far below the trailing edge, and resharpen.

When the finished bit tip has a silvery color, centered point, and cutting edge slightly above the trailing edge, you have a sharp bit that's every way as good as a brand-new, factory-sharp bit, ready to cut through any material within its hardness range. And, if the worst happens and you dull the bit, there's little reason to worry. You can resharpen it and be back at work in a few minutes . . . if you have a drill-bit sharpener.

RULES FOR SAFE USE

● For safe electrical use in a garage or basement, a bit sharpener should be of double-insulated design. Even then, a ground-fault interrupter (gfi) outlet is a sensible precaution for operation of the sharpener, because it will instantly shut off power should a failure that threatens electrical shock occur.

● Place the sharpener on a flat, uncluttered bench surface, where it won't be easily knocked over or otherwise abused. (Cluttered work areas and crowded benches invite accidents.)

● For your own protection, wear safety glasses. They cost little, and they protect your precious sight against the chance that stray filings or abrasive dust will inflict injury.

● Do not operate the sharpener in gaseous or explosive atmospheres. Motors in these tools normally spark, and the sparks might ignite fumes.

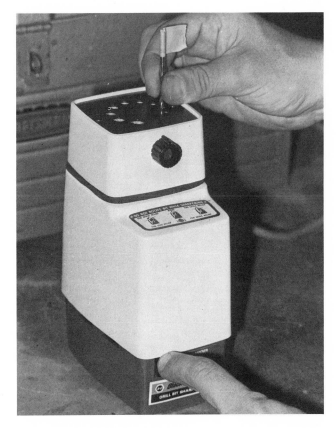

Figure 3-4. Push the bit downward and rotate it clockwise until it stops. Lean bit toward index line at the outside edge of the hole. This is the proper sharpening position. Do not rotate bit while sharpening. GRAF-WHALEN photograph.

4

Electric Engraving Tools

There was a time when electric pencils were found only in the hands of jewelers skilled in engraving syrupy sentiments on rings and charm bracelets. That was in the leisurely days when most homes had but a single door lock and when "ripped off" meant only that something had been torn!

Today, a "rip-off" occurs every 15 seconds in the United States. Burglaries by pros and drug-hungry amateurs account for losses of 300 million dollars annually in New York City alone. In light of these unsettling statistics, the electric pencil has assumed a new, crime-deterrent role in antitheft campaigns across the country.

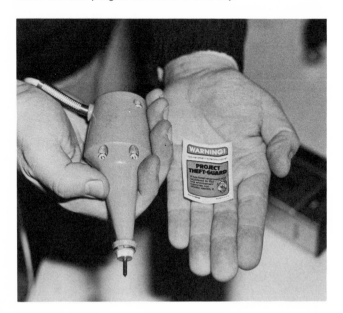

Figure 4-1. Some engraving tools come with special decals that can be affixed outside any premise that contains engraved items. GRAF-WHALEN photograph.

The plan is simple and successful: A homeowner uses an electric pencil to engrave identifying numbers on valuables, and furnishes a list of these numbers to the police. Prominent signs around the home then warn the would-be thief that all valuables are permanently marked for easy identification. Goods have to be anonymous to be cash worthy, so few thieves will risk being caught with easily traced loot. They pass up protected homes for easier, unmarked pickings elsewhere. The pencil engraver is so named simply because it is held in one hand like a pencil. Rather than using the rotary action associated with jeweler and wood-carving tools, these clever little machines have tough tips, which impact a surface at 7,200 strokes a minute. They produce a series of dots that look like a line to the naked eye. The width of the line is determined by the depth of the stroke, which is adjustable.

The pencil engraver, with a solid carbide or tungsten-carbide tip, can mark steel, glass, plastic, wood, stone, ceramic, brass, aluminum, copper, iron, pewter, silver—in fact, just about any household surface. Thus, the range of objects which one might choose to engrave, whether to prevent loss through theft or loss through negligent borrowing, is just about limitless. Included are power tools, toys, sporting goods, firearms, garden tools, jewelry, cameras, lawn mowers, radios, and televisions. Homeowners have also been using the engravers for such varied projects as identifying house keys or marking metal storm windows and screens with proper room locations to make installation and storage easier.

The pencil engraver also has craft uses. Because it is used like a pencil, little practice is required before you can confidently write your name or draw a design on a gift cigarette lighter, tray glass, or what have you. There's no need to press down on the engraver; just move the hand slowly and evenly and let the vibrating point do the work.

HOW THEY WORK

All electric pencils get their motive power from the 60 cycle-per-second, alternating-current power line. A simple vibrator motor converts the varying current flow through the motor's single winding into 7,200 mechanical tapping strokes per minute. Each tap strikes the end of a long steel rod, tipped with a tungsten-carbide cutting point. A spring, girdling the rod, gives with each tap, but pushes the rod back up to meet the motor tapper between strokes. Actual stroke motion of the rod is slight, but the tough carbide point is only a few mils in circumference. Thus, indenting force is focused on but a tiny area, producing the equivalent of hundred-pound-per-square-inch blows.

The special vibrator motor has an E-shaped core of silicon steel, drilled through lengthwise to accept the rod. A coil of fine insulated wire nestles snugly within the "E" core. The single moving part of the motor—the steel tapper—sits above the "E" core, held in position by the spring-loaded cutting point rod, below, and the nylon-tipped depth-of-cut control screw, above.

Some tools include a mercury switch to eliminate the annoyance of having to hold down a mechanical switch. A small blob of mercury is sealed into a glass tube fitted with two contacts. When the tool is held upright, the conductive blob bridges the two contacts and power is applied to the motor winding. The alternating current flow sets up a varying intensity magnetic field that alternately pulls and releases the tapper, causing it to sharply strike the rod and drive its point down against the work. The depth-of-cut control bears against the motor tapper. Turning it in or out controls the length of the strokes applied to the cutting point via the rod. Short strokes make fine lines; longer strokes make bolder lines. Because the motor does all the hard, stroke work, little sidewise effort is needed to guide the pencil through the shapes of numbers, letters, symbols, or even artful scrollwork and curliques.

Figure 4-2. Depth-of-cut adjustment is set to assure proper cutting depth for different materials. GRAF-WHALEN photograph.

Figure 4-3. Valuable equipment is easily marked for permanent identification. GRAF-WHALEN photograph.

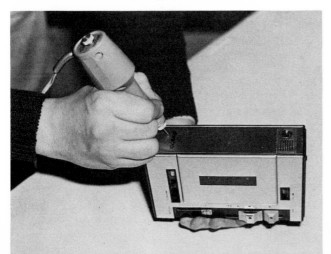

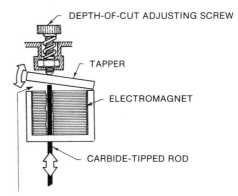

DEPTH-OF-CUT ADJUSTING SCREW

TAPPER

ELECTROMAGNET

CARBIDE-TIPPED ROD

ELECTROMAGNETIC FIELD PULLS TAPPER DOWN

Figure 4-4. A simple electromagnetic motor drives the carbide-tipped steel rod.

5

Electric Glue Guns

Of the bewildering array of adhesive products now available, the intriguing *hot-melt* adhesives are the latest to invade the home craftsman's shop. Look around your home, shop, or business and try to count the things made possible by glue. Chances are you'll run out of breath before you run out of things to count. Strong, thermosetting, plastic compounds, called hot-melts, make neat, permanent bonds that set in less than a minute and cool to a resilient, waterproof finish. These properties have made hot-melts a favorite in industrial circles for years. Problem was, though, they had to be applied *hot* to a surface (about 350° F hot), and handling was a tricky, tacky task. While this was no problem for industry, nobody wanted to use such hot, messy stuff for home repairs and mending chores.

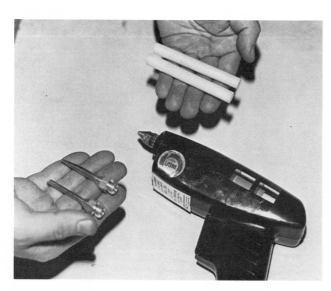

Figure 5-1. Electric glue gun. GRAF-WHALEN photograph.

The electric glue gun changed all that. A compact tool that fits the hand comfortably, the glue gun makes application of hot-melt adhesives and caulking compounds about as simple as writing your name with a ball-point pen. Today's glue guns conceal some clever engineering beneath their innocuous exteriors. Actually, they contain most of the essential parts of a hydraulic hot-melt applicator, mimicking their big, automated cousins in the furniture and container factories. These electrically operated glue guns consist of a heating element, nozzle, and glue chamber. Solid glue sticks are moved into the chamber where they are melted and then released in controlled amounts through the nozzle.

HOW THEY WORK

The one-piece heavy cast-alloy heating chamber nestles inside the halves of the insulating plastic casing. The upper portion of the chamber is tapered, becoming progressively narrower toward the pointed nosepiece. The bottom portion of the chamber casting contains a ceramic insulated coil of heater wire. Directly below the chamber, but mounted close to it, is a bimetal thermostat. One end of the heater coil is wired to one contact of the normally closed thermostat; the second contact goes to the AC line cord. The opposite end of the heater coil is wired directly to the other line cord wire. When the gun is plugged in, power is immediately applied to the heater. Electrical energy is converted to heat along the entire length of the heater coil and transferred through the ceramic body to the heavy alloy casting. The heat spreads uniformly throughout the casting, raising its temperature to about 350° F within 3 minutes.

Temperature has to be constant, from heel to nose of the chamber, in order to keep the glue fluid up to the time it exits from the gun. As the chamber warms up, part of its heat energy is radiated toward the bimetal thermostat.

Each arm of the thermostat is made from a metal alloy "sandwich," having the unique characteristic of expanding more on one side than on the other when heated. As the arm absorbs heat, a "tug-of-war" commences—one face lengthens faster than the other, causing the strip to bend. When sufficiently hot, the thermostat arms bend far enough away from each other to break the circuit between the AC line and the heater coil. As long as the chamber remains hot enough for gluing, the circuit stays open. But, if it cools slightly, the thermostat arms contract and close the circuit, reapplying power to the heater to bring it back to temperature.

When the chamber is hot, you're ready to glue. Sticks of hot-melt adhesive snugly fit the heel end of the heating chamber. You drop one stick in and back it up with another. Inside the hot chamber, the glue stick flows and turns liquid. But the stick behind it remains solid at least two-thirds of its length. Because the heat chamber is tapered, only the very end of the backup stick softens, forming an effective seal and allowing pressure on the hard end to be exerted, pistonlike, against the liquified glue further down the tapered chamber. Some models operate by thumb pressure on the rearmost glue stick, while others operate by forefinger pressure on a trigger mechanism. Pressure on the backup stick raises the hydraulic pressure on the fluid hot-melt. The fluid pushes against a spring-loaded ball check-valve between the forward end of the chamber and the nosepiece, opening the valve and escaping through a narrow opening to the pointed applicator nose. Releasing pressure closes the ball check-valve and stops hot-melt flow. Control is far more exact than would be possible with a squeeze-tube

adhesive, and the hot-melt sets as soon as it has given up its heat to the surface to which it is applied. As glue is used up, the backup stick sinks deeper into the heating chamber, making a novel self-feeding arrangement. When you can't push it anymore, you simply slip another glue stick in behind it and continue as before. There are no messy cleanup tasks either. When you're finished gluing, the gun is simply unplugged and left to cool with the hot melt inside. Though it hardens when cool, the next time you need it, just bring it to temperature and glue effortlessly.

With no caps to lose, no deadly vapors to breathe, no tubes that keep on flowing long after you've stopped squeezing, and no hit-or-miss squirting in the hope that some glue gets into the right places, the *art* of gluing may gradually give way to the *science* of gluing, thanks to the electric glue gun and hot-melt adhesives.

TIPS FOR USING YOUR GLUE GUN
Most glue guns are fitted with a standard short-nose nozzle that dispenses a 1/16-inch bead for use where open or easy-to-get-at surfaces are being joined. Accessory nozzles that can apply different configurations of adhesives for special job requirements are available for some guns. For example, the USM Thermogrip® model 260 is shipped with a standard 1/16-inch short-nose nozzle that can be replaced by a 2-inch-long, 1/8-inch-diameter nozzle for gluing surfaces that are difficult to get at or with another long-nose nozzle that is flattened so that it dispenses a 1/4-inch-wide bead of glue.

All adhesives work by flowing into place as a liquid and then solidifying by drying, curing, or, in the case of a fam-

Figure 5-2. Glue sticks are easily fed into the rear of the gun, to be advanced into the heating chamber by pressure on the finger-operated trigger control.
GRAF-WHALEN photograph.

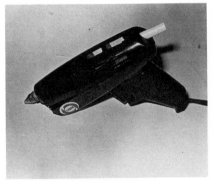

Figure 5-3. After adhesive is applied to the surface to be bonded, stand the tool on the handle and the front of the melt chamber. As long as the heated tool is placed in a standing position it will cause no damage. GRAF-WHALEN photograph.

Figure 5-4. When hydraulic pressure is applied to the fluid hot-melt in the heating chamber by the yet-to-be melted solid adhesive stick in the rear of the tool, adhesive flows readily from the nozzle. GRAF-WHALEN photograph.

ily of adhesives called hot-melts, cooling. Hot-melts dispensed by glue guns are odorless, ready-to-use, non-toxic, waterproof, 100 percent solid thermoplastic adhesives. They do not use any malodorous and flammable solvents like alcohol, ketones, or toluene in their formulation. Furthermore, they also do not suffer from shortcomings such as short shelf-life, long setting-time, or the need to mix or apply from tubes or bottles that can break or leak. Neither is there a need to use a brush or other applicator.

Heat performs the liquifying function in hot-melts that solvents bring about in wet adhesives. Yet, solidification need not be a permanent process as it is with all other adhesives or thermosetting materials. Hot-melts liquify repeatedly upon the application of heat, with no consequent loss in their adhesive strength when cooled.

The general-purpose and extremely versatile, cream-colored, opaque, polyethylene-based hot-melt has an average active working time of 20 to 25 seconds and yields a complete bond in about 60 seconds. It has good flexibility and a softening temperature of about 170° F. Hot-melts bond a variety of materials, and the more porous the material, the better the bonding ability. Best applications include the bonding of wood, paper products, leather, fabrics, metals, linoleum, ceramics, glass, plastics, and even concrete. Once you've tried a glue gun you'll stick with it!

Figure 5-5. Nozzle temperature is approximately 380° F. Care must be taken never to touch the nozzle or hot glue when the tool is plugged in. GRAF-WHALEN photograph.

Because the cooling down from the application temperature (as high as 450° F) to the set temperature is rapid, the following treatment of substrates will enhance the strength of the finished bond:

Roughing: When joining extremely smooth materials such as painted wood or metal, roughen the surface with emery cloth, steel wool, a wire brush, or sandpaper.

Cleaning: Remove oils and especially solvents from all surfaces to be bonded.

Preheating: When gluing large surfaces, it is important that the glue remain liquified until the parts to be glued are pressed together. Best results are achieved by heating these materials with a flatiron, a flood lamp, or a heat gun to about 150° F before glue is applied. The surfaces should be hot to the touch, not merely warm.

Hot-melts are quick and easy to use. Application is a simple two-step operation: Apply the hot adhesive to the joint line or surface of one substrate, join the two surfaces, and hold them together for a few seconds while the adhesive cools. No need for clamps, jigs, or fixtures! Why? Because hot-melts set up quickly. The adhesive solidifies rapidly as heat is dissipated throughout the substrate. The bond normally reaches 60 to 80 percent of its maximum strength in a matter of a *few seconds*, 90 percent in 60 seconds, and the remaining 10 percent in the following 24 hours.

If the glue hardens before you have a chance to adhere other work to it, it can be reactivated by running the tip of the glue gun over it. Excess glue can be stripped away with the tip of the gun or it can be shaved off with a razor, knife, or sharp plane. No ordinary solvent can be used to remove it, nor can it be sanded.

RULES FOR SAFE USE

Hot-melt glue is extruded as molten thermoplastic material from a *very hot* nozzle at temperatures that may be as high as 450° F. This temperature far exceeds that of boiling water and, therefore, demands caution and common sense.

• Do not touch the molten glue. Skin contact with molten glue can cause severe burns and extreme care must be taken to avoid such contact.

• Should contact with molten glue occur, immediately immerse the contacted area in cold, clean water. Do not attempt to remove the set hot-melt from the skin. Cover the contacted areas with clean, wet compresses, and see a physician as soon as possible.

6

Bench Grinders

Even though space on your bench top may be harder to find than a left-handed monkey wrench, you should consider giving something the old heave-ho to make room for a bench grinder. That's especially true if you have a frequent need to true up metal workpieces; or put a keen cutting edge on chisels, axes, rusted garden tools; or restore the bite of worn screwdrivers, lathe tools, punches, and drill bits. More than this, though, a bench grinder gives you a do-almost-everything tool that can sharpen, shape, deburr, and smooth almost anything—metal, wood, plastics, or stone. And, with accessories in place of its abrasive wheels, you can wire-brush surfaces clean of rust and corrosion, as well as restore the gleam of common or precious metals with a buffing wheel. Ever-present and ever-handy, the grinder is a tool that rounds out a shop's real value.

Stripped to its bare essentials, a bench grinder consists of a horizontally mounted electric motor that has shafts extending left and right, to which abrasive grinding wheels or other attachments are fitted. The drive is direct and there are no gears or belts to change speed or torque. Most motors revolve at a no-load speed of 3,450 rpm.

WHAT'S AVAILABLE

The size of a grinder is given in terms of wheel diameter. For example, a 7-inch grinder is designed to turn 7-inch abrasive wheels. Home shop sizes run from 5 to 7 inches, with motors ranging from 1/4 to 1/2 horsepower.

Heavy-duty units typically use 6- to 7-inch diameter, 3/4-inch-thick wheels, and light-duty types drive 4 1/2- to 5-inch wheels that are about 1/2 inch thick. The heavy-duty grinders have more powerful motors than the light-duty models. Though there are probably few home or shop jobs beyond the power capabilities of a light-duty grinder, a heavy-duty grinder does almost any job faster because of its more powerful motor. Also, the grinding wheels of heavy-duty models are slightly larger. The more powerful a bench grinder is, the more firmly the work can be pressed against the spinning abrasive wheel, without slowing it excessively or possibly even stalling it, and the quicker material is removed from the work. The typical heavy-duty grinder removes three times as much material as a light-duty model in the same grinding time.

Heavy-duty models are approximately 15 inches wide, 8 or more inches deep, and they take up considerably more space on the workbench than the typical lighter-duty models, which are only about 10 inches wide.

Grinders whose wheels are smaller than 6 inches generally do not have sufficient power for serious grinding or sharpening. However, for lighter and only occasional

Figure 6-1. Bench grinder. GRAF-WHALEN photograph.

work, a 4 1/2-inch or 5-inch grinder may be a good choice. In between, there's a 6-inch, 1/4-horsepower unit, and for heavier than average work a 7-inch unit is probably best. Because all wheels rotate at about the same speed, the working surface of a larger-diameter wheel moves faster, and, as a consequence, it also grinds faster. As the grinding wheels get thicker and larger, the horsepower requirement goes up, and so, naturally, does the price. The extra thickness also helps in sharpening wide tools. The larger open space around the wheels of a heavy-duty model makes it easier to handle bulky jobs.

To meet safety requirements, all grinders, regardless of size, must have strong wheel guards covering three-quarters of the rim. Shatterproof eye shields—preferably adjustable—conveniently positioned between your eyes and the work are a *must*. Work rests should be large and sturdy enough to safely support the work. They must be adjustable (tilt and distance) in order to keep wheel gap at less than 1/8 inch. A gap wider than 1/8 inch—the maximum clearance recommended by the American National Standards Institute's safety code for abrasive wheels—poses the danger of jamming a tool between the rest and the wheel, with possible danger of injury to the user and damage to the grinder. Most rests are removable, if nec-

essary, for grinding odd-shaped or large work. Some rests have a formed slot that holds drill bits at the correct angle for sharpening. Work rests can be locked in position, either with finger-tightened wing nuts or a bolt-and-nut combination that requires a wrench for removal and installation.

Heavy-duty, higher-priced grinders are equipped with spark arresters at the top of each wheel to intercept hot, flying shards, as well as chutes at the bottom to divert the sparks down and toward the back of the grinder, away from you. A goosenecked lamp to illuminate the work is a worthwhile accessory, as is a built-in water trough for cooling the work to prevent overheating.

A good bench grinder, regardless of size, has a finely balanced motor and wheels. It will quickly attain running speed, run quietly, and, when it is shut off, will coast freely for a long time. This is a sign of good balance and quality bearings.

Wheels

Grinding wheels are composed of innumerable very small, abrasive grains that are held fast by any one of a number of special bonding materials. Each tiny grain is an active cutting tool that dulls as it does its job. Eventu-

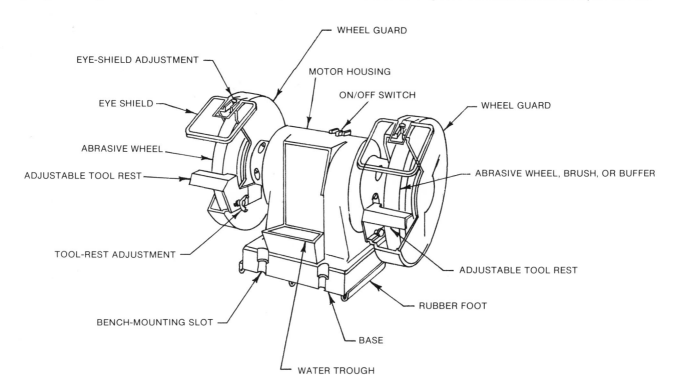

Figure 6-2. Principal parts of a bench grinder.

ally, it tears loose from the bonding material, so that another new, sharp grain can take over. Grinding wheels are characterized by their size (diameter, thickness, hole size), as well as by the type of abrasive, grain (grit) size, grade, structure, and bond. Let's look at these in detail.

The *abrasive* is the material that does the cutting, and synthetic abrasives are used for almost all wheels. Tough aluminum oxide is suitable for grinding most ferrous metals, such as high-speed steels and carbon steels. Silicon carbide abrasive is used for working on cast iron, tungsten carbide, and other low-tensile strength materials, such as bronze, brass, aluminum, or copper.

Grain sizes (relative coarseness of the abrasive) range all the way from 12 to 24 (coarse), 36 to 46 (medium), and 60 to 80 (fine); to 100 to 180 (very fine). Wheels that are supplied as standard equipment with a new grinder usually fall into the "medium" category. Fine grain wheels are appropriate for grinding hard materials, because they have more cutting edges and, therefore, cut faster than do coarse wheels. A coarse wheel can be used on soft materials for rapid removal, but a finer-grain wheel always produces a smoother finish.

Grade defines wheel hardness. It has no relation to the hardness of the abrasive or bond, but rather is a measure of how fast the wheel wears down—how fast bonding material releases dulled grains. Grade ranges from A to I (soft), J to O (medium), P to R (hard), and from T to Z (very hard). To grind hard materials that dull the wheel quickly, it is best to use a soft grade. But for grinding soft materials, a hard wheel is generally more economical.

Structure has to do with the amount of open spaces between the abrasive grains. Open-grain wheels with widely spaced grains are best for grinding soft materials, such as aluminum or brass, that tend to "load up" the wheel. Close-grain wheels produce a fine finish and are also recommended for hard and brittle materials.

The *bond* of a wheel consists of special clays and other ceramic materials that are used to hold the grains together. The bonding material and the abrasive grains are fused together to form a vitrified, porous, high-strength wheel. Some tool-sharpening wheels use a silicate bond for cooler operation, others use a resinoid bond. Rubber and shellac are also used as bonding materials. A letter code is used to denote the material used in the bond. V designates vitrified; R, rubber; B, resinoid; and so on. Bonds run the gamut from *very soft* to *very hard*. Hard wheels hold abrasive grains in place even under extreme pressure. Soft wheels permit them to loosen easily. In general, harder wheels should be used for grinding soft materials, while the softer wheels are recommended on hard materials. Between these two extremes, a medium-hard grade is best for average work.

TIPS FOR USING YOUR BENCH GRINDER AND ITS ACCESSORIES

Standard grinders are usually fitted with two different general-purpose wheels that are appropriate for most grinding jobs. One wheel, probably 60-grit, is suited for sharpening knives, drill bits, axes, and other wood-cutting tools. The coarser, probably 36-grit, wheel on the other side can easily tackle rough- or fast-grinding of most materials. To bolster this basic pair, consider a carbide wheel for grinding very hard items, such as carbide-tipped tools. Other wheels in various grit sizes can be added for work beyond routine grinding. For example, a 100-grit, or finer, wheel is needed for keen-edge tools, finishing, grinding, and polishing.

A *soft-buffing wheel* is a useful accessory. To aid the buffing action, purchase a supply of special compounds to enhance a specific finish. Use *red rouge* for polishing gold, silver, and other precious metals; *white rouge* for nickel, chrome, stainless steel, iron, cast brass, and aluminum. To polish copper brass or pewter, use *brown tripoli*. An *emery compound* is necessary for removing rust, tarnish, or scale. *Wire-brush wheels*, either coarse or fine, are the best choice to remove rust and corrosion from metal and to produce a scratch-brush (medium-luster) finish. Use fiber-brush wheels for less abrasive scrubbing.

A *variety of jigs* are sold as accessories for grinders. Some are simple and hold only a few tools, while others are quite complex and make it possible to hold objects like tools, blades, scissors, screwdrivers, or garden implements at the recommended angle. There are three steps

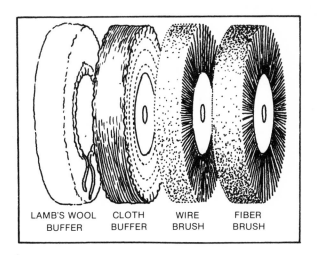

LAMB'S WOOL BUFFER   CLOTH BUFFER   WIRE BRUSH   FIBER BRUSH

Figure 6-3. Accessory wheels that can be used on a bench grinder to brush, clean, or polish a variety of materials.

involved in sharpening tools—grinding the edge to the correct bevel, removing the burr or wire left on the edge in the grinding operation, and honing or polishing the cutting edge.

Take light passes when grinding tools; keep the blade moving across the wheel and stop to cool the work often. If part of the edge turns blue, it's burned. The temper at that spot is gone, and it is necessary to grind off the burnt spot. Next, remove the wire with one or two almost-flat passes over an oilstone, and then strop the blade on leather charged with rouge or fine emery.

Figure 6-4. A bench grinder is just the tool for keening up edge-worn surfaces like this battered chisel. GRAF-WHALEN photograph.

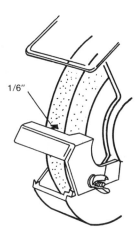

1/6"

Figure 6-5. The tool rest should be adjusted to be within 1/8 to 1/16 inch of the wheel, slightly below the centerline.

RULES FOR SAFE USE

• Be sure that the grinder's speed does not exceed the maximum safe speed stated on the grinding wheel.

• Examine the wheel for cracks or chips and "ring" the wheel before you mount it on the machine, as well as from time to time thereafter.

• To ring a wheel, hold it by placing a pencil in the hole or hang it on a piece of string, and tap it lightly with a wooden handle, 25 degrees each side of the vertical center line. Rotate the wheel 180 degrees and repeat. If the wheel is in good condition, it will ring clear. A dull sound could indicate a crack that may not be readily discernible by the naked eye. *Don't take a chance!* Discard that wheel, or run the risk that it will fly apart one day, hurling shrapnel in all directions.

• Fasten the mounting nut securely, but not overly tight, so that the wheel can be driven without slipping. Recessed flanges are used to mount grinding wheels and only the outer part of the flange is supposed to make contact with the wheel. To distribute the clamping force evenly, blotters are placed between the wheel and the flanges (torn blotters should be replaced with ones cut from ordinary blotting paper). The diameter of these paper washers must not be less than that of the flanges.

• Before using the machine, be sure the guards are in place. Adjust the tool rest so that it is within 1/16 to 1/8 inch of the wheel and slightly below the center line of the wheel, to reduce the possibility of accidental jamming by work wedged between the tool rest and the wheel. If it is necessary to adjust the work rest, *stop the machine first.*

• Whenever possible, work on the face of the wheel. For some jobs, it is necessary to use the side of the wheel. Do this very carefully and be sure to inspect the wheel frequently to be sure that its thickness is not reduced to the point where further use becomes risky.

• As with any power tool, ground the three-prong plug properly. You may wish to consider use of a ground-fault interrupter with your grinder (and for all the power tools you use in your shop) to provide extra protection against electrical hazards.

• *Always wear safety goggles*, even if you're just touching up a screwdriver. Do this even though the machine has its own guards and shields. Don't count on regular eyeglasses, which may break if hit by flying debris. Never wear dangling or loose clothing that could be caught in the wheel.

• Whenever you start to use the grinder, always stand aside for a moment and let the wheel come up to full speed before applying the work, just in case an undetected crack should cause the wheel to fly apart.

• When grinding, always keep the work moving across the face of the wheel; grinding against the same spot on the wheel will cause weakening grooves to be worn into the face of the wheel.

• Never force work against a cold wheel; apply work gradually to give the wheel an opportunity to warm, thereby minimizing the possibility of breakage. A grinder works best and most safely when feed pressure is light. Too much pressure can break the wheel, overtax the grinder's motor, and overheat and damage the workpiece.

BENCH GRINDER MAINTENANCE

• Tool rests require occasional adjustment to keep them within 1/8 inch or less of the rotating wheels.

• Since most grinders have brushless induction motors, there are no brushes to be replaced.

• Because bearings are generally sealed and impregnated with sufficient lubricant for the average life of the grinder, that chore is also not required, unless it is specified in the owner's manual. In that case, apply recommended lubricant—sparingly—in the oil holes or grease cup provided.

• A spinning wheel may develop excessive vibration because of imbalance. If that should happen, stop the motor, loosen the mounting nut, rotate the wheel around the arbor (about a half turn), and then retighten. It may be necessary to repeat this step several times to find the correct orientation that stops the annoying vibration.

• Occasionally, remove the wheel guards to clean the wells of any accumulation of debris that may clog the grinder's internal mechanism. Also, inspect the air vents underneath the motor housing. Keep them clear so the motor does not overheat.

Dressing the Wheel

The grinding wheel, like every other cutting tool, requires attention every now and then. A built-up layer of dull, abrasive grain, as well as metal particles or other foreign materials that load up the surface of the wheel—and are not removed by the normal self-sharpening action of the wheel—can be quickly ground off by using a *star-wheel dresser*. This mechanical sharpening device consists of a row of free-to-rotate star wheels that are supported on a handle. During the "dressing" operation, the star wheels turn as the dresser is firmly passed across the rotating grinding wheel. This removes the surface layer of contaminants, exposes new abrasive, and restores much of the original sharpness of the wheel.

7

Hand-Held Grinders

Complementing the shaping, sharpening, and smoothing capabilities of the bench grinder (see chapter 6) is the dandy little hand-held Moto-Flex Tool® by Dremel Manufacturing Company. This compact handful uses miniature abrasive wheels, sanding discs, wire-brush wheel, and polishing wheel to duplicate in small scale the operations performed by its husky bench-bound cousins. The truly remarkable feature of this hand-held tool is that it can get into areas no larger tool can get near; and, it offers precise, controllable operation that big power tools can't match.

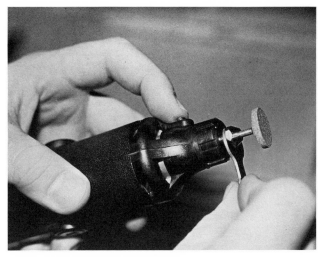

Figure 7-2. Readily interchangeable tool bits are secured by a locking nut that is tightened while the motor shaft is kept from rotating by finger pressure on the locking button. GRAF-WHALEN photograph.

Figure 7-1. Hand-held grinder. GRAF-WHALEN photograph.

Figure 7-3. Infinitely variable speed control adjusts tool-bit rotation to the job at hand. GRAF-WHALEN photograph.

Pint-size emery wheels in a wide variety of shapes make grinding practical in jobs where tedious and less precise hand work would otherwise be the only answer. And there are silicon grinding points for hard steel, glass, ceramics, and similar tough materials. "Moto-Tool" models are available with built-in electronic speed control for fast or slow grinding and with flexible drive heads for really precise grinding, smoothing, shaping, and polishing jobs.

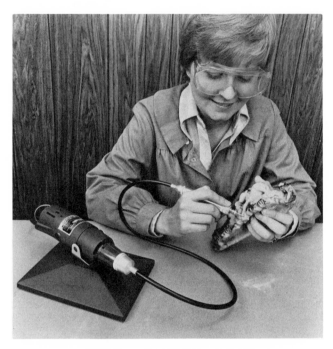

Figure 7-4. DREMEL MODEL #232 "MOTO-FLEX TOOL"®. The slim-grip hand piece of this flexible shaft power tool is driven by a 25,000 rpm, 1/15-horsepower universal motor through a 34-inch-long, vinyl-covered flexible shaft. To extend its versatility, motor speed can be varied from zero to full rpm, by the use of a foot or manually operated speed control. Photograph courtesy of Dremel Manufacturing, Div. of Emerson Electric Co.

8

Lathes

Of all the power tools used by home craftsmen, the wood lathe is undoubtedly one of the most satisfying. Only on the lathe can beginners and experts alike produce at a time—and all in the same continuous operation—intricately shaped, finished masterpieces of exquisite and beautiful design. To work with the wood lathe is to know the complete satisfaction of watching ideas take form under the seemingly magical touch of the chisel in your hands!

The lathe is a general utility tool that produces round forms by spinning wood between its centers, while shaping it with various chisels and gouges. The lathe can be used to perform a greater variety of operations than any other single power tool. It can be adapted to boring, routing, sawing, sanding, finishing, and buffing of work; and, by varying the spindle speeds, to turning, spinning, sanding, buffing, and polishing of metals, plastics, and other materials.

Figure 8-1. This modern lathe has a built-in, solid-state, infinitely variable speed control that provides any speed between 800 and 2,800 rpm simply with the turn of a knob. GRAF-WHALEN photograph.

The major parts of a lathe are the *headstock*, which is in a fixed position (it provides driving force to the workpiece); the *tailstock*, which is movable; and an adjustable *tool rest*. These three main parts are mounted on a *lathe bed* that assures alignment between the headstock and the tailstock. This bed can be flat or tubular, depending upon the particular lathe's design. The tool rest and the tailstock can be independently moved laterally, so they can be adjusted to suit the height of the workpiece.

The workpiece, which is mounted between the headstock and the tailstock, is commonly referred to as a *spindle*. Two types of turnings are made on a lathe—*spindle and faceplate*. Spindle turnings—lamps, legs, and similar workpieces—are turned between centers mounted in the headstock and the tailstock. Faceplate turnings—lamp bases, cups, bowls—are mounted to the headstock only on a faceplate. When the workpiece is mounted either as a spindle or a faceplate turning, sharp chisels and gouges are employed to cut away waste material, as the workpiece material spins between centers or on the faceplate.

Two lathe centers are required to hold a spindle—one in the headstock and one in the tailstock. As drive is applied to the headstock, the headstock center holds the spindle on center and also engages the end of the spindle to rotate it. The tailstock center simply holds the spindle on center and allows it to revolve freely.

Any workpiece that is to be made into a disc or other large circular object having the major portion of the work on the end, instead of around the circumference (such as a bowl or a tray), is generally mounted on the headstock alone. Such a workpiece is called a faceplate turning, and it is mounted on a faceplate which must be large enough in diameter to hold the workpiece steady. Faceplates are circular discs with threaded hubs that come in sizes from 3 to 10 inches. They are always mounted in the headstock.

Any workpiece that can't be mounted between centers or is too small to be done on a faceplate, requires the use of a *screw center*. This accessory, designed to hold small workpieces, is also mounted in the headstock.

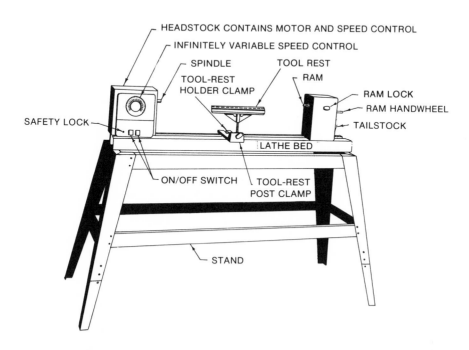

Figure 8-2. Principal parts of a lathe. GRAF-WHALEN photograph.

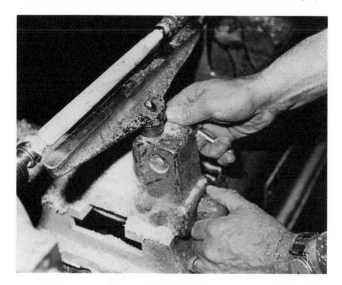

Figure 8-3. Spindle turnings are mounted between centers in the headstock and the tailstock.

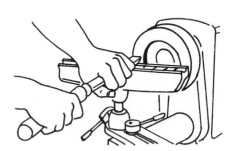

Figure 8-4. To make a faceplate turning, the tip of the chisel is steadied by the left hand, which holds the edge against the tool rest while the right hand guides the tool. Note that the tip of the chisel is held higher than the handle.

WHAT'S AVAILABLE

Lathe capacity is given in terms of maximum spindle length (20 to 28 inches for home shop use) and maximum diameter of the workpiece that can be swung over the bed. This diameter is usually used to indicate lathe size. Thus, on a 12-inch lathe, the bed is approximately 6 inches from the headstock, which makes it possible to swing a 12-inch faceplate turning.

Motors used on lathes are 1/4, 1/3, or 1/2 horsepower, and they rotate at 1,725 rpm. Lathes that are 6 to 10 inches usually use 1/3-horsepower motors; 1/2-horsepower motors are for lathes larger than 10 inches. A three- or four-step cone pulley that matches the lathe pulley is used on the motor to achieve various speeds, such as 990 rpm, 1,475 rpm, 2,220 rpm, and 3,250 rpm. Some lathes use electronic solid-state speed controls that give variable speed adjustment, so no cumbersome belt changes are required. Large-diameter stock requires low spindle speed, while smaller items can be turned faster. A spindle speed chart like the one on page 39 is usually supplied with the lathe. These tables list the ideal rpm rate for metal turning, wood-boring, sanding, buffing, and freehand turning.

Figure 8-5. DREMEL MODEL #700 "MOTO-LATHE"®. This miniature lathe can be used with wood, plastics, and soft nonferrous metals by anyone who likes to work small or has frequent occasion to work on models. Photograph courtesy of Dremel Manufacturing, Div. of Emerson Electric Co.

Motors of different power rating and type of bearings can be used for the same basic wood lathe. Heavy-duty motors designed for rugged shop service come equipped with ball bearings. A less expensive motor with sleeve bearings is generally sufficient for the home handyman.

The stability of the lathe bed affects the work, and to achieve rigidity and low vibration, professional lathes are made with heavy cast-iron beds. A well-constructed bed of steel tubing, however, should be sufficient for home shop use. To check for smooth, gliding motion, move the tailstock over the rails. You should be able to make all lathe adjustments with precision and ease and the lathe should lock securely.

The headstock should be sufficiently sturdy to withstand the pressures that develop when heavy materials are turned. If you wish to do outboard turning of large bowls and other wide items that can't swing over the lathe bed, then the lathe must be able to accommodate the work outside, to the left of the headstock.

TIPS FOR USING YOUR LATHE

The most common lathe operation is *spindle turning*, where the work is mounted between head and tailstock and either of two basic techniques—scraping or cutting—is used. The technique used depends on the choice of tool and how the tool is held. Scraping is the easier approach for the beginner.

To prepare wood for turning, each end is marked for its true center. At the headstock side, a spur center is inserted in one end of the wood by pressing it in or driving it with a mallet. If the wood is hard, pilot holes or shallow saw cuts may be needed to seat the center. After the spurs are embedded in the wood, that end is installed on the headstock spindle. Then, the tailstock is moved toward the wood, until the center just touches and holds the work. The tailstock is further adjusted until the work starts to bind as it is rotated by hand. Then the adjustment wheel is backed off by about one-half turn, so that the piece freely revolves about the tailstock center. Oil or graphite should be applied to reduce friction at the contact point between wood and center. This is not necessary if the tailstock has a ball-bearing center, which turns with the work. Give the mounted workpiece a few turns by hand to see if it strikes any lathe parts. Only when everything clears and is locked in place should power be applied.

"Roughing off" is the first basic step in the turning operation. This is done with a *gouge* and it reduces the raw stock to a cylinder. Next, a *parting* tool can be used to mark the workpiece along its length with the outlines of desired decorative curves or other design elements. The amount of stock removed depends on the gouge angle

Figure 8-6. To prepare wood for turning, mark the true center on each end. Use a pointed tool (or nail) to make a starting center hole. GRAF-WHALEN photograph.

Figure 8-9. To make a number of identical turnings use a template made of thin wood or cardboard. Hold the template against the workpiece frequently to check your work progress. GRAF-WHALEN photograph.

Figure 8-7. The spur center holds the stock and imparts rotary motion. GRAF-WHALEN photograph.

Figure 8-10. To obtain a smooth surface, secure a piece of sandpaper onto a contoured piece of wood and apply it to the rotating workpiece. GRAF-WHALEN photograph.

Figure 8-8. The ram hand wheel advances the ram to hold the workpiece securely between centers. GRAF-WHALEN photograph.

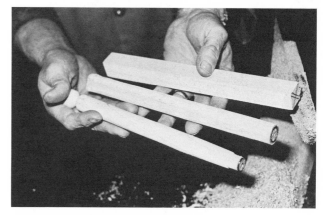

Figure 8-11. Spindle turnings in various stages of completion. GRAF-WHALEN photograph.

and on how the tool is moved over the work. Scraping removes less material, but has the advantage of easier control. Cutting, or shearing, is fast and creates a smoother finish—but it takes experience to master. The gouge is held approximately level for scraping and advances slowly. Cutting is done with either tool angled against the workpiece.

A good, safe starting location for the tool rest is slightly above the centerline of the work and 1/8 inch from the edge. If the rest is too low, the chisel may chatter or produce forcible kickback of the chisel. This can be aggravated if the rest is set too low and the chisel angle is too high, or if both the rest and the tool ride too high on the work.

To make an item such as a bowl, the faceplate is mounted to the headstock and the work fastened to the faceplate with small wood screws. Should the screws interfere with the turning operation, the problem can be cured by mounting a backing block on the faceplate and then gluing the work to the block with a sheet of paper in between. The paper permits separation of the finished work from the block without damage. Screws should be heavy enough to hold the workpiece securely, but not so long that they are cut into during the faceplate turning operation.

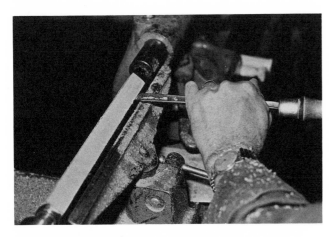

Figure 8-12. For spindle turning adjust the tool rest so it is slightly above the centerline of the work and 1/8 inch from the edge. GRAF-WHALEN photograph.

Figure 8-14. A properly applied chisel quickly reduces the workpiece to the desired diameter. GRAF-WHALEN photograph.

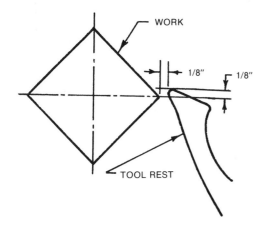

Figure 8-13. Recommended tool rest position.

Figure 8-15. The faceplate turning, which is securely mounted on the headstock spindle, will soon become a beautiful wooden bowl. GRAF-WHALEN photograph.

Lathe Chisels

There are six commonly used chisels that scrape, cut, or shear, specifically designed for lathe turning—the *gouge*, the *round nose*, the *parting tool*, the *flat nose*, the *skew*, and the *spear point*.

Rough cuts, which are cuts that shape a workpiece into a cylinder to reduce it to approximate working size (about 1/8 inch from finish size), are best made with a gouge. This tool is also used to make concave cuts and round grooves. The gouge cuts away large areas *rapidly*, so be sparing in its application! It is placed on the tool rest with the convex side down and the cutting edge angled in advance of the handle. Because the gouge is a cutting tool, it is held with the handle down. The gouge is a hollow, round-nose tool with an outside bevel of 30 degrees. Size ranges from 1/4 to 1 1/4 inches with 1/4, 1/2, and 3/4 inch most common for home workshops.

The round nose is an easy-to-work-with tool used for diameter and circumference scraping operations, such as rounding edges and bowl contours and for smoothing any surfaces that accommodate the chisel width. When held in one position, the round-nose chisel will scrape a round bottom groove the opposite shape of the tool itself. If the chisel is moved sideward, the groove is expanded into a cove. This tool is held in a horizontal position on the tool rest, with the beveled side down. Round-nose chisels are very much like ordinary hand chisels, but with the end ground round. The cutting edge is beveled on one side to 40 to 45 degrees and widths are 1/4, 1/2, 3/4, and 1 inch.

The parting tool is most generally used to establish approximate finish-size diameters at various points along the workpiece. It cuts narrow grooves, which are used as depth guides to facilitate the turning of the workpiece. It is also used to part (cut off) the workpiece and to square ends and shoulders; thus, it cuts straight into or through the workpiece. The parting tool is held with the narrow edge of the blade on the tool rest and with the point of the tool above the centerline. The parting tool is a V-shaped chisel ground on two sides at approximately 60 degrees. It is available with 1/8-, 3/16-, and 1/2-inch cutting edges. The 1/8-inch size is most useful.

The flat-nose chisel (also called square-nose chisel) is used just prior to sanding for smoothing a workpiece and making it perfectly straight or for scraping long, flat surfaces. The flat-nose chisel is held firmly against the tool rest, with the beveled side down and the scraping edge parallel to the workpiece. It is used for diameter, as well as circumference, scraping operation. It has one ground edge beveled on one side at an angle of 45 degrees. The edge is perpendicular to the handle. The tool is available in several widths, from 1/4 inch to 1 1/4 inches, increasing in 1/4-inch increments.

The skew is a fast-cutting, flat chisel with an end cut at an angle used for smoothing cylinders and for cutting square shoulders, beads, deep V-grooves, undercutting, and tapers. The skew makes finishing cuts that are the smoothest cuts possible with a chisel. It is a double-ground chisel similar to the flat chisel, except that the cutting edge is 60 degrees with respect to the handle. Skews are available in increments of 1/4 inch, from 1/4 to 2 inches. The generally used sizes are 1/2 and 1 inch.

The spear point (also called a diamond point) is a scraping chisel used to delicately scrape shallow V-cuts, corners, chamfers, beads, and parallel grooves. It can also be used to mark the workpiece for other operations. The spear-point chisel has a diamond-shaped tip with two beveled edges. It produces clean lines, edges, and corners. Widths of 1/2, 3/4, and 1 inch are available; the 1/2-inch size is most often used.

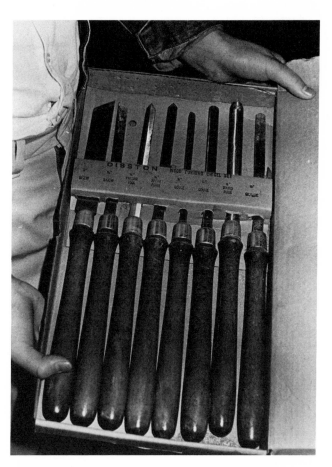

Figure 8-16. This eight-piece set of wood-turning tools contains two skew chisels, a parting tool, a spear point, a round nose, and three gouges. GRAF-WHALEN photograph.

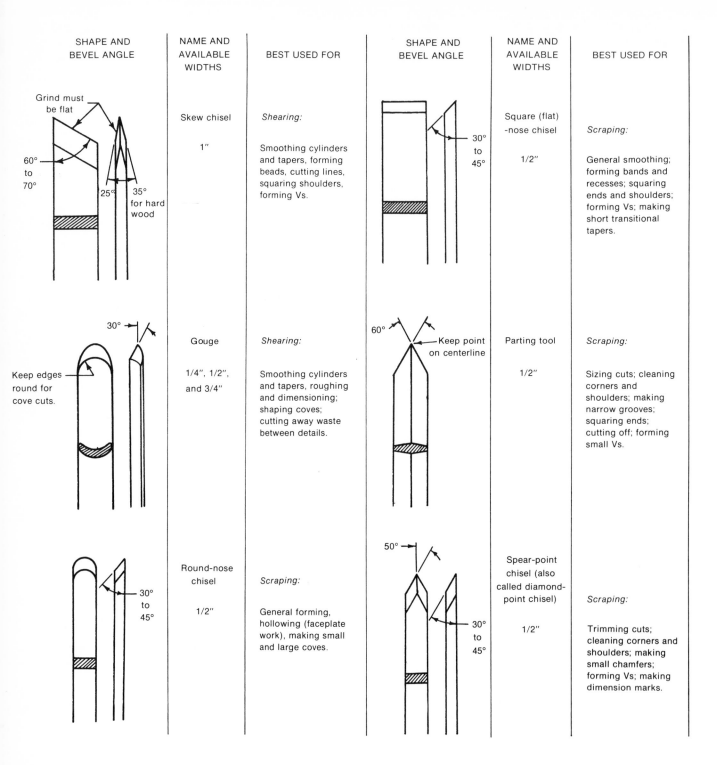

SHAPE AND BEVEL ANGLE	NAME AND AVAILABLE WIDTHS	BEST USED FOR	SHAPE AND BEVEL ANGLE	NAME AND AVAILABLE WIDTHS	BEST USED FOR
Grind must be flat / 60° to 70° / 25° 35° for hard wood	Skew chisel 1"	*Shearing:* Smoothing cylinders and tapers, forming beads, cutting lines, squaring shoulders, forming Vs.	30° to 45°	Square (flat) -nose chisel 1/2"	*Scraping:* General smoothing; forming bands and recesses; squaring ends and shoulders; forming Vs; making short transitional tapers.
30° / Keep edges round for cove cuts.	Gouge 1/4", 1/2", and 3/4"	*Shearing:* Smoothing cylinders and tapers, roughing and dimensioning; shaping coves; cutting away waste between details.	60° / Keep point on centerline	Parting tool 1/2"	*Scraping:* Sizing cuts; cleaning corners and shoulders; making narrow grooves; squaring ends; cutting off; forming small Vs.
30° to 45°	Round-nose chisel 1/2"	*Scraping:* General forming, hollowing (faceplate work), making small and large coves.	50° / 30° to 45°	Spear-point chisel (also called diamond-point chisel) 1/2"	*Scraping:* Trimming cuts; cleaning corners and shoulders; making small chamfers; forming Vs; making dimension marks.

Figure 8-17. Commonly used chisel types.

It is essential to maintain a keen edge on all the chisels. Keep a stone handy. Study the shape of the tool before you start using it, and, as you work, touch up the cutting edge occasionally.

Carbide-tipped chisels are available in various sizes. They can be used on wood, but they are used most on material like metal and plastics at woodworking lathe speeds. Slow speeds are best, especially on hard materials. Waste should come off cleanly. Should the work begin to chatter, or if you find you are getting a ridged surface instead of a smooth cut, it's a pretty good indication that the work is turning too fast, that you are feeding the tool too fast, or that you are trying to remove too much material in one bite. The angle of the tool is important with carbides. For wood and plastics, the tool handle should be slightly below the tool rest; for steel about level and for nonferrous metals, slightly above the tool rest. Tungsten carbide is very hard, but quite brittle, and will hold a keen edge for a long time.

General Procedures for Lathe Turning
Projects should be done in this order:
- Mounting the workpiece
- Rough cutting the workpiece to cylindrical shape
- Cutting to rough dimensions
- Final cutting
- Sanding
- Finishing

The following steps should first be practiced with the power off; and when power is applied, the lathe should first be run at low speed:
- Center the workpiece and place it in the lathe.
- Set the lathe for proper speed.
- Place yourself in a natural position in front of the workpiece. One side of your body should be slightly nearer the lathe than the other side.
- Use a gouge to rough cut the workpiece to approximate dimension. The tool rest should be 1/8 inch from the workpiece and 1/8 inch above the workpiece centerline.
- Use the parting tool to make approximate depths of cut at proper points along the workpiece.
- Always cut a larger diameter toward a smaller diameter when making tapered cuts. Work from the center of the workpiece toward each end, and roll the tool off of the ends. Never start at an end, because of the danger of the tool catching on the workpiece. Make no cuts to a depth likely to risk hitting the headstock or tailstock center.
- The tool tip must not get so hot that the cutting edge is burned. Cool the tool frequently.
- To finish a cut, use a chisel and take thin cuts to remove stock slowly. Use light force and a lot of control. Removing stock too quickly may cause the tool to dig into the workpiece.
- When the finishing cuts are completed, sandpaper the workpiece with abrasive strips. Keep them in motion, while using light pressure against the workpiece, which should be revolving at a high speed. Use progressively finer abrasive grits, ending up with small pieces of steel wool.
- Stains and waxes can also be applied while the workpiece is spinning at a slow speed by applying a little stain or wax to a cloth and holding it against the workpiece. The lathe must be stopped when staining or polishing square portions of the workpiece.

Lathe-Spindle Speeds
The following are suggested approximate lathe-spindle speeds for various workpiece sizes. Use the closest lower speed that your lathe can provide. In general, use low speed for all rough cuts, for heavy faceplate turnings, and until the workpiece is cylindrical. The higher speeds are for light and finishing work. If the workpiece chatters or vibrates at any speed, slow down. For safety larger workpieces are turned at slower speeds.

Wood Turning Lathe Speed Guide in Revolutions Per Minute

Diameter of Workpiece	Speed		
	First Cut	Shaping Cut	Finishing Cut
Under 2"	900–1200 rpm	2400–2800 rpm	3000–4000 rpm
2–4"	700–900 rpm	1800–2400 rpm	2400–3300 rpm
4–6"	600–800 rpm	1200–1800 rpm	1800–2400 rpm
6–8"	400–600 rpm	800–1200 rpm	1200–1800 rpm
8–10"	300–400 rpm	600–900 rpm	900–1200 rpm
over 10"	300 rpm	300–700 rpm	600–900 rpm

RULES FOR SAFE USE
The lathe is not a difficult tool to operate safely. However, like any tool with revolving parts, carelessness can lead to trouble. Safety depends upon common sense and alertness at all times, and there are certain precautions that should always be taken.
- Wear snug-fitting sleeves or roll them up. Never wear long, free apron strings, which could wrap around or be entangled in a revolving part. Even the smoothest shaft can catch and almost instantly wind up the ends of loose, dangling objects with brutal force, causing serious injury to the careless operator.

Figure 8-18. When operating a lathe always wear safety goggles and proper working clothes. Use only sharp tools and position yourself slightly to the side of the cutting tool to avoid serious injury in the event the tool catches in the workpiece and is thrown out of your hand. GRAF-WHALEN photograph.

Figure 8-19. The workpiece must be securely clamped between lathe centers with the tailstock and tool rest safely locked in position. GRAF-WHALEN photograph.

• Only use sharp tools, because they are safe and cut rapidly with little pressure.

• Never stand in the line of the workpiece when the lathe is first turned on. In the event that the workpiece is not correctly attached it can be thrown from the lathe.

• Hold turning tools firmly in both hands.

• When operating the lathe, position the body slightly to the side of the cutting tool, so as not to get hurt in the event the tool catches in the workpiece and is thrown out of your hand.

• The tool rest should be 1/8 inch from the workpiece, parallel to the surface to be cut, and 1/8 inch above the centerline of the workpiece—unless otherwise directed. If a chisel is applied to the workpiece below centerline or if the tool rest is too far out, the chisel can be jammed between the workpiece and the tool rest and be thrown from your hands (or the workpiece could be split and fly apart). Always adjust tool-rest height to above centerline and close to workpiece, so that the chisel end cannot be dragged down. Hold the chisel firmly, and never thrust it forcefully and carelessly into the workpiece.

• Use the tool rest to maximum benefit for tool support in all operations.

• As material is removed from the workpiece, reposition the tool rest as necessary.

• Turning, sanding, etc., produce flying particles. Always wear safety glasses, goggles, or a face shield, if the operation is dusty.

• A loose or too-large workpiece can be thrown off or split into parts, which will fly off and can cause injury. After mounting a spindle or faceplate turning, check the security of its mounting.

• Revolve the workpiece a full revolution by hand to make certain it will clear the tool rest and lathe bed before applying power to the motor.

• A workpiece revolved backwards can throw the chisel back at you. If you have a lathe with reversible motor, check spindle or faceplate rotation each time before beginning work.

• Make certain all locks are tight before beginning work.

• Any large, badly unbalanced workpiece (especially a faceplate turning) can set up a severe enough lathe vibration to shake the workpiece loose from its mounting. To avoid this potential problem, it is best to saw-cut turnings to approximate balance before mounting.

• Always do the roughing-out turning at the slow speed.

• Avoid awkward hand or foot positions.

• Never operate the lathe with guards removed.

LATHE MAINTENANCE

Occasional lubrication and a simple alignment check are the only maintenance steps necessary. There are no numerical calibrations to confirm, however, so an occasional verification of the coaxial alignment of the tailstock (cup) center with the spur center in the headstock is in order. How this is done varies from one lathe to another. On some lathes, the tailstock has a threaded cross-shaft beneath the ways that can be adjusted to align the ram center precisely with the headstock center. To achieve this alignment, bring the tailstock close to the headstock, and adjust the threaded cross-shaft with a screwdriver for perfect alignment.

The points on the centers must be adjusted to meet when they are viewed from above (vertical alignment) and also when they are viewed from the side (horizontal alignment). Since the spur center has a fixed position, adjustments are made by moving the cup center.

Sealed ball-bearing spindle mounts require no lubrication. Bronze-bearing chambers should be filled at recommended intervals with light machine oil through appropriate holes located in the headstock. A few drops of oil on the ram stock assembly are also recommended. To assure smooth travel of the carriage, wipe the ways with an oily rag or wax them. Of course, lathe tools should always be kept sharp, and this is readily achieved with a few wipes on an oilstone.

Figure 8-20. This lathe cannot be turned on unless a "key" is first inserted into the safety lock. GRAF-WHALEN photograph.

9

Routers

The portable electric router is a high-speed, rotary, cutting and shaping implement that ranks as one of the most versatile of all power tools. With just a moderate amount of skill, this handful of power can produce true artistry in wood or composition material. No other tool fully duplicates its features or capabilities. A router can cut dadoes, rabbets, ploughs, and grooves of all kinds; make fancy moldings or molded, beveled, curved, carved, or rounded edges on existing lumber. It also speeds up and simplifies the task of making almost any type of accurate and strong woodworking joint, including mortise and tenon, tongue and groove, splined dado, rabbet, and—that aristocrat of all joints—the dovetail joint.

The router is the only portable power tool that can do a first-rate job of trimming off excess material when applying rigid plastic laminates to countertop surfaces or edges; it is used for such special jobs as carving recesses for decorative inlays or carving numbers, letters, and other decorative designs in wood surfaces.

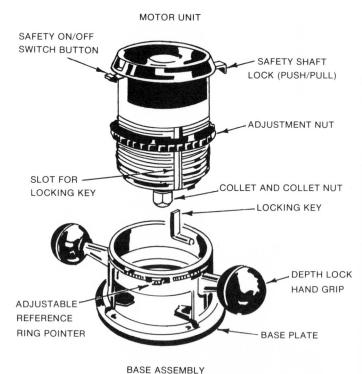

Figure 9-2. Principal parts of a router.

Figure 9-1. Router. Photograph courtesy of Black & Decker Mfg. Co.

HOW THEY WORK

The router is deceptively simple in principle. It basically consists only of a high-speed motor that develops from 1/3 to 1 1/2 horsepower, with a chuck at one end, securely mounted in a housing that holds it in a vertical position for routing. Also incorporated is a vernier mechanism that permits precise height adjustment of the motor to vary the depth of cut. In some routers, this adjustment is achieved by rack-and-pinion gearing, while in others, precise height setting is accomplished by a spiral cam. Scale markings are usually in sixty-fourths of an inch, so cutting depth can be controlled very accurately.

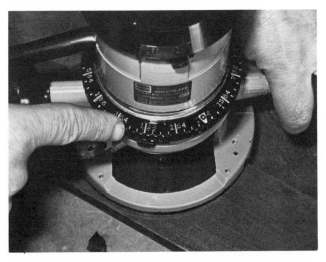

Figure 9-3. Easy-to-read scale markings on the adjustment nut make precise depth-of-cut adjustment effortless. GRAF-WHALEN photograph.

Figure 9-4. The base plate should be waxed occasionally to assure smooth, friction-free movement along the surface of the workpiece. GRAF-WHALEN photograph.

The housing also supports two easy-grip handles for guiding the tool over the work. It has a flat-bottom, smooth-surface, circular base, which protects the work from being marred as the router is moved about. The bottom end of the motor shaft is fitted with a special collet chuck that retains the keen-edged cutting tool—the bit. Most routers will accept bits of 1/4-inch shank diameter.

WHAT'S AVAILABLE

The differences between various router models are mainly in construction, power, and method of depth-of-cut adjustment. The majority of models are in the 3/4- to 1-horsepower range. Low-power models are fed at a slower rate for deep cuts to avoid loading the motor, thereby slowing it; or else the router is passed over the same area several times, with each bite set more deeply.

The greater the rotational speed, the smoother will be the cut. The bearings in low-cost models are sleeve type. Better routers have ball bearings or a combination of sleeve and ball. The occasional user will probably find sleeve bearings satisfactory for light-duty work. Before settling for a particular router, check to see if the handles are comfortable to grip, if the depth scale is easy to read, and if the depth of cut is easy to set. Are bits easy to change? Some models require the use of two wrenches for changing bits—one for holding the motor shaft and the other for loosening or tightening the collet chuck into which the bits are inserted. Others need only one wrench

Figure 9-5. A built-in bar temporarily holds the motor shaft stationary in this router, so only a single wrench is needed to change bits. GRAF-WHALEN photograph.

for the collet chuck. These models have a built-in lever or bar which temporarily holds the motor shaft stationary while bits are being changed. The router's versatility is further enhanced by the availability of nearly 200 bits and cutters.

Most housings have a flat top, which can be inverted and placed on a table surface to ease bit installation. Your hands are then free to manipulate wrenches that tighten the bits in the collet. The shank of the bit or cutter should be inserted as far as possible to keep run-out and deflection to a minimum. Routers operate at speeds averaging anywhere from about 20,000 to 35,000 rpm. At that speed, a sharp bit can produce a smooth edge that requires no further sanding. It is easy to cut a circle or other shape from plywood or other panels as true and smoothly finished as if it had been turned on a lathe!

Horsepower and bearing construction constitute the main differences between routers. The greater the workload to be performed, the greater the horsepower needed and the heavier the bearing construction required. The power of the router's motor determines its cost and how deep and how fast the tool can cut through work. A lower-powered router can do many of the jobs a high-powered router can do, providing it does them in stages. To make a deep cut, for example, simply requires a number of shallow passes.

Check that brushes are readily removable for inspection. Compare several models, and, if possible, check the balance and feel of each tool before you buy.

Bits and Cutters

Router bits and cutters are made of carbide-tipped steel or high-speed tool steels. High-speed steel bits are suited for most uses in hard or soft woods. For plastic laminates and plywood, the more expensive carbide bits and cutters are to be preferred. Also, for extended use, carbide bits will stay sharp longer and are a better choice for heavy use. High-speed steel bits can be resharpened on standard grinders, but carbide bits must be professionally sharpened with a special grinding wheel.

Bits and cutters come in three mounting arrangements, two materials, and an almost infinite variety of sizes and shapes. *One-piece bits* that combine the cutting head and shank are by far the most popular. Routers use 1/4-inch shank bits that are interchangeable among different manufacturers' routers. *Arbor bits* thread onto separate shanks. *Shaper cutters* can be used on some higher-powered routers. Here, the bit collet is unscrewed and a spindle installed in its place on its router motor shaft. A cutter with spacing collars and a smooth hole through its center is mounted on the spindle and clamped tight with a nut. Combinations of cutters and collars are also

used together. Shaper cutters are particularly useful in routing edges of boards, as the tool's subbase rides on the flat side of the board, rather than on the edge.

Some bits are fitted with noncutting *pilots* that control the sidewise depth of cut. These pilots are either a solid rod or a high-speed ball bearing. Carbide bits (solid- or carbide-tipped) cost 2 1/2 to 3 times more than tool steel. They are well worth the investment for the serious craftsperson because they stay sharp much longer.

An assortment of fifteen to twenty different router bits and cutters should satisfy the needs of almost any woodworker. Furthermore, by controlling the depth of cut, several decorative contours can be realized from a single bit. Here are some basic router bits and cutters:

Straight bits: Used for routing.

Veining bits: Used for narrow and decorative grooves. The ends can be either rounded or square. Some veining bits are double-ended and use a special collet.

Core-box bits: Used to scoop out a semicircular channel for hollowing out trays or for making concave quarter-round edge moldings.

Cove bits: Used for molding edges only. They are shaped like core bits except that they have pilots.

Rounding-over bits: Used for making rounded edges. They have pilots flush with the edge of the cutter.

Beading bits: Similar to rounding-over bits, except they form a molded edge with a sharp break at each end of the round. Other shapes include *rabbetting bits, roman ogee bits*, and *dovetail bits*, which make the bottom of a groove wider than the top.

Edge bits: Used for trimming edges, these bits are generally guided along their path by a small pilot projection below the cutter portion that slides against the edge of the work.

Laminate trimmers (carbide only): Special edge bits used for trimming veneer and plastic laminate (such as Formica®) used for countertops. Designed to combine bevel and flush cutting in a single bit.

Grooving bits: These are lowered to a controlled depth for cutting a variety of shapes.

V-groove bit: Routes the familiar "V" seen in wall paneling. It is used for chamfering.

Straight-sided bit: Cuts square grooves that are useful for inlay work.

Shaper cutters: Used primarily for molding board edges and cutting tongues and grooves or other joints. They work fast, but require a powerful router (1 horsepower or better) to drive them efficiently.

Bits must be kept sharp or they will burn the work. They are best kept stored in individual compartments to protect their edges. Bits can be sharpened with a sharpening kit attachment available for some routers.

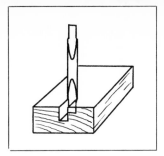 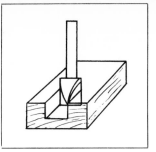 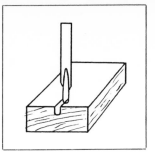 

Straight, single flute: For general stock removal, grooves, dadoes, and rabbets.

Straight, double flute: For general-purpose routing.

Veining: For decorative free-hand routing; raised or cut-in designs or letters.

Dovetail: For dovetailing joints on frames, shelves, bookcases, and cabinets.

  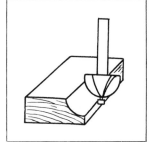

Corner round: For edge rounding.

Beading: For decorative edging of furniture parts.

Cove: For cutting canes.

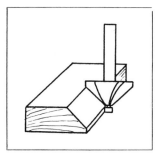 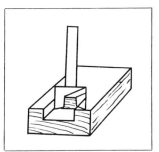 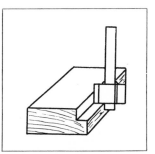 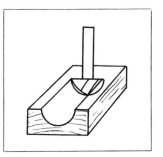

Chamfering: For decorative edging and concealed joints.

Mortising: For stock removal, dadoes, rabbets, and hinge-butt mortising.

Rabbeting: For rabbeting or step-cutting edges.

Core box: For fluting and general ornamentation.

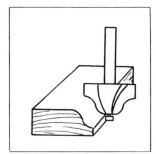 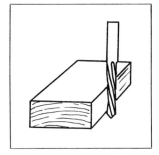 

Roman ogee: For decorative edging on furniture of different periods.

Spiral: For outside and inside curve cutting.

V-groove: For simulating plank construction, lettering, and sign work.

Figure 9-6. Much of the versatility of the router lies in the vast variety of bits and cutters that it can use. These are some of the most widely used bits.

45

TIPS FOR USING YOUR ROUTER

Select the bit for the work at hand and clamp it in the collet chuck. Be sure it's in all the way and secure! A slightly loose bit can "walk" partially out of the chuck and destroy depth accuracy, particularly when making a heavy cut.

Next, adjust the motor in the base until the tip of the bit is just flush with the subbase and then set the depth gauge at zero. The router can now be set for any depth of cut directly with the gauge. When the power switch is turned on, there will be a sudden twisting force from the motor, so be sure to grasp the handles firmly. Moreover, there is a continuous gyroscopic "feel" to the router all the time it's on. Get used to it and remember who's the boss! Besides tool sharpness, the most important other factor that affects the smoothness of routing is the rate of feed, which boils down to how much material you try to remove in one pass. Clean, smooth routing can be done when the router is running close to its no-load speed. Too deep a cut or a too-fast feed will slow the motor down, forcing the cutter to take bigger bites than it can handle. Direction of feed should be from left to right, along an edge, so that the cutter blades will have a chipping action, rather than a gouging action, which can cause splintering.

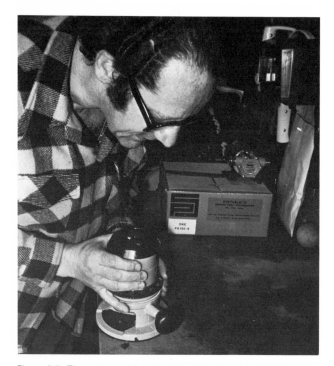

Figure 9-7. The motor unit is adjusted until the tip of the bit is just flush with the subbase. Then the depth gauge is set at the zero mark. GRAF-WHALEN photograph.

The simplest way to make a straight cut with a router is to clamp a straightedge to the workpiece and let the edge of the router subbase ride along it. A 6-inch-wide strip cut from the edge of a sheet of plywood or 1/4-inch tempered hardboard makes an excellent straightedge for long cuts.

Most routers come with fairly complete instruction books that tell how various cuts can be made and how adjustments can be made to take care of various cutting situations. Practice is advisable on scrap material to get the "feel" of the tool and to learn its capabilities and limitations.

Basic Router Cuts

Rabbet: An L-shaped groove cut along an edge of the workpiece. It can be cut with a straight bit and edge guide or with a piloted rabbeting bit. Some drawer fronts and doors are rabbeted to make a neater joint with cabinet frames. The router can be guided with a straightedge, T-square, or edge guide to reduce splintering. Route across the grain first, then with the grain.

Dado: One of the most basic cuts to be made with the router. It is a straight cut across the grain of the workpiece. The dado is often used for making shelves. It is also the basis for the overlap joint, combining the dado and the rabbet. A stopped dado is one that is closed at both ends.

Groove: A simple cut, parallel to the grain of the workpiece. It is chiefly decorative, as for example "V" grooves cut into plywood sheets to simulate a "planking" effect. Veining grooves are also frequently found in traditional furniture.

When making edging cuts, it is advisable to do the edges across the grain first. Then, if there is any breaking loose at the corners of the workpiece, it will be removed by the cuts following the grain. Be sure that the router is being fed from left to right or in a counterclockwise direction around the workpiece.

Guides and Accessories

There are a number of attachments available (some of which you can even make yourself) that enable the router to do all kinds of precision work. These guides vary greatly in flexibility, however. All allow you to guide the router along the edge of the work for rabbeting and for dadoes, ploughs, and grooves up to several inches in from the edge. All can be made to follow a circular edge. More complex edge guides can also guide your router in order to make parallel, equally spaced dadoes, to pivot about a point, or to let you plane edges. Here are some details of the most common guide types.

Straight and circular guide (also called edge guide): This can guide the router parallel to a straightedge or concentrically inside a round edge, always keeping the bit at

RABBET

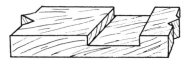

DADO

OVERLAP JOINT

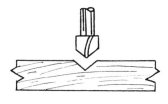

V-GROOVE

Figure 9-8. Basic router cuts.

END LAP

BLIND MORTISE AND TENON

SPLINE JOB

OPEN MORTISE AND TENON

RABBET

RABBET AND GROOVE

TONGUE AND GROOVE

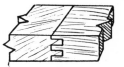

GLUE JOINT

DOVETAIL

Figure 9-9. Common wood joints that can be made with a router.

precisely the same distance inside that edge. The guide is a frame on which two sockets for guide rods are fixed. At one end of the rods is a flat, arc-shaped bracket, by which the guide is attached to the top of the router base with four screws. By loosening the wing nuts, the head can slide along the rods.

Slot and circle-cutting attachment: With a similar bracket for mounting on the router base, this attachment has a plate that is adjustable on two rods. On the inner edge of the plate is a pivot pin held by a screw. With this pin set into a 1/4-inch hole drilled in the work, the router can swing to make perfectly circular slots, grooves, rosettes, and the like. It can also cut out perfectly circular discs with a straight bit, lowering it a little at a time after each pass until it cuts through. A molding cutter can cut out a disc with a shaped edge and leave a circular opening with a similar molded edge, all in one operation.

Remove the pivot pin, replace it with a straight bar, and you can rout grooves along short or long edges; or you can cut evenly spaced grooves across a surface.

Template guides: These are circular, stepped plates with a projecting neck or flange around a hole, through which the bit can pass. Mounted on the router base, the guides are used with templates (thin sheets of metal or hardboard), in which the pattern to be routed has been cut out oversize. The template is temporarily fastened to the workpiece and the bit dropped inside the cutout pattern.

Then the router is moved freehand, with the flange of the template guide bearing against the edge of the template cutout. (The routed groove is actually inside the guide flange, so the template must be cut that much larger all around.)

Dovetail-joint fixture: This consists of two slotted plates, a finger template, and a clamping device. Using this device, the male and female joints may be cut in the same operation. Making dovetail joints with chisel and mallet is difficult, demanding, and time-consuming. With a router and this fixture, fine joints that provide just the right spacing and depth for dovetail joints in both drawer and box construction can be cut quickly and accurately.

Hinge-mortising template: This is used for setting hinges in doors and shutters and includes template frames that are temporarily fastened to doors and their frames, a template guide that tracks the router in them, and a special bit and chisel for cutting the corners square. After hinge mortises have been routed in the door, the frames are transferred to the door frame—there to enable you to rout perfectly aligned mortises.

Veneer and laminate trimming: A veneer or laminate is a thin layer of fine hardwood or plastic glued to a base of more common wood. Trimming is done with a bit or trimmer equipped with a pilot or ball bearing, which guides along the edge of the workpiece and controls the amount of material removed. When a piloted bit is not

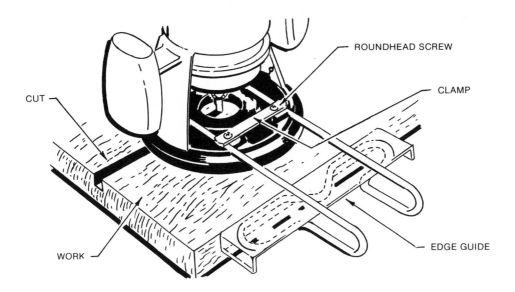

CUT

WORK

ROUNDHEAD SCREW

CLAMP

EDGE GUIDE

Figure 9-10. The edge guide attachment guides the router smoothly along the workpiece at the preset, fixed distance.

available, the edge guide may be used in combination with an unpiloted bit, if great care is exercised in properly setting the guide. Because of the extreme hardness of some laminate materials, carbide-tipped bits and cutters are to be preferred.

Tools for decorative edges: Many cutting tools are available to be used with the router for doing decorative edging for furniture, moldings, and picture frames. Some of the more common ones are illustrated in figure 9-6. A piloted bit can follow the edge of a workpiece, making it unnecessary to use an edge guide to obtain a straight cut.

Homemade router guides: A template can be made by jigsawing or scroll-sawing a design into thin plywood or tempered hardboard. The template is then sanded smooth and clamped to the workpiece. The design can then be cut, simply by following the template. The pattern on the template must be somewhat larger than the design desired on the workpiece to allow for the distance between the outside diameter of the template guide and the cutting edge of the bit.

RULES FOR SAFE USE

The shaft and bit of the router turn extremely fast and cut very swiftly. This means that special care is needed in the operation of a router, for the rotating bit can cause severe injury! Always have the router under control! *Never* start the router when the cutting edge of the bit is in contact with the work. Wear safety glasses or goggles to protect eyes from splinters and chips. Always *disconnect* the supply cord plug from the outlet before installing or changing bits and cutters. (Merely switching off the tool is not enough, as switches can be turned on accidentally.) Stand the machine on its head (the motor generally has a flat top for this purpose), insert the shank to a depth of at least 1-2 inch, and be sure the bit is locked tightly before power is applied.

When starting, hold the router firmly, for the initial torque will tend to twist it out of your hands. Always keep the router base flat on the work surface. Hold the tool firmly to the work and feed from left to right or, on circular work, counterclockwise. Let your sense of feel control the feed. To protect the tool, use sharp bits, and try to get the feel of the most efficient cutting movement. The bit should cut easily with only very slight reduction in motor speed. Too slow a feed creates friction that can burn the wood, whereas too rapid feed wears bit edges and leaves a rough surface. Feeding speed depends largely on the hardness and density of the wood through which the bit must pass. The sound of the tool is an excellent guide. Motor slowdown is a signal that the cut is being forced, so, if the going is difficult, it is better to set the cutter to a more

shallow depth and then make several passes to achieve the desired full depth.

ROUTER MAINTENANCE

The amount of cooling air that reaches the router motor affects its life, so it is important that all air passages are kept free of obstruction. Blow them out frequently when the tool is in service. After about 50 to 100 hours of operation, check the brushes for wear—unless the user's manual warns that the job should be done at a service center. Bearings in some models are lubricated for the life of the router and, therefore, need little attention. Others require periodic lubrication. Check the user's manual. A silicon carbide hone—an exceedingly hard material—is a useful maintenance item that can be used to sharpen router bits to keep them cutting at peak efficiency.

Figure 9-11. The router must always be under control. Hold it firmly by the handles. Safety glasses or goggles are a must to protect the eyes from splinters and chips. GRAF-WHALEN photograph.

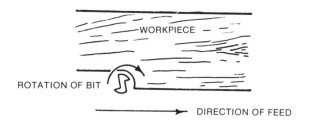

Figure 9-12. When cutting along an edge, the router should be moved from left to right, so that the cutting edge is fed directly into the material and no chatter or vibration occurs.

10

Power Sanders and Polishers

Surface smoothing and finishing are key parts of just about every wood or metal project. Power sanders can be used to advantage in securing a surface that's right for painting, staining, and varnishing. Polishers, on the other hand, are often used to bring up the luster of the surface after it has been coated with a finishing agent and to apply the final coat of wax that gives the finished project an enduringly beautiful sheen.

In sanding, an abrasive (flint, garnet, aluminum oxide, or silicon carbide) is rubbed over the surface of a softer material (wood, plastic, most metals) to wear down "hills and valleys" or "pores" by friction, and thus present a smooth, uniform surface to which the finishing material (paint, varnish, etc.) will evenly conform. Polishing (more precisely, *buffing*) is a greatly refined extension of the idea behind sanding. Here, relatively soft materials are rubbed across a coated surface of somewhat harder material. The object is to smooth the microscopic pores in the finish, so that its surface scatters less light, presenting a more reflective, mirrorlike appearance. Of course, "polishing" has farther meaning with regard to working with bare metals. It is the first of three steps used to produce a gleaming surface—*polishing, cutting down,* and *coloring.* Polishing is a coarse-finishing operation to remove pitting and scratches. Next follows cutting down, which is a buffing operation with emery, stainless, or tripoli compound. Finally comes coloring, which is a final buffing with a soft wheel or disc, using a fine agent such as jeweler's rouge.

Figure 10-1a–1d. Four sander and polisher types. Figure 10-1d is the BLACK & DECKER NO. 7960 POLISHER®. Photographs courtesy of Black & Decker Mfg. Co.

WHAT'S AVAILABLE
Hand power-sanders are available in three basic types— *belt, orbital/reciprocating,* and *disc.*

a

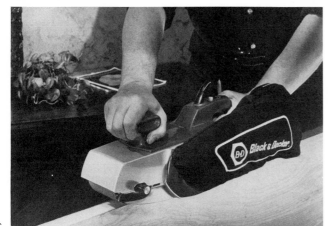

b

c

d

Belt Sanders

These heavy-duty tools consist of a hand-held housing containing a husky universal (series-wound AC, DC) motor with a gear-tooth drive belt that turns a continuous abrasive belt between fore and aft rotating drums. A rear pistol-grip handle and a front-mounted knob provide for two-handed control of the tool, so that the large abrasive

Figure 10-2. The belt sander is a workhorse among power sanders, capable of removing great areas of surface material from a workpiece, floor, or other household surface. GRAF-WHALEN photograph.

Figure 10-3. For dust collection, this sander features a built-in vacuum bag. An impeller creates suction, which draws dust into the bag to keep the workpiece free of material that might obstruct your view of the sanding progress. GRAF-WHALEN photograph.

area of the belt can be guided over the surface to be sanded with relative ease. Abrasive belts come in 3- and 4-inch widths, in different grits ranging from coarse to fine. Sanding speeds of most models range from 900 feet per minute to 1,500 feet per minute, with some models offering dual-speed switches. Most often used for large-area sanding (floors, furniture, production work, etc.), belt sanders raise a considerable amount of dust. Some models include a built-in vacuum bag attachment and a motor-driven impeller that suck up dust for easy disposal later.

Orbital/Reciprocating (Finishing) Sanders

For general home use and for fine finishing operations, either an orbital or reciprocating sander is a good choice. (Today, many manufacturers offer one tool with a selector mechanism that produces either sanding pattern.) Abrasive paper is held against a flat, rectangular, cushioned pad, supported on flexible rubber mounts on the bottom of the tool. The motor sits vertically within the housing, and its shaft drives an eccentric mechanism attached to the pad. In the reciprocating type, the pad is free to move only fore and aft, about 3/16 inch. In the orbital type, the pad can move in any direction by about the same amount, thus following the rotation of the eccentric mechanism. In either type, the restricted movement of the pad makes the tool easy to use, without the skilled handling needed to prevent gouging and rippling with a belt sander. For fine polishing, a lamb's wool pad can be attached in place of the abrasive paper.

Disc Sander/Polishers

There are two styles—*horizontal type,* with rear and side hand grips and right-angle gear drive, and *vertical type,* with side-mounted handles and in-line gear drive. The horizontal type is larger, but gives easier control of surface pressure, because the motor weight is not directly over the disc. However, the more compact vertical type has advantages when working where maneuvering space is limited. Both accept fine-, medium-, and coarse-abrasive discs, offering simplified attachment of the disc to the fiber or rubber backup pad. A lamb's wool polishing bonnet is easily attached to the disc with a drawstring closure for fine surface buffing. Other attachments are available, such as a grinding wheel (usually aluminum oxide) for fine surface finishing; a wire cup brush wheel for removal of paint, rust, or scale; and a drill chuck. The sanding disc diameter ranges from 6 to 9 inches in most common types, and a two-speed switch is standard in all but the least costly models. For general rough-sanding of wood, a disc type used at high speed is adequate. However, it is difficult to obtain a completely flat, evenly

sanded finish, because the rotary action of the disc tends to cause hand pressure to be uneven. What's more, the disc radius limits travel into corners (when resurfacing a floor or interior of furniture). Follow-up finishing with an orbital/reciprocating sander or manual sanding will usually be required. As a polisher, the disc type requires some skill in use; too much pressure and high speed can wipe paint right off the surface of your car. Slow speed and a gentle pressure are all that's needed for polishing. For general auto body refinishing, however, the disc type has the versatility to cover all tasks, from old paint removal, through smoothing, and all the way to final buffing after the paint job has cured.

Figure 10-4. Compact orbital/reciprocating finishing sander removes material more delicately than other types that are used before final surfacing. GRAF-WHALEN photograph.

Figure 10-5. This disc polisher can accept a lamb's wool bonnet for polishing or abrasive discs for rough-sanding. Photograph courtesy of Power Tool Division, Rockwell International.

IMPORTANT FEATURES TO LOOK FOR
General Points

Double insulation or a three-prong grounding plug, in those units having metal housings, are important to electrical safety. So is its mechanical design. Check the balance of the tool in your hands and be sure that the switch is easy to reach and comfortable to operate. The front handle should permit comfortable guidance of the tool without excess pressure. What's more, the handle should be set back from the front of the tool, so that your knuckles won't be bruised if the tool is run sharply into a corner. Good ventilation of the motor is essential, since it runs quite warm and can overheat if air vent holes are blocked. The housing should be shaped to prevent accidental contact with the rotating abrasive or its sharp edges. Abrasive belt, disc, or sheet installation and removal should be simple and, preferably, should not require disassembly. Ask for a demonstration of belt, disc, or sheet changing.

Selecting a Belt Sander

Weights of these tools range from 5 to 25 pounds. Heavy sanders usually have greater work capacity than light-weights, but their husky motors may also give the tool more "muscle" than your own muscles can comfortably stand. Lighter sanders are favored for vertical work (doors, walls, etc.) because they are more easily held and guided over the work surface. The work capacity of a belt sander depends upon its *size* and *belt speed.* These will often be found on the tool's nameplate or in its literature. The size is listed as the width and circumference of the abrasive belt that fits the sander. Common belt sizes are 3 by 18 inches, 3 by 21 inches, 3 by 24 inches, 4 by 21 inches, and 4 by 24 inches. (Generally, the larger the sander, the greater its work capacity.) The speeds of belts on different models, given in surface feet per minute (sfpm), range from 900 to 1,600. The greater the sfpm, the greater the work capacity of the tool for its size, or the faster it removes material from the surface being sanded.

The housing covers the motor, the upper surface of the abrasive belt, and one side of the sander. The other side is mostly open to make belt changing easier. Check to see if the housing allows you to sand close to a wall. Areas the belt can't reach must be sanded by other means. On some models, the rear roller, powered by the motor, has a soft, outer layer that grips the abrasive belt and helps prevent slippage. Other models provide a soft lining belt, over which the abrasive belt is placed for good traction. A trigger switch on the rear handle starts the sander, and most models have a button to lock the trigger switch on during prolonged sanding. The lock releases the instant the trigger switch is squeezed. A few models that offer two

speeds have separate slide or toggle speed-selection switches. To change a belt, you first retract the front, free-turning roller of a belt sander. Then, after the new belt is on and the front roller returned to operating position, you must align the belt so it won't run off to one side during sanding. Look for a simplified approach, so that belt-changing doesn't become a nuisance.

A belt sander produces large quantities of waste, or dust, from a work surface. Any one of three systems of dust collection is recommended—a built-in dust bag, a bag bought separately that can be attached as required, or an accessory flexible hose that connects to a vacuum cleaner. In the first two systems, dust collection is powered by a motor in the sander. In the third, the vacuum-cleaner motor sucks dust away from the sander. Look for simplified attachment and placement of hose or bag, so that it won't obscure your view of the work or impede your progress.

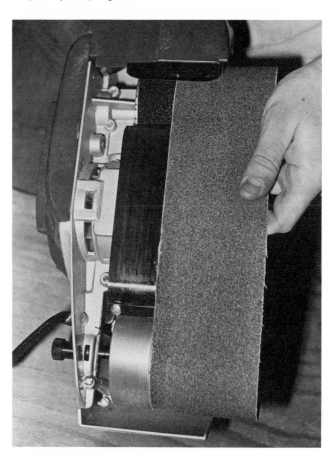

Figure 10-6. New belt slips onto drums of belt sander in seconds, so that you can change the grit from coarse to fine as your sanding job nears completion. GRAF-WHALEN photograph.

Selecting a Finishing Sander

Least expensive models commonly have vibratory motors and back-and-forth, or "reciprocal," sanding motion. Models that are moderately priced usually have rotary motors and a circular, or "orbital," sanding action. More expensive models with rotary motors are capable of both motions. Quality, special features, and size also affect price.

The work capacity of a finishing sander depends on the size of its sanding pad and the speed and length of the sanding strokes. These specifications are found either on a model or in its sales literature. The pad sizes of most models for home use range from 3 1/2 by 7 inches to 4 1/2 by 9 inches. Many catalogs and brochures list only the size of the abrasive sheet required to fit the pad. To determine the pad size, subtract 2 inches from the sheet

ABRASIVE AND GRIT	SANDING UNFINISHED SURFACES														
	SOFTWOODS (PINE, FIR)			GOOD WOODS (BIRCH, MAPLE)			HARDWOODS (FURNITURE)			PLASTIC			SANDING END GRAIN		
	ROUGH	SEMI	FINAL	ROUGH	SEMI	FINAL	ROUGH	SEMI	FINAL	ROUGH	SEMI	FINAL	ROUGH	SEMI	FINA
ALUMINUM OXIDE															
FINE (120—3/0)			■			■			■			■			■
MEDIUM (80—1/0)		■			■			■			■			■	
COARSE (50—1)	■			■			■			■			■		
GARNET															
FINE (120—3/0)			■			■			■						
MEDIUM (80—1/0)		■			■			■							
COARSE (50—1)	■			■											
NO-LOAD															
EXTRA FINE (240—7/0)												■			
MEDIUM FINE (180—5/0)															
FINE (120—3/0)															
RUBWET															
SUPER FINE (400)												■			
VERY FINE (320)											■				
EXTRA FINE (220)										■					
EMERY															
FINE															
MEDIUM															
COARSE															
FLINT															
FINE		■													
MEDIUM		■													
COARSE	■														

Figure 10-8. Quick-Reference Abrasives Application Chart. Courtesy of Stanley Power Tools, Division of Stanley Works.

length and about 1/8 inch from the width. Generally, a bigger pad means greater work capacity.

The speeds and lengths of sanding strokes are coordinated in three different ways in finishing sanders. On some models the speed is between 3,000 and 4,500 orbits per minute (opm); on others, the speed is doubled to around 10,000 opm, but the stroke length is halved. The sanding capacities of the two arrangements are similar, but shorter strokes give a glossier surface. Reciprocal sanders with vibratory motors have a speed of 7,200 strokes per minute (spm), the equivalent of 7,200 opm, and a short stroke. They can produce a fine finish, but they smooth more slowly than orbital models.

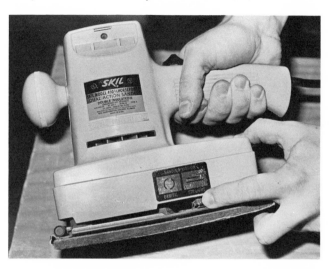

Figure 10-7. Orbital or reciprocating (straight-line) action is selected by flipping a lever on the side of the tool. GRAF-WHALEN photograph.

Figure 10-9. Sanding sheets of many different grit sizes are available for all orbital/reciprocating sanders, as well as a lamb's wool pad for polishing jobs. GRAF-WHALEN photograph.

SANDING FINISHED SURFACES

WET SANDING BETWEEN FINISHING COATS			REMOVING PAINT AND VARNISH			PREPARING AND POLISHING METALS		
ROUGH	SEMI	FINAL	ROUGH	SEMI	FINAL	ROUGH	SEMI	FINAL

If the housing extends beyond the edges of the sanding pad, hand sanding will be necessary, close to perpendicular surfaces and in corners.

Most models have separate handles, but some simply have a housing palm-grip. Try such a tool under power to find if it becomes uncomfortably hot to hold with extended use. Heavier units may have auxiliary handles, such as a front knob, to provide better control and more uniform pressure with two-handed use.

The on/off control on a finishing sander is either a slide or a trigger switch. A trigger switch usually has a locking button nearby. A slide switch locks on automatically.

To take a worn abrasive sheet off the pad of a finishing sander and replace it with a fresh one, you must operate a special mechanism. On some models, a lever opens and closes clamps at the front and back of the sanding pad. On others, you use a special key or a screwdriver to loosen and tighten pad clamps. Still others have spring-loaded clamps that must be held open while an abrasive sheet is inserted. Before you purchase a model, test the ease of abrasive changing.

Finishing sanders produce less waste than belt models, but you may still want a dust-collection system to keep your work and work area clean. You can buy either a model with a built-in dust bag or one that will accept a kit. A kit contains a plastic skirt to fit over the sanding pad, a flexible hose, and an adapter to connect the hose to your vacuum cleaner. Some manufacturers make dust-collection kits to fit all their models; others make kits only for some styles.

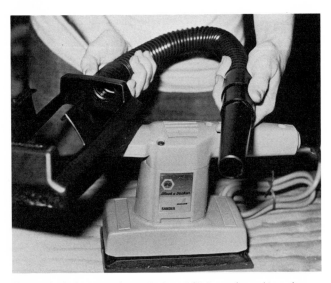

Figure 10-10. A vacuum base attachment fits to sander and to a shop vacuum to suck away dust from the area you're sanding. GRAF-WHALEN photograph.

Selecting a Disc Sander/Polisher

Least expensive models generally have small motor ratings and a disc diameter in the range of 6 inches or less and are usually of the vertical type. These offer somewhat less control over the sanding and polishing operation, because the disc straddles a small area of a large workpiece. However, for small jobs, low-cost disc sanders are adequate. Larger disc size and greater motor power of more expensive models can pay dividends in large-area sanding. No disc sander should be thought of as a finishing tool, where a superfine mirrorlike finish is required. However, for removal of large amounts of material and for scaling irregularly shaped surfaces, the disc sander is a good choice.

Most disc sanders have two separate handles, so you can hold the tool with both hands for best control. In some vertical models, the side handle is removable. This is rarely an advantage, except when working in tight quarters. One-handed operation of a disc sander is not recommended.

Work capacity of a disc sander is determined by the abrasic disc diameter and the motor rating. A husky model suitable for most homeowner jobs and many commercial tasks will have a 9-inch disc and a 1 1/4-horsepower motor, with selectable no-load speeds of 4,600 rpm and 3,600 rpm.

Disc sanders of the vertical type look very much like the common hand drill. And, just as a drill can accept a sanding disc as an accessory, so can some disc sanders accept a drill chuck. This can multiply the usefulness of the polisher, because it will then accept many of the accessories designed to be used with electric drills.

TIPS FOR SANDING AND POLISHING
Belt Sanders

Select the abrasive belt appropriate for the job to be done and install as directed by the tool's manufacturer. Pay particular attention to adjustment of tracking, so that the belt runs true with the tool's rollers.

Hold the belt sander firmly. With motor running full speed, apply sander to the work with a forward motion. Let the back of the platen touch the work first, then bring the platen into full contact as the stroke moves forward. The sander should be fed back and forth, parallel to the grain of the wood. Do not apply heavy pressure on the sander, as this will only reduce the speed of the sanding belt and cut down the rate of stock removal.

As the sander is fed back and forth over the surface, guide the sander sideways, overlapping the strokes. Work the whole surface down evenly, and do not let the sander dwell or a hollow will be made. Avoid tilting the sander when feeding, as the belt will make a gash in the work.

When removing old paint or varnish, use only open-type belts to prevent clogging. Make short, backward strokes lifting quickly at the end of each stroke to prevent burning the finish. Start each new stroke in a new area.

When sanding very small areas, make a small felt pad, about 1/8 inch thick in a proportional size to the area to be sanded, and insert under the sander's pad to reduce sanding area. Use this trick for sanding glue joints, smoothing plaster patches on walls, or feathering out taped joints on Sheetrock® walls. When sanding doors, trim, and other mill work, be careful not to sand cross grain at the joints, where the direction of grain changes.

Since grain is not present in metal, plastic, or stone, simply use a sweeping, rotary movement which overlaps every stroke. This will produce an even surface. Never use oil or other coolants, as the belt will throw the liquid.

Finishing Sanders

Select the appropriate abrasive sheet for the job and fit it to the sander pad. Most sanders use a pair of gripper rollers, which are tightened with a screwdriver to tense the sheet over the pad. Orbital sanders are not ideal for fine wood-finishing work, because half of the circular strokes made by the pad will be across the grain. This means that swirl marks produced by the motion must be removed by final with-the-grain sanding, either by a reciprocating sander or by hand. Combination orbital/reciprocating sanders solve this problem with ease, giving the user the fast removal of orbital action, plus the smoothing, straight-line reciprocating action for fine finish-work.

For either type of operation, hold the sander by both its handles and turn its power switch on. Apply the workpiece and move the sander with the grain of the wood. If much material is to be removed, orbital action will do it quickly. On the other hand, if fine finishing is desired, use reciprocating action, with the wood grain. Don't apply pressure to the machine; its weight will usually be sufficient to hold the abrasive to the workpiece when sanding a horizontal workpiece. For vertical work, light pressure is permissible.

For most work, the soft pad of the sander will give adequate support to the abrasive sheet. However, when smoothing a wooden workpiece, combining both hard and soft grains (such as fir), you may find it helpful to slip a thin stiffening piece of hardwood between the pad and the abrasive paper. This will spread the abrasive action evenly, so that hard and soft grain are evenly leveled.

If sanding causes the abrasive to clog, stop and clean the abrasive surface with a stiff-bristle brush. This will result in more even and efficient surface smoothing.

For polishing, a finishing sander can be a delight to use.

In place of the abrasive paper, use a piece of felt or lamb's wool material cut to match the size of an abrasive sheet. The fine motion of the tool is ideal for working wax to a high luster on finished wood and metal surfaces.

Disc Sander/Polishers

Select the appropriate abrasive disc and fit carefully to the tool as recommended by the manufacturer. Apply to the workpiece, tilting the leading edge slightly for better sanding action. Move smoothly along as the surface is

Figure 10-11. A polishing bonnet attaches to disc of polisher with a drawstring. GRAF-WHALEN photograph.

Figure 10-12. Light, gentle pressure is all that's needed to buff up a painted surface to a high luster. GRAF-WHALEN photograph.

cleaned, and avoid dwelling too long in one place or gouging and swirl marks may result. Similarly, avoid cross-grain motion, if possible, as this leaves more work to be done in the final touch-up, with a finishing sander or hand sanding.

For removal of surface coats from metal (such as car finish), use a moderate to high speed, with fine abrasive. Avoid excess pressure that will score the metal. If removed paint clogs the abrasive disc, stop and clean it with a stiff brush. When working on irregularly shaped objects, the disc will follow contours, with careful manual guidance. However, recognize that some touch-up manual sanding will be required, using abrasive rope or paper. Don't force the disc into impossible positions; the abrasive paper may tear or the disc pad may be damaged.

For polishing, a lamb's wool bonnet can be attached right over the abrasive disc pad and held snugly by a drawstring. Polish only a clean, well-cured surface, free of abrasive material that might damage the finish. Use the lowest possible speed, and avoid pressure on the tool. High speed and excess pressure can create sufficient friction to melt and wipe off a painted finish. Ideally, the polisher should "float" over the finish, as if riding on the pad's fibers. Some practice is essential to gain the proper "feel" of the tool before embarking on ambitious polishing tasks.

Abrasives for Use With Sanders

The materials commonly used as abrasives are garnet, which is a natural mineral, and aluminum oxide and silicon carbine, both of which are man-made. All are available in grain sizes and shapes suitable for tasks, ranging from rough-sanding of wood to finish-sanding of wood, plastic, stone, glass, ceramics, and metal.

The density of abrasive grains on a sheet or belt is termed "closed coat" or "open coat." Each abrasive grain has a space around it; such stock is for rough-sanding of wood and soft metals or removing finishes. In closed coatings, the abrasive grains completely cover the sanding surface and tend to produce a smooth, even finish.

The grit, or grain, size is the most important consideration in selecting either a belt or sheet abrasive to do the job wanted. It is designated by numbers. In the system commonly used, the numbers range from 36 for coarse, to 400 or more for extra-fine. In another system, which is being discontinued by most manufacturers, the numbers range from 2 for coarse, through 1/0 for medium, to 3/0 for fine.

The accompanying table shows the grit sizes recommended for common uses. Some experimentation may be necessary to get the best results with your particular sander and the pressure you exert using it.

Where hand-sanding is required for the final touch-up, care should be given to select the right abrasive. Three types of sandpaper grit are used on wood—flint, garnet, and aluminum oxide. These abrasives come backed with paper or cloth. Emery cloth is good for removing small amounts of rust from a surface, and crocus cloth polishes metal surfaces. An aluminum-oxide-based cloth is good to use on metal that is to be finished with a coat of paint or lacquer.

Recommended Grits for Specific Jobs

Name	Grit Number	Use
Coarse	36	Removing paint and heavy rust.
	40	Rough-sanding of wood, plastic,
	50	and metal.
Medium	60	Semifinish-sanding on hard
	80	wood, plastic, and metal.
	100	Finish-sanding on soft wood.
Fine	120	Finish-sanding on hard wood,
	150	plastic, and metal.
Extra-fine	220	Final-sanding for extra-smooth
	320	finish.
	400	

Figure 10-13. A worn sheet sands unevenly and may rough up the work surface. Inspect frequently and replace with a new sheet when wear pattern shows up. GRAF-WHALEN photograph.

RULES FOR SAFE USE
Electrical
When sanding or polishing outdoors or in a garage or basement, apply the usual safety precautions. A tool equipped with a three-prong, grounding-type plug should have its metal housing safely grounded. Even so, wear stout rubber-soled shoes to minimize chances of grounding your body. For added protection, even if the tool is double-insulated, a portable ground-fault interrupter is a very sensible precaution. (See chapter 40 for more information.)

Mechanical
Match the tool to the job, and don't overload a small sander by forcing it to work on a big job. Excessive heating of the tool signals that it is operating beyond its ratings or that its ventilation has been obstructed. Stop at once, and allow the sander to cool. Find the cause of the overheating before resuming work.

Personal
Cheap, plastic safety glasses are such low-cost protection that there is no reason to use a sander or other tool without this extra insurance. Dust and particles expelled by a sander can cause serious eye inflammation, so do all in your power to prevent dust from entering your eyes. Similarly, the fine dust will remain suspended in the air you are breathing, if you're working indoors. A low-cost inhalator will filter out these particles, so that they cannot enter your respiratory tract. This protection should be considered positively mandatory, if you are sanding an old surface painted with lead-content paint. Take no chances and use breathing protection. Individuals with sensitive skin or known allergies should wear gloves, long-sleeve shirt, and work pants to prevent contact with the materials removed by sanding.

SANDER AND POLISHER MAINTENANCE
Sanders accumulate dust as a natural consequence of their operation. This necessitates a careful cleanup at periodic intervals to prevent early failure. The motor is especially susceptible to dust infiltration and should be given a thorough brushing and vacuuming after lengthy use. Dust blocking motor vent holes causes the motor temperature to rise sharply. Similarly, dust which filters into bearings or the motor commutator acts as an abrasive on these parts. Its removal prolongs sander life. The two carbon brushes which supply power to the commutator section of the motor will usually be protected from dust. However, these components do wear with time, and after 100 hours or more use, they should be inspected and replaced, if necessary. (The typical sign of excess brush wear is unusual arcing and sparking and uneven operation of the motor with wide speed variations.)

In belt sanders, felt oil reservoirs are sometimes used to retain lubricant and are fed to the tool's bearing surfaces, as required. This reservoir should be saturated with oil at least annually. Check manufacturer's recommendations for details and other maintenance requirements.

11

Circular Saws

Not so long ago, the basic tool of the carpenter and home builder was the handsaw, and progress in home construction was measurable in the material-cutting operations a skilled worker could perform by hand in a day's work. But the invention of the circular saw changed the emphasis from material cutting to material placement and finishing, thus spurring the greatest improvement in home construction efficiency since home building began. First a professional's tool, the circular saw has gradually become as indispensible as the electric drill to any home craftsman who is confronted by a need to cut and fit wooden building materials in a fair-size home project. The principal reason is that it brings truly time-saving, large-scale, cutting power right to the job, in place of laborious "cut-it-here, place-it-there" work.

The circular saw can save better than 50 percent of the time and drudgery in home carpentry projects, and it is a handy adjunct to even the best-equipped shop with stationary cutting aids, such as a table saw.

HOW THEY WORK

The circular saw consists of a motor and gear train connected to a circular blade, all of which are supported in a housing fitted with blade guards, an adjustable base, guides, and convenient pistol-grip handle. (Some models also include a built-in slip clutch between the motor and blade, so that if the blade jams in the cut, the motor will freewheel and not burn out. The clutch also will tend to minimize kickback and loss of control should the blade bind in the kerf.)

WHAT'S AVAILABLE

Circular saws are rated by the blade diameter, motor current draw, and cutting depth. They range from the small 6-inch, light-duty models, to professional models of up to 10-inch blade diameter. Current ratings range from 6 to 13 amperes, and depth of cut (usually rated as a vertical cut) ranges from a minimum of 2 inches (adequate for a 2×4) to more than 3 1/2 inches. It's important to note that large blades usually cut deeper, but depths are not always consistent with blade size among different brands due to variations in tool design. Also, because a circular

Figure 11-1. Circular saw. Photograph courtesy Black & Decker Mfg. Co.

saw can be used for bevel (angle) cuts up to 45 degrees, as well as vertical cuts, the depth of cut at the most severe angle is an important point to check. Often, it will be up-wards of 1/2 inch less than the vertical-depth capability, varying widely with design and built-in features of differ-ent models.

Apart from differences in acceptance of accessories and different blade types, a basic choice exists between the type of gear drive used between the motor and saw blade. *Worm-drive* gear systems provide very high torque to the blade, giving it the power to overcome grain dif-ferences, knots, and other obstructions that would other-wise bog down the blade. Saws with this system are gen-erally top-of-the-line models and principally used by the building and construction trades. The high torque output and irreversibility of the drive provide smooth cutting of lumber, metal, stone, brick, particle board, and other composition materials in use today.

Helical gear-drive is used in moderately priced saws, rated for general homeowner use. Though generally a sound investment, a saw with such a drive system needs the help of a slip clutch to withstand the same loads that a worm-drive saw can handle. That's because helical gears can't take the sheer forces of repeated blade jam-ming indefinitely. The clutch is designed to "give" and let the blade slip, thus protecting the helical gears and motor should the blade bind or jam.

IMPORTANT FEATURES TO LOOK FOR
Size and Rating
For most homeowner and handyman jobs, saws in the 6 1/2- to 7 1/2-inch range are the best all-around choice. It's wise to err toward the large side in making a saw choice, as insurance against the day you'll tackle a bigger-than-usual cutting job. Also, don't be misled by the rpm (revolutions per minute) rating of the saw. It's usually rated with the saw biting nothing but air (no-load)! The real measure of cutting power is the speed under load. The closer this is to the no-load rating, the better the cutting tool you've got. If you can get a demonstration of the saw's cutting power before buying, by all means, take it. Your ears and hands are a good judge of a saw's cutting quality, and it's better to rely on "feel" than on a salesperson's chatter. Significant change in note of the tool's sound under load may mean a motor rating that's just not great enough for occasional big jobs. Also, sense the way the tool lies in your hands while you are cutting. If it's easy and natural, you'll cut longer and more accurately without fatigue. If it feels heavy and strange in your hands, requiring constant correction, support, and guidance, try another few brands before settling on a final choice.

Safety Features
No portable tool has quite the same capacity to inflict in-jury as a circular saw. And so, tool manufacturers have lavished great care in providing safeguards as built-in features of their circular saws. Most important is the *upper guard*, a fixed part of the housing that overlaps the vicious rotating blade, protecting you from accidental contact or from dust or chips being thrown back at you as the saw blade chews through its cut at high speed. The upper guard should be of tough, durable material that can withstand rough handling without chipping or breakage. It should completely cover the blade from top rear to top front, so that no portion of the teeth are accessible to contact from the working (upper) surface of the work-piece. Next is the *lower guard*, which has a multiple pur-pose. When the tool is not engaged to a workpiece, the lower guard pivots close about the bottom blade surface, protecting you, the blade, and any surface on which the saw is resting. Once the blade is spinning, the lower guard moves backward only enough to accommodate the blade's bite into the workpiece, shielding the user's body from accidental contact with the rear portion of the blade protruding through the workpiece. The lower guard is usually counter-weighted, so that it is normally closed unless the saw is in the kerf of a workpiece. In use, the guard is pushed back by the workpiece and telescopes into the upper guard, so that the blade is exposed only when you are cutting.

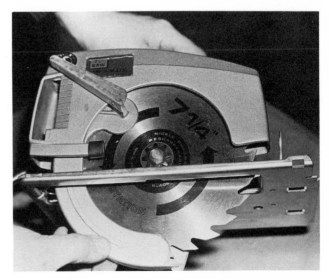

Figure 11-2. The upper and lower guards surround the rotating blade of the circular saw. The lower guard pivots backward and telescopes into the upper guard so that only the workpiece is exposed to the blade's vicious teeth. Lever at upper left allows lower guard to be manually retracted. GRAF-WHALEN photograph.

From the electrical safety standpoint, many saws offer double-insulated construction, affording antishock protection without the use of a grounding-type outlet or extension cord. Others require grounding for assurance of safety. Regardless of the type of protection offered, a portable ground-fault interrupter, between the saw and outlet, will provide an extra measure of safety, especially when you are working in areas where accidental ground contact is unavoidable. (See chapter 40 for additional details on ground-fault interrupters.)

Easy-To-Operate Power Switch

Trigger-type switches are universal on these tools. Be sure that it is easily and comfortably operated to minimize hand fatigue while you're cutting. But be sure the switch doesn't work on a "hair-trigger," enabling the tool to start by accident while you are changing hand positions or laying it aside.

Positive-Locking Blade-Depth and Tilt Adjustments

The cutting depth of the saw blade is usually set by adjusting a knob or lever on the housing. This knob should have a locking feature so that vibration won't change the depth of cut while you are working. On some models, blade tilt is set by a wing nut. This must be kept snug to prevent loss. If lost, it should be replaced before attempting use of the tool. Working a saw with a loose foot is an invitation to accident and at least a sure way to make a sloppy cut.

Adaptability to Accessories

Versatility and the ease with which a circular saw can be used increase with its ability to accept helpful accessories. A "riving" knife attachment that fits to the saw housing behind the blade will keep the kerf in the workpiece spread, so that the blade is not bound up as it moves ahead. An edge guide is another handy helper for ripping cuts, especially on long cuts. Some commercial guides are equipped with protractors, so that you can accurately set your saw for angle or bevel cuts.

Types of Blades

Over the years, a variety of blade types has been developed to meet a broad range of cutting jobs. Most, however, are special-case types. For all-around use in crosscutting, mitering, and ripping wood, the *combination blade* is the best general choice. It's the blade that comes with the saw at the time you buy. Depending upon diameter, it has from 36 to 44 teeth, is made of tool steel, and is suited to softwood, plywood, and occasional hardwood cutting. It provides rough, fast cutting, with and across the grain.

Figure 11-3. The trigger switch of a circular saw is naturally operated when you have a firm grip on the saw's handle. Releasing the switch causes the saw to shut off for safety. GRAF-WHALEN photograph.

Figure 11-4. The depth-locking adjustment sets the blade depth to the desired cut. A secure locking arrangement is necessary to ensure that this adjustment doesn't change while cutting. Solid shoe support means smooth cutting at desired blade depth. GRAF-WHALEN photograph.

Figure 11-5. Blade changing is a two-handed operation done only with the saw safely unplugged. The lower guard is retracted and an open-end wrench is used to loosen the bolt, securing blade to drive arbor. GRAF-WHALEN photograph.

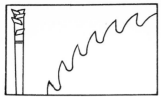

RIP
For ripping all hardwoods and softwoods.

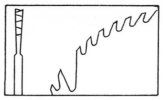

THIN-RIM COMBINATION
For fine trim and finish work and can rip, cross-cut, and miter.

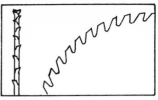

CABINET COMBINATION
For cutting in any direction in hardwoods and softwoods.

COMBINATION (CABINET-MAKER'S BLADE)
For free, smooth, and accurate cuts in any direction on hardwoods.

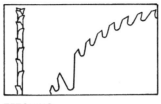

TETONING
For all-purpose cutting; wide-kerfed for cutting tenons and splines in all hardwoods and softwoods.

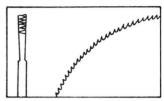

THIN-RIM VENEER
For satin-smooth finish cuts in plywood or thin veneers; no splintering.

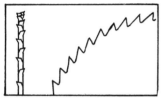

HARDBOARD SIDING
For cutting tempered hardboard (Masonite) underlayment, siding, perforated board.

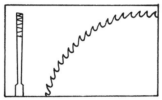

METAL CUTTING
For aluminum, brass, bronze, copper, zinc, and lead.

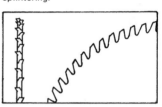

NAIL CUTTING
For rough-cutting through all woods that have an occasional nail.

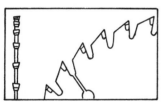

HARDBOARD CARBIDE—TIPPED
For wood or for cutting hardboard siding.

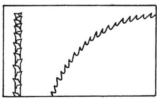

PLYTOOTH
For plywood, composition board, and soft board; smooth cutting.

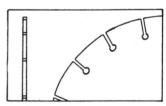

STEEL-SLICER
For light-gauge sheet steel, roofing, guttering, and downspouts up to 1/16" thick.

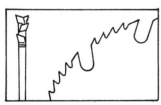

COMBINATION
For ripping, cross-cutting, and mitering on all hardwoods and softwoods.

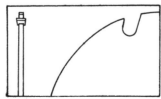

CARBIDE-TIPPED
For long cutting life; good for abrasive materials.

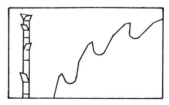

CHISEL-TOOTH COMBINATION
For all-purpose, fast cutting in all woods; excellent contractor's framing blade.

Figure 11-6. Use the right saw blade for the job.

If you plan to do a lot of ripping, you may do well to purchase a *rip blade*. Similar to the combination blade but with larger teeth for better chip clearance and less binding, the rip blade is well suited to rough, fast, with-the-grain cutting of softwood and hardwood.

For smooth cross-grain cuts, choose a *crosscut blade*. Its greater number of finer teeth (between 70 and 80, depending upon diameter) give a less splintered appearance to cuts across the grain, reducing your work in the final smoothing stage. A crosscut blade is also a good choice as a rip blade or cutoff blade when working extremely hard woods.

For the smoothest possible cross-grain cut, choose a *miter*, or *"planer" blade*. This is a slow-cutting, hollow-ground blade with fine teeth, but it permits very accurate cross-grain or rip cuts and is useful in fine cabinet and furniture work. The fine-tooth pattern also allows this blade to be used for cutting soft metals, such as aluminum or copper. The use of a lubricant is recommended when cutting these.

For tempered laminates, exterior plywood, and similar materials that tend to dull blades rapidly, your best choice is a *hard chisel-tooth combination blade*. The chisel-tooth pattern and small number of teeth make this a fast-cutting blade, and its hardened steel construction keeps it sharp up to four times longer than ordinary steel blades.

Paneling, ceiling tiles, wallboard, and thin plastic materials need the tender treatment of a *paneling*, or *fine-tooth blade*. Both have up to 180 teeth (depending upon diameter) and are slow cutting, but nonchipping, in their cutting action. This means a clean-cut edge requiring minimal finishing for those hard-to-cut materials.

Metal-cutting blades are offered in *coarse-tooth* and *fine-tooth* patterns for nonferrous metals and in *friction* types for cutting ferrous metals (such as light-gauge flat or corrugated steel sheet). Blades for cutting nonferrous metals (copper, brass, aluminum, magnesium, etc.) must be used with a lubricant. What's more, the binding nature of all metals makes choice of a worm-drive saw particularly prudent, because sudden jam-ups will be less likely to occur.

Grit blades are knifelike blades with an abrasive cutting coat on either side, extending 1/2 inch in from the blade perimeter. They are helpful for cutting and sanding in one operation and are a sound choice for use on veneers, plywood, hardwood, fiberglass, and plastics. Used with art and skill, they can be especially versatile in plough and dado cuts. They cannot be used on metal or for stone cutting. Tungsten-carbide, 36-grit abrasive is the usual coating, and long blade life is achievable when judicious care is taken in the material you choose to cut.

Carbide-tipped blades are true virtuoso performers when it comes to circular saw applications. They're costly, but they pay back the investment by staying sharp up to thirty times longer than tool-steel blades do when cutting new lumber. They are offered in coarse- and fine-tooth sizes, giving you the alternatives of fast, rough cutting or slow, accurate cutting. The carbide tips are brazed to the saw teeth and come ground in four basic patterns—*square*, *triple-chip*, *alternate top bevel*, and *alternate top and face bevels*. The square pattern cuts fastest, is strongest, and stays sharp the longest, but it produces a rough cut and may tend to wander with the grain in some hardwoods. The alternate top bevel pattern is a good choice for cabinet and furniture work, because it produces a quality cut, scoring the work before cutting it. For general carpentry and the occasional foray into cutting plastics and laminates, the triple-chip pattern is best. In this pattern, the first tooth chops out the center of the cut, the next clears the corners, and the third completes the cut. This gradual cutting action does not fracture brittle materials and minimizes splintering for a high-quality cut. The alternate top and face bevel patterns are especially smooth-cutting, accurate blades for the very highest-quality furniture work. The bevel in the cutting edges shears material in an alternate, one-two pattern that leaves a silky finish in the cut.

Rougher carbide-tipped blades are also available for handling stone, masonry, asbestos sheets and siding, asphalt roofing materials, and more. However, no carbide-tipped blade will last long if it encounters nails or other embedded metals in the material you're cutting.

TIPS ON USING YOUR CIRCULAR SAW

To make a good, clean cut with your saw, be sure that the blade is sharp. Next, set the correct depth of cut with the tool's adjusting knob. Don't expose excessive blade depth beyond that which you need for a good cut. Mark the workpiece with a pencil line to give you a cutting reference to follow. Grasp the tool and place it and yourself in proper position; then activate the switch and move the saw smoothly into the work, applying minimal pressure. (Forcing the saw will cause binding and overheating.) Keep the pencil line sighted in the notch in the saw's base as you move ahead. The high-speed blade cuts cleaner than a handsaw and cuts on the "up" stroke, rather than the "down" stroke. This means that the "good" side of the lumber should be facing down when you cut to minimize splintering on the finished-side cut edge. For most purposes, the saw-cut edge will be adequately smooth without further finishing. However, even for furniture-quality work, less sanding will be required than with handsawn edges.

In general, blades with few, coarse teeth cut quickly,

roughly, and need the most finishing. Those with numerous fine teeth progress more slowly, leave a finer finish on the cut edge, and require a minimum of finishing.

Cross-Cutting
Easiest of the straight cuts, cross-cutting is mastered with very little practice. A guide is handy, if you want to cut without marking the workpiece. The guide attaches to the saw; it is adjusted to place the blade the required distance from the board edge, and then it rides the edge and maintains this distance exactly, as the blade cuts across the grain of the workpiece. For cutting small pieces off a larger workpiece, a board can be clamped along a line marked on the stock. The saw base edge then rides the edge of the board, cleanly slicing off the desired amount of the workpiece. Where high accuracy is not the most pressing consideration, a freehand cut can be made, following a pencil line.

Ripping
A stock piece that is too wide for use and must be cut along the grain is *ripped* to size. Rip cuts should be made with a guide, since the cut is usually too long to permit freehand control. If a gauge is used, measure the distance from the far edge of the saw-blade tooth to the edge of the desired part of the stock. Set the gauge to this dimension; or pencil a layout line along the stock and clamp or tack a board along this line (on the waste part of the stock) to serve as a guide for the saw-base edge as the blade advances through the grain. A guide is important to prevent the blade from wandering and following a weakness in the grain structure of the workpiece. On long cuts, a riving knife may prove helpful to keep the kerf from binding the blade.

Angle Cuts
For crosscut or rip bevels, set the saw to the desired angle with its tilt adjustment. However, you should make a test cut before considering this adjustment final. Check the cut with a protractor and compensate, as required. In making the actual cut, a clamped-on guide strip or edge guide is an indispensable aid. Where many identical cuts are required, a kind of miter-box jig can be fabricated to guide the saw across each workpiece. You'll need a guide strip and a shelf support for the saw, and it is wise to immobilize the jig by clamping it to a sturdy bench.

Dadoes and Grooves
Notch cuts can be made by setting the blade depth to the required depth of the groove, and then making a series of overlapping cuts. Outermost cuts should be made with a guide. Internally, your cuts can be freehand, since

waste removal is the main objective. The cut can be cleared with a chisel. Where an angled notch is required, set the depth to slightly more than the notch required and make two cuts which overlap at the required angles.

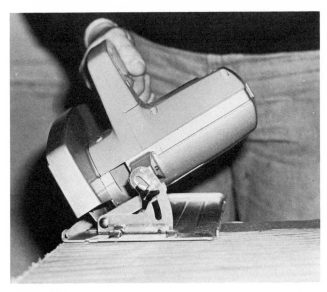

Figure 11-7. For beveled cross or rip cuts, the circular saw's angle is set and locked in advance with its built-in adjustment knob and scale. Bevel cuts can be made without a guide, but, where accuracy is essential, clamp a guide strip of scrap wood to the workpiece before you make the cut. GRAF-WHALEN photograph.

Figure 11-8. To cut a precise notch or groove (dado cut) the saw's blade depth must be precisely set in advance. Where accuracy is essential or the workpiece is large, a guide should be clamped to the workpiece. GRAF-WHALEN photograph.

Plunge Cut

To enter a surface from the top, rather than an edge, retract the bottom guard (power off) and tilt the saw on the base-plate shoe, over the desired cutting area. Apply power and gradually lower the saw so that the blade sinks into the workpiece. Once the blade is seated, cutting can continue in the usual manner.

RULES FOR SAFE USE

Your personal safety is the first concern when using a circular saw. All other considerations are secondary. In every cutting situation, think of yourself *first!* Don't take chances or act rashly. Keep your work area free of obstructions that can cause accidents. Be sure of your grip and control over the saw at all times. Wear snug-fitting clothes that won't catch, snag, or unbalance you. Support your workpiece solidly; it partially supports the saw while you're working. If a makeshift support collapses while you are in the middle of a cut, you could be in for trouble. Use clamps and other hold-down devices to give yourself a solid cutting surface.

Figure 11-9. Solid support of the workpiece, a firm grip on the saw, standing to one side of the saw's path, and knowledge of exactly where your hands are at every instant are the key points that will make your use of a circular saw safe and sound. GRAF-WHALEN photograph.

The saw should never be roughly handled while plugged in. The power cord should always be safely draped out of the cutting area, and the plug should be firmly seated in the outlet or extension cord socket to minimize the possibility of jerking or bucking due to poor contact and intermittent power flow.

Hold the saw in such a way that your body is not directly behind the blade. This way, if kickback occurs, there is little chance of injury. Also, don't use the saw for overhead cutting. The risk is very high and the rewards in time saving are not worth it. Finally, don't leave the saw where children can get at it. Keep it under lock and key when you are not around.

CIRCULAR SAW MAINTENANCE

Blade condition is the chief determinant of your saw's cutting qualities. After a blade has been in use for some time, you will notice a need for increased pressure to get the same cutting action. When this happens, remove the blade and sharpen it or have it professionally sharpened.

Clear away accumulated sawdust from the motor, and vent holes periodically to assure free passage of cooling air through the motor housing. A clean, dry paintbrush is useful for clearing dust.

Seasonally, remove and inspect the saw motor's brushes, replacing as necessary. Worn brushes rob the motor of full power due to poor contact, and replacement means full cutting power will be available when you need it. Do not allow worn brushes to remain in your saw beyond the point where replacement is called for. Excessively worn brushes lead to severe arcing at the motor commutator and can damage the contact surfaces to the point where costly repair is required.

Lubrication is rarely required by circular saw manufacturers. However, the periodic lube requirements set forth in the instructions accompanying your saw should be carefully followed to ensure longest service life for the money you've invested.

12

Scroll and Jigsaws

For all the brawn and cutting power of circular saws, table saws, radial-arm saws, and saber saws, they're no match for the scroll or jigsaw when it comes to delicacy of cutting, control of sawing pattern, and fineness of detailing. In finishing work and fine decoration, these thin-bladed saws are unsurpassed. They give you almost unlimited control over direction of cut and smoothness of sawed edges and an unhindered ability to practice true artistry in the little details of curve and shape that can transform a homemade workpiece into a masterpiece of the woodcrafting art.

The scroll or jigsaw consists of a motor-driven fine-tooth blade, which cuts vertically over a horizontal table that supports the workpiece. The cutting edge of the blade faces outward and is sufficiently thin to incise the work, while following the delicate urging of finger pressure applied to the work from either side. This makes it possible for the blade to follow curves and shapes penciled onto the workpiece in advance, to produce cuttings and scrollworks of great complexity with comparatively small effort. Blade thickness is of greatest importance here because the cut is not hindered by a blade, which tends to perpetuate the cutting direction. Curves, recurves, circles, openings, scrollworks, designs, and cuts of virtually any direction and of the smallest radius can be made with this tool, adding immeasurably to the craftsman's skill in producing a finely detailed end product.

WHAT'S AVAILABLE

Scroll saws are classed by the *throat size*; that is, the opening of the U-shaped blade support-arm, measured from the rear of the blade to the rear support. This determines the size of the workpiece that can be passed through the blade and maneuvered about the blade. Typical range of throat sizes is from 10 to 26 inches. Next, the depth of cut must be considered. Rarely does this exceed 2 inches, and speed of cutting is, frankly, slow. Within the range of available sizes lie the small, hobby jigsaws; the mid-size, multipurpose saws; and the large woodworker's saws.

The hobby jigsaw is dandy for small workpieces, such as dollhouse furniture, model planes, model ships, railroad layout pieces, some jewelry work, and soft-metal cutting. Magnetically operated by a vibrator-type motor,

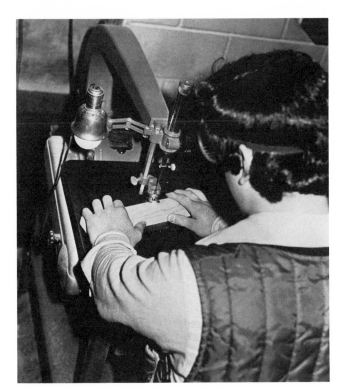

Figure 12-1. Scroll saw. GRAF-WHALEN photograph.

jigsaws have limited cutting power, but are capable of fine cuts when used within their limitations. Cutting is slow because saw movement is relatively slight.

The mid-size, multipurpose scroll saws are powered by smoother-running rotary motors that do not vibrate the workpiece, giving greater cutting capacity and precision. Larger throat size means bigger workpieces can be handled, too. One of the decided "extras" of the mid-size saw is its adaptability to a broad range of blades, plus its unique power takeoff. This latter feature allows attachment of sanding discs, buffing and polishing wheels; and a flexible, shaft-driven, hand-held attachment accepts miniature bits for grinding, carving, shaping, and smoothing. The potency of this combination is very great, because it gives you everything you need to finish a workpiece without resorting to use of bigger tools not meant for delicate crafting.

Large, woodworker's scroll saws are generally dedicated to cutting operations only and feature belt-driven mechanisms powered by a substantial motor. In these, the sawing speed is usually selectable by use of pulleys of different diameters. Featuring a large throat, heavy table, and rotatable blade (allowing sawing from the side, rather than into the throat, to handle larger workpieces), these top-line models have enough muscle to handle stocks of up to 2-inch thickness with reasonable cutting speeds.

IMPORTANT FEATURES TO LOOK FOR
Blades
The range of blades offered for scroll and jigsaws represents an attempt to match specific cutting jobs to saws of different cutting power. Generally speaking, however, the *jeweler's blades*, which attach by pins to the top and bottom members of the saw, provide a diversified choice of cutting tools. Offered in 12 to 32 teeth-per-inch (tpi) sizes, this blade type can accommodate materials as fragile as a seashell, or as tough as mild steel. The following table relates blade size to specific jobs. Blade width is a factor in making the right selection, too. Narrow blades are the choice when you need to cut complex, curved work. Wider blades are the choice for making progress through straight cuts or around gentle curves on fairly large pieces. Be aware, however, that narrow blades are tough to control, easily changing direction so that the cut line may not be as precise as desired. This means extra finishing work later. You'd do well to choose the widest blade that will let you follow the most intricate shape in the workpiece. Not all blades made by different manufacturers will fit all currently available saw models— a point worth looking into before you make your buying decision.

Figure 12-2. This mid-size, multipurpose scroll saw features a smooth-running rotary motor, plus a deep throat for large workpiece handling. The spring-loaded, hold-down foot acts as a "third hand" to keep the blade on course as you cut. GRAF-WHALEN photograph.

Figure 12-3. The rubber suction-cup feet on this saw's base keep the saw from "walking" on the bench during cutting, ensuring a cut that's true to the line marked on the workpiece. GRAF-WHALEN photograph.

Figure 12-4. A large, belt-driven scroll saw, featuring adjustable speed through use of stepped pulleys. The belt is slipped from one pulley to another to change blade speed. GRAF-WHALEN photograph.

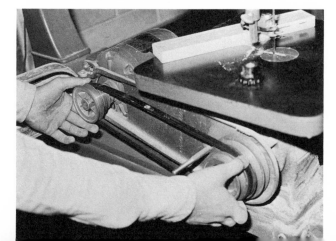

Choosing the Right Blade

Material to Be Cut	Blade Size (in Teeth Per Inch)	
	Fine-Tooth	Coarse-Tooth
Aluminum, lead, copper, steel	32 tpi (.07") 20 tpi (.25") 20 tpi (.35")	15 tpi (.07") 15 tpi (.11")
Wood, plastic, Bakelite®, hard rubber, ivory	15 tpi (.05")	7 tpi (.07") 7 tpi (.11")
Hard and soft woods, hard leather, shell	30 tpi (.054") 20 tpi (.054")	10 tpi (.11") 10 tpi (.187") 7 tpi (.25")
Asbestos, pewter, brass, hard aluminum, iron	30 tpi (.054") 20 tpi (.25")	12 tpi (.085")

Figure 12-5. Correct blade adjustment and tensioning is the single most important factor in accurate scroll-sawing. A too-loose blade will vibrate and bow, producing a ragged result in the workpiece. GRAF-WHALEN photograph.

USING YOUR SCROLL OR JIGSAW

Blade selection for the material and type of cut is the first task. Choose a narrow blade for tight curves, complex shaping cuts, and detailing. Wider blades are used for straight cutting or larger-radius work. The table on this page lists recommended blades, tooth counts, and blade widths for cutting different materials. You should practice with several of these to gain the invaluable "feel" for the right blade. Coarse blades will cause more chipping of material, but cut faster than fine blades; and narrow blades will be tougher to control through precise cuts than wide blades. The mix of characteristics for each cutting job needs study and experience.

Once you've selected the blade, fit it to the saw's chucks and set tension. You need enough to keep the blade from bowing under pressure, and narrow blades will need more tension than wider, more substantial blade types. Here again, experience is the teacher. With the blade in place, apply power and view the blade from front and side to ensure that it's running truly vertically. Adjustment may be needed. Stop the saw and set the table so that it is truly horizontal with respect to the blade, unless you are making a bevel cut. A square placed on the table, beside the blade, will make this adjustment a simple matter.

Many saws provide a spring-loaded, hold-down foot that applies pressure against the workpiece, to keep it flat against the table as it enters the blade. Most provide a tension adjustment, so that pieces of different thickness can be held with equal pressure as you cut. A light "drag" pressure is the setting you want; just enough to keep the blade from vibrating the piece, but not enough to hinder movement of the piece as you guide the cut. In no event should the arm pressure be so great that it scores the piece or leaves tracks.

It's wise to lightly mark the piece with a reference line beforehand, so that you can cut to this reference. Alternatively, you can glue a tissue paper outline drawing of the finished cut pattern on the piece with rubber cement and cut through both. The tissue is easily removed afterward, and any residual rubber cement can be rubbed off without damage to the piece.

To begin a cut, place the piece on the table, align with the blade, and press gently forward with both hands to prevent the piece from turning about the thin blade. The saw cuts fairly slowly, and you should time your forward movement to the tempo of its cutting action. Resist the temptation to rush. Craftsmanship should be unhurried. Don't apply sudden, jerky twisting force to the workpiece; it will be transmitted to the blade and may cause it to bind, and possibly, to break. Cut at the natural pace of the saw and feel its rhythm through your fingertips.

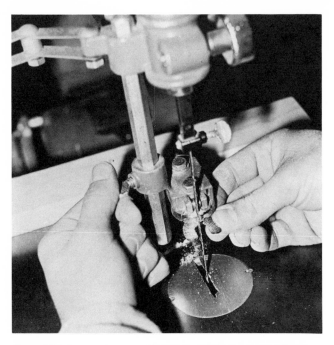

For straight cuts, it's wisest to clamp a square or straightedge to the table to serve as a guide. This will minimize finishing work. Freehand straight cuts most often have ripples, because slight feed-pressure variations give the thin blade a chance to wander slightly in the cut.

Metal cutting requires patience and skill. It may also require a cutting lubricant (such as wax or soap) applied to the blade as a preparatory step. Slow speeds are best, and finer blades produce least chattering and deformation of the workpiece. If you are cutting very thin metal stocks, you'll find it prudent to "sandwich" the piece between two thin wood sheet scraps. These will prevent curling and give you a finer-quality cut.

Low melting-point materials, such as plastics, pose a cutting problem, because the frictional heat of the cutting blade may soften the cut edges to the point where they rejoin if allowed to come together behind the blade. Here, a "splitter" inserted into the saw kerf may help. A toothpick, cardboard, or even a piece of waxed paper slipped into the kerf will minimize chances of the heated edges closing on one another and solidifying into a single piece.

Figure 12-6. In some large scroll saws, the hold-down foot can be adjusted to the workpiece size by loosening a thumbscrew and sliding a collar up and down a rigid shaft parallel to the blade. A light drag on the workpiece top is the ideal setting. GRAF-WHALEN photograph.

Figure 12-7. Hand position and pressure on the workpiece is critical to the scroll-saw cut. Careful, steady pressure, free of sudden jerks that will bend or warp the blade, are the sure way to a precise cut. GRAF-WHALEN photograph.

Figure 12-8. The power takeoff of this Dremel model operates a cable-driven head that accepts miniature brush, sander, grinding wheels, and other cutting and finishing tools for careful detailing of the workpiece after cutting. GRAF-WHALEN photograph.

Scroll saws that are equipped with attachments for grinding, sanding, and polishing make cleanup of the sawed piece convenient. These are especially valuable features when you are working with small pieces, because the attachments deliver finishing treatments scaled to the workpiece. Fine work thus need not be attempted with other, larger shop tools (such as a bench grinder or sander) meant to handle bigger jobs. Lacking this capability, you are best advised to hand-finish fine work with manual methods.

RULES FOR SAFE USE

Most scroll and jigsaws come equipped with three-wire, grounding-type plugs or are double insulated. Both methods afford effective antishock protection as a first line of defense against breakdown of electrical insulation. However, if you are working in a basement or garage shop, where you're likely to come in contact with damp concrete floors or other grounded surfaces, assume that your body will be grounded when you're using the saw. When all is well, this poses no hazard. But, if an accidental electrical failure should occur that makes metal parts of the saw "hot" with respect to ground, you could receive a shock. Failures are rare, but possible; and so, you may find it prudent to add a second line of protection by powering your saw through a ground-fault interrupter (gfi). This is a prudent investment in personal safety. Refer to chapter 40 for more information about gfi's.

Scroll saws can inflict nasty cuts if used carelessly, although not nearly as severe as the wounds that can be caused by the more powerful saws of the circular, table, and radial-arm variety. Regardless, it's prudent to protect yourself by knowing exactly where your fingertips are at every instant, relative to the blade. Don't let your attention wander or become so fixed on the cut that you lose sight of the blade. Remove rings and jewelry from hands and wrists before cutting. They'll only be in the way and they interfere with the manual dexterity needed to make a complex cut. Don't wear bulky clothes that restrict your movement or that might catch on the saw. *Do wear eye protection*. Plastic safety glasses will protect eyes from dust and chips. Keep a pair handy and have a spare for visitors, too.

Be sure that the blade is securely fastened and the saw ready for operation before applying power. Don't try to start the saw with a workpiece engaged to the blade—it sets up huge stresses that can snap the blade, possibly sending pieces flying at you. Likewise, while you are cutting, try to minimize pressure against the blade to reduce chances of breakage.

When you've finished using the saw, give some thought to securing your work area against inquisitive, but inexperienced visitors. This is especially important if you have small children. Pull the plug, turn the power switch off, and, if you have a master switch that will kill power to all your shop outlets, turn it off too. These barriers should adequately protect against most hazards of unauthorized use. However, the best recipe for safety is the homemade mix of ingredients you provide.

SCROLL OR JIGSAW MAINTENANCE

Scroll saws need little maintenance. A few drops of ordinary motor oil, applied to the bearing of the drive mechanism, will keep the saw operating smoothly for months at a time. The motor requires no lubrication, and, in smaller models, is of the shaded-pole induction type, which has no brushes. This means long, trouble-free operation. In larger models, fitted with belt-drive mechanisms, the belt should be periodically checked for wear, fraying, and stretching.

As blades wear dull in one spot on the blade length, it's possible to raise the table of some scroll saws to bring a workpiece into contact with an unused cutting section. This extends blade life and lowers your costs.

13

Radial-Arm Saws

If woodworking craftsmen were limited to owning one power tool, the overwhelming majority would choose the radial-arm saw. This would hold true for carpenters, cabinetmakers, and home builders, as well as home hobbyists. The reason is that no other single piece of shop equipment can perform such a wide range of woodworking operations so efficiently. Basic sawing operations such as cross-cutting, ripping, mitering, and beveling, plus more complicated operations, such as compound-angle cutting, can be performed quickly and more easily on the modern radial-arm saw than on any other powered shop tool. With accessories and attachments, the radial saw can quickly be adapted to dadoing, molding, shaping, sanding, drilling, boring, and routing—all with professional speed and accuracy. That's why the radial saw is regarded by many as "the one-tool workshop."

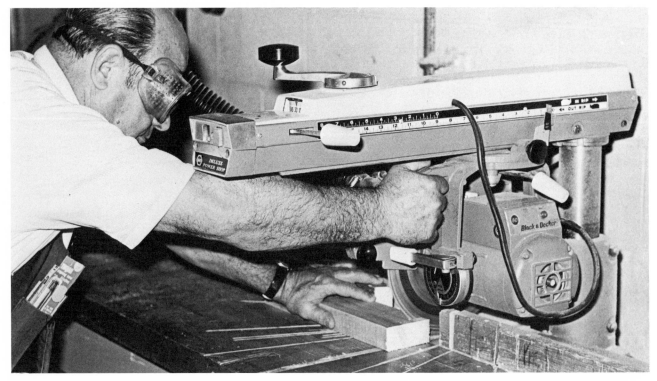

Figure 13-1. Radial-arm saw. GRAF-WHALEN photograph.

HOW THEY WORK

Unlike the table saw, in which the motor is *under* the table and the blade protrudes through a slot in the work surface, the radial-arm saw's blade-and-motor assembly is suspended *over* the work surface. Instead of feeding the work into the blade—as with the table saw—the workpiece remains stationary for most cuts, and the overhead blade travels *through* the cut, pulled across the track on the radial arm.

The motor is an integral part of the radial-arm saw and is mounted in the yoke. The motor shaft is a directly driven, threaded arbor that holds and turns the blades or other accessories. This arbor is usually 5/8 inch in diameter, with a threaded (left-hand) end for the arbor nut. The size of the radial-arm saw is specified in terms of the diameter of the maximum-size blade that can be placed on the arbor. For home workshops 9-, 10-, and 12-inch blades are recommended, with 10-inch blades probably being the most common size. Motors powering 9- and 10-inch saws are 1 or 1 1/2 horsepower, while 12-inch models use a 2-horsepower motor. Input power is 120 volts for the smaller horsepower motors and 240 volts for the larger models. Some motors can be used on either 120 or 240 volts by making the simple wiring changes specified by the manufacturer.

The arbor turns clockwise at about 3,400 rpm. Some motors incorporate auxiliary spindles that revolve at about 3,400 to 20,000 rpm to power accessories like routing bits and drill chucks. These auxiliary spindles are on the opposite side of the motor from the arbor and rotate in the opposite direction.

An important safety feature incorporated in the motor of many radial-arm saws is an automatic braking device that arrests the revolving cutter and eliminates coasting when electical power is removed. Others have manual braking, which is effective, but needs your quick action to ensure a safe, instant stop.

The radial-arm-saw blade is protected by a blade guard that attaches to the motor housing. This guard is removable and is adjustable in position around part of the blade. The blade guard *must* be kept in position whenever possible, because it safeguards your hands by keeping them out of the cutting area. It also aids in preventing the workpiece and sawdust from being hurled forward, toward you. Antikickback devices are a standard attachment. Metal fingers (pawls), suspended from the blade guard, trail along the work surface during ripping. The work can move through the blade (under the protective fingers) with little opposition, but on kickback (where the workpiece reverses direction) the fingers dig into the wood and arrest its backward motion.

A mounting frame (yoke) holds the motor to the carriage. This allows the motor and blade to tilt for bevel cuts. The yoke swivels 90 degrees (360 degrees is possible) in the carriage assembly, from a crosscut position to a rip position. The yoke is never to be placed at any intermediate angles between crosscut and rip; it must always be in either one position or the other. Part of the yoke is the operating handle that is used to pull the blade through the workpiece.

The carriage supports the yoke on the radial arm. Sealed roller-bearing guides allow it to move smoothly over the length of the radial arm. The carriage can be locked in a fixed position. The carriage, yoke, operating handle, motor arbor, auxiliary spindles, blade, blade guard, splitter, and antikickback pawls are collectively called the *head* of the saw. The radial arm, which supports the head and allows it to travel from one end to the other, rotates 90 degrees left and 90 degrees right to set miter angles. The vertical column, which supports the radial arm, raises and lowers in the base that attaches the column to the saw table. The dust chute helps to collect dust from the blade guard. Many saws also have a vacuum connection. A shop vacuum cleaner can be attached to this connection to reduce cleanup time and the amount of dust floating in the air.

The table is a workpiece support made of two or four pieces of 3/4-inch or 1-inch plywood, Masonite®-covered core, or chipboard, on top of a frame that is adjustable, so that the table can be leveled. The *fence* is a piece of 3/4-inch or 1-inch stock that fits between any of the table sections or behind the table. The workpiece is held firmly against the table and fence for crosscut and miter cuts or

Figure 13-2. The yoke clamp handle provides a friction lock between the upper face of the yoke and the bottom face of the roller head. GRAF-WHALEN photograph.

is slid along the table and fence for rip cuts. The fence and table are both sawed during normal operation of the saw and are easily replaced if it becomes necessary. The size of the radial arm and the table size determine the maximum crosscut capacities and the maximum rip capacities.

WHAT'S AVAILABLE

Saws come with a combination, or general-purpose, blade suitable for both crosscuts (across the grain) and rip cuts (parallel to the grain), and all can be used with accessories of their own or with accessories of most other brands. Blade sizes range from 8 to 10 inches in diameter.

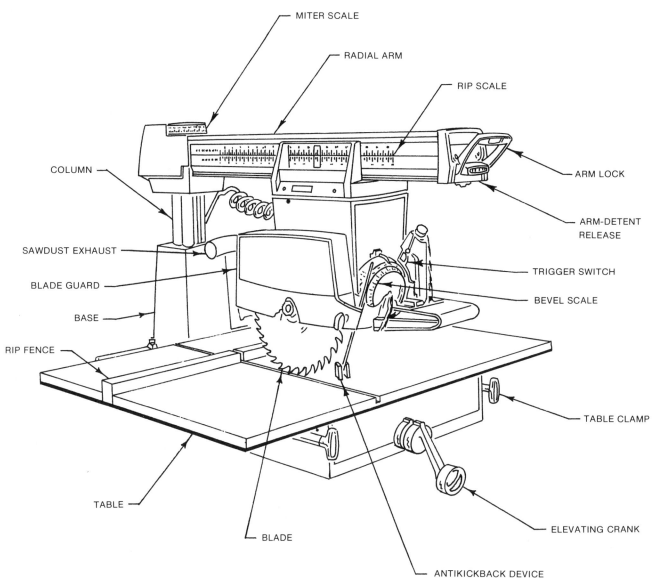

Figure 13-3. Principal parts of a radial-arm saw.

As the price of a radial-arm saw increases, certain improvements become more noticeable. The table is thicker, and greater mechanical rigidity improves cutting accuracy. On a large table, the maximum ripping-width may increase from 20 inches in a moderately priced saw, to 26 inches; and the maximum span of a crosscut may jump from 18 to 22 inches. Higher-priced saws have a number of extra spindles for running accessories at various speeds. Notable is a 20,000-rpm spindle that develops the high speed rotation needed by routing and shaping attachments.

IMPORTANT FEATURES TO LOOK FOR

A radial-arm saw's blade can be set in virtually any position over just about any point on the table. All models have a blade guard, but the guard on most radial-arm saws covers only the upper half of the blade. To supplement that protection, some saws include a floating lower guard. Others offer a floating guard as an option, in the form of a pair of rings or crescents attached to the upper guard and straddling the lower part of the blade. They glide lightly over the work, as the blade makes its way through the workpiece. The guard should be reasonably effective in preventing you from brushing into the blade's teeth from the side or from a quartering position, but won't do a thing to prevent anyone from pulling a crosscut through a misplaced thumb.

Saws incorporate an antikickback device, consisting of dangling metal pawl fingers that trail along the wood being rip-sawed as it's fed past the blade. These fingers are designed to dig into and arrest any backward motion of the wood. Some saws have a splitter disk mounted between sets of antikickback fingers. This disc follows into rip cuts as they are made, to keep the wood from pinching and stalling the blade. Kickback is a hazard peculiar to rip cuts. Do not compromise safety by removing the antikickback feature when making crosscuts!

Some saws have switches that can be locked in the off position with a padlock through a pair of ears that bracket the switch. Other saws can't be started unless a special key or button is inserted into a lock built right into the switch. These features make the radial-arm saw considerably safer for use in a home shop that is accessible to children. Consider your own safety when choosing a good-quality cutting tool, but don't forget those extra safety precautions that will keep young people from using or being injured by the tool when you're not around to shoo them away.

TIPS FOR USING YOUR RADIAL-ARM SAW
What a Radial-Arm Saw Can Do
Here's a brief description of some of the many cuts that can be made with a radial-arm saw. Specific instructions on setting up a particular saw are given in the user's manual.

Crosscut: A cut made across the grain of the workpiece at an angle of 0 degrees; that is, 90 degrees to the length of the workpiece. The blade is perpendicular to the table and drawn across the table and workpiece.

Rip cut: A cut along the grain of the wood. The blade is turned 90 degrees (left or right) and the carriage is locked in a fixed position on the radial support-arm. The workpiece is fed through the blade by using a fence as a guide.

Miter cut: A cut made across the grain of the workpiece at an angle other than 0 degrees. The radial support-arm is at an angle between 90 degrees left and 90 degrees right. The blade is drawn across the table and the workpiece.

Bevel cut: A cut made with the grain (cut) or across the grain (rip) at an angle to the surface of the workpiece. The blade is set at any angle other than 90 degrees to the workpiece. In other words, the saw is set for either a crosscut or a rip cut and the blade is tilted.

Chamfer cut: A bevel cut along the edge of the workpiece that does not cut all the way through.

Compound-angle cut: A cut that includes both a bevel and a miter cut or a rip cut and a bevel cut.

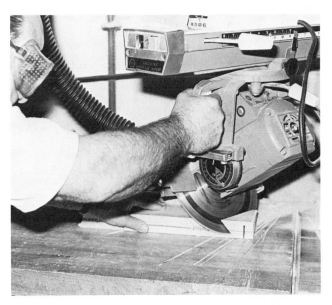

Figure 13-4. A compound-angle cut, which includes both a bevel and a miter cut, is easily made on a radial-arm saw. The yoke is locked in a crosscut position, the radial arm is secured at the proper miter angle, and the head is set at the desired bevel angle. GRAF-WHALEN photograph.

Making the Cuts

Your first cut should be a *crosscut*. Clamp the rip fence securely on the table, and be sure the blade is locked in line with the arm. Use a carpenter's square to check that the blade is at right angles to the fence *and* perpendicular to the table surface. These relationships must be accurate. Next adjust blade height. Turn the elevating crank to lower the blade, so that the bottom edge is about 1/8 inch below the underside of the work. At this depth, the blade naturally cuts slightly into the table surface, as well as through the rip fence on the first pass. This sets up reference lines on the table and fence that show the actual track made by the saw. Before starting the crosscut, move the head with the handle to position the blade behind the rip fence, near the vertical column. Then, position the workpiece on the table and press it evenly against the fence. Be sure to keep your fingers away from the blade. Now, line up the pencil line on the board with the slot in the rip fence. Remember that any saw blade has width, so place the kerf on the waste side of the work.

Once the work is lined up on the table, *and only then,* turn on the motor. Now pull the blade head toward you, through the slot in the rip fence and the workpiece. Move slowly so you can develop the right feel for the blade's best cutting pressure. A forced cut produces a rough cutting-edge. After the whirring blade clears the work

Figure 13-5. The rip fence and table are both sawed during normal operation of the saw. They can be easily replaced if it becomes necessary. To help collect sawdust, a hose from the exhaust port can be connected to a shop vacuum cleaner. This reduces cleanup time and the amount of annoying sawdust floating in the air. GRAF-WHALEN photograph.

completely, push forward on the handle and return the blade to the starting position beyond the fence. Now turn off the motor.

When cutting extra-thick material, you may not have enough blade surface to accomplish the full cut in a single sweep. In this case, make one pass, then invert the workpiece and pass it through the saw a second time. It is most important that the workpiece be carefully aligned before the second pass, so that the two cuts match and merge into a single smooth line.

The next most important operation is the *rip cut*, in which you move the work and not the saw. This is much the same as a table-saw cut. The blade is turned 90 degrees *parallel* to the rip fence and locked at the desired *width* of the finished piece. Be sure to adjust the anti-kickback device carefully, for there is a danger of kickback in a ripping operation. This danger can be reduced by adjusting the curved pawl fingers of the safety device until they just contact the surface of the workpiece. After the fingers are locked at the proper height, they will not impede the blade's progress—unless, of course, a kickback suddenly changes the direction of the feed. The workpiece must never feed toward the edge of the blade that carries the antikickback device; it must travel toward the rising edge of the blade. (Most blades have one or more arrows imprinted on their sides to indicate direction of rotation.)

To start a rip cut, turn on the power. Then, carefully place the workpiece flat on the table and securely align its edge with the rip fence. Using the fence as a guide, gradually feed the material into the blade. As the work progresses and your hands move closer to the blade, *be very careful.* Always use a "push stick" when the work is narrow or when your hand tends to move dangerously close to the vicious blade. Most saws have a movable blade guard that can be lowered to provide protection against accidental hand or finger contact with the blade. As soon as the cut is completed, turn off power. Be sure to wait until the blade comes to a complete stop before you remove the work.

Another important cut is the *miter cut,* which is basically a crosscut, but with the overhead arm swung to the desired cutting angle. After the required number of degrees has been set on the miter scale near the top of the arm, the blade is pulled through the work, as in crosscutting.

A *bevel* is cut by following the general procedure for ripping, except that the bevel clamp-handle is loosened and the blade adjusted to the desired degree of slant. The complete assembly must be resecured with the locking clamp before the cut is started.

Using Accessories

The combination blade supplied as standard equipment with all radial-arm saws is sufficient for most routine work. However, optional blades are available for best results on specific jobs. The choice is not limited to a given manufacturer's selection, because most blades are interchangeable if they have the same or smaller outside diameter.

Rip blades: Cutting *along* a wood's grain takes a lot more power than cutting *across* it, for in ripping, you are actually planing out wood fibers. Rip blades are specifically made to handle that planing job and for throwing out the resulting long chips.

Dado sets: This blade assembly mounts on the saw arbor and cuts grooves up to about 1 inch wide in a single pass. This makes it possible to cut slots that support shelves or staircase steps, as well as certain mortise-and-tenon joints, tongue-and-groove joints for flooring, and the like. The same results can also be achieved but not as easily, by making a series of overlapping cuts with a regular blade. Dado sets consist of two outer cutter blades, sandwiching a number of chipper blades. The more chippers, the wider the slot. For tenons or tongues, a few chippers can be replaced with spacing washers.

Plywood or planer blades: These are fine-toothed blades designed for cutting plywood without splintering it. They also can cut solid stock smoothly, which minimizes the sanding required for finishing.

Miscellaneous blades: Other blade possibilities are extra-thin cabinetwork combs (for fine furniture work), blades suitable for cutting ferrous and nonferrous metals, blades for Masonite®, and blades for flooring. Durable carbide-tipped blades are a good investment, if you frequently cut material that puts a severe demand on the blade. Blades differ from one another in silhouette and head-on view which tells, for example, whether the ends of the teeth are bent to the left and right or if they are bent at all.

Molding cutters: These consist of a slotted head to accept knives of many shapes. As the cutter spins, the knives cut a decorative profile in the wood workpiece.

Sand discs: These discs cut fast, so you have to be careful to avoid taking off too much stock. A shade too much pressure and the end grain being sanded may tend to burn; a light touch is in order.

Sanding drums: These accessories, which are less apt to char wood, are particularly good for curved surfaces. However, they also do well in straight work, such as finishing a rabbet. Most saws have at least one auxiliary shaft, protruding from the motor housing on the side opposite the arbor, in addition to the blade arbor. Attachments for that shaft usually need special adapters for connection.

Router bits: These are a class of attachments that cut grooves in wood, gouge out patterns in relief, shape molding profiles, make short, blind mortises for furniture work, and make other similar cuts. Most saws do not have an auxiliary high-speed accessory shaft; consequently, they do only a fair job of routing, because the accessory shafts run at the low (3,500 rpm) speed of the blade arbor.

Sawdust collector: This is a valuable accessory. It consists of a plastic shroud that catches waste and directs it to a box, bag, or vacuum below the chute.

Figure 13-6. Saw blades and wheels used with radial-arm saws.

NAME AND USE	DIAMETER (INCHES)	NUMBER OF TEETH
	4 1/4 to 12″	20 to 44

COMBINATION
For cross-cutting, rip work, and general carpentry.

NAME AND USE	DIAMETER (INCHES)	NUMBER OF TEETH
	6 1/2 to 8 1/4″	30 to 32

RIP
For quick cutting with grain. Has better chip clearance and less binding than combination blade.

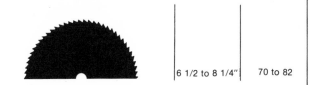

NAME AND USE	DIAMETER (INCHES)	NUMBER OF TEETH
	5 1/2 to 8 1/4″	20 to 28

HARD/CHISEL TOOTH COMBINATION
For cross-cutting and rip work. Teeth stay sharp longer. Good for tempered laminates, exterior plywood, and other materials that tend to dull blades. Resharpen by grinding.

NAME AND USE	DIAMETER (INCHES)	NUMBER OF TEETH
	6 1/2 to 8 1/4″	70 to 82

CROSS-CUT
For smoother cross-grain cuts. Also for use as rip and cut-off blade on very hard woods.

continued on page 78

continued from page 77

NAME AND USE	DIAMETER (INCHES)	NUMBER OF TEETH
	5 1/2 to 10"	50 to 80

MITER OR "PLANER"
For smoothest cut cross-grain or rip. Can cut soft aluminum or copper with lubricant.

NAME AND USE	DIAMETER (INCHES)	NUMBER OF TEETH
	6 1/2 to 8 1/4"	90 to 100

FINE TOOTH (NONFERROUS METALS)
For copper, brass, 3/8" or thinner aluminum and magnesium, 1/16" or thinner aluminum and magnesium, 1/16" and thicker plastics. Must be used with lubricant.

	DIAMETER (INCHES)	NUMBER OF TEETH
	5 1/2 to 8"	120 to 176

PANELING
For smooth, splinter-free cutting or plywood and other laminates. The smooth cut often eliminates the need for further finishing.

	DIAMETER (INCHES)	NUMBER OF TEETH
	5 7/8 to 10"	72 to 76

FRICTION (FERROUS METALS)
For cutting light-gauge flat or corrugated steel sheets, such as metal roofing.

	DIAMETER (INCHES)	NUMBER OF TEETH
	5 1/2 to 8"	120 to 176

FINE-TOOTH
For fine cut-off work. Can cut soft wallboard or thin plastic materials.

	DIAMETER (INCHES)	NUMBER OF TEETH
	5 7/8 to 8"	6 to 20

CARBIDE-TIPPED BLADES
Stay sharp up to thirty times longer in cutting lumber. Good for cutting hard-to-cut materials, such as asbestos sheets and asphalt siding, but should not be used for stone, masonry, metal, or wood where nails may be hit.

	DIAMETER (INCHES)	NUMBER OF TEETH
	6 1/2" to 7 1/8"	70 to 76

FLOORING
For repairing old floors; cutting crating or used lumber where nails might be hit.

SPECIAL PURPOSE BLADES

	5 7/8"	

KNIFE BLADES
For cotton sampling and for cutting rubber (up to 1/4" thick), Neoprene, rugs, fabrics, and similar materials.

METAL-CUTTING BLADES

	DIAMETER (INCHES)	NUMBER OF TEETH
	6 1/2 to 8 1/4"	30 to 32

COARSE TOOTH (NONFERROUS METALS)
For 3/8" and thicker aluminum, magnesium, or lead. Must be used with lubricant.

	6 to 8"	

PERMA-GRIT BLADES
Five tools in one that saw, sand, shape, dado, and plough. Can be used on thin veneers, plywood, hardwood, fiberglass, and plastics.

Assembly and Installation of the Saw

A radial saw has to be set up and installed in accordance with the manufacturer's instructions before it can be used. It must also be checked for calibration and corrected, as required. Only a properly installed, calibrated, and adjusted saw can be expected to give safe and satisfactory performance. While the initial setup is a fairly straightforward procedure, it will most likely take a bit of time and patience. Assistance will probably be needed to set the saw on the stand—for most saws weigh about 150 pounds.

Tabletops are made in several pieces—all have the front piece fixed; the rear piece (or pieces) are movable. Saws are equipped with a rip fence—a low, vertical plank, clamped in place that can be moved as necessary. In cross-cutting, the action of the blade's teeth tends to force work downward and toward the rear of the saw as the blade is pulled forward. The rip fence (against which the work should butt) opposes the backward motion. Next comes blade alignment. With the arm in its crosscut position, the blade has to be set so that it is at right angles to the rip fence—parallel to its track on the arm and perpendicular to the table surface. That's not as difficult as it sounds, and most manufacturer's instructions are generally quite clear. A carpenter's square or combination square will also be needed. All saws provide locating pins, wedges, or detents to help position the blade or motor yoke at any of several of the most common cutting angles, after which the blade or yoke can be locked into position. Miter scales also have detainers at commonly used points (45 degrees left and right and 0 degrees for normal crosscut).

The blade is set upright and parallel to the arm for crosscuts, tilted for a beveled cut, or swiveled at a right angle to the arm for rip cuts. The radial arm is set to point straight or to the right or left for square or miter cuts. The arm is raised or lowered to adjust blade height, so that the blade protrudes no more than necessary beyond the wood. Bevel, miter, and rip scales give the numerical angle-value of each adjustment. Locating pins, detents, etc., generally indicate a commonly used setting. The depth of cut is conveniently set in most saws.

Most saws are best connected to a 15-ampere household electrical circuit, dedicated to themselves alone. To protect the saw's electrical-supply circuit, use a time-delay fuse or a circuit breaker. Some models' motors can be internally converted for use on 220-volt lines. These saws will run a trifle more efficiently, because the line-voltage drop will be a bit less, and slightly more power will be supplied to the blade. That reconnection is a useful idea if you anticipate continuous heavy-duty use or if the supply voltage is often low.

Because the work is always placed lengthwise on the worktable, for crosscut *and* ripping operations, the relatively large radial-arm saw can be conveniently located against a wall in the workshop. There should, however, be room on either side to permit long workpieces to be placed on the table for cross-cutting or to be pushed through the saw blade for rip cuts.

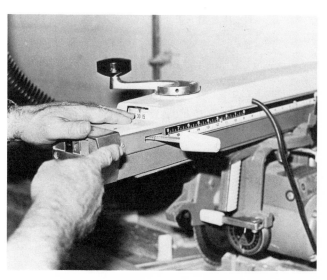

Figure 13-7. The miter clamp handle holds the radial arm securely in place once it is set at the desired angle. GRAF-WHALEN photograph.

Figure 13-8. The bevel lock holds the motor/blade assembly at any required bevel angle by locking it securely at the angle indicated by the pointer on the bevel scale. For vertical cutting, the pointer should be set at exactly 0 on the scale. GRAF-WHALEN photograph.

RULES FOR SAFE USE

• Always make sure that the blade is mounted on the arbor, so that the teeth of the saw point toward you and so that the saw can cut on the "pull" stroke.

• Make sure that stock is flat on the table and the back edge of the stock is held firmly against the fence when cross-cutting.

• The saw should be back as far as it will go before you start to use it for cross-cutting work.

• Be sure that the workpiece ends are supported at the same level as the table when cross-cutting long stock.

• The blade guards must be in place when the saw is in use.

• Before starting, make sure that the saw is adjusted for the correct depth.

• Make sure that the blade you use is sharp. Pinching or binding indicates a dull saw blade, *which should not be used.*

Figure 13-9. As the blade is pulled forward, its whirring teeth force the stationary work toward the rear of the saw. To avoid possible injury, it is most important that the work is held firmly against the rip fence. GRAF-WHALEN photograph.

Figure 13-10. Always wear safety goggles! The sharp chips hurled off by the high speed blade as it cuts through the workpiece can result in serious injury to unprotected eyes! GRAF-WHALEN photograph.

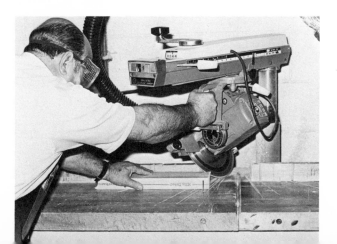

• The antikickback guard must be properly adjusted when ripping stock.

• Be sure that the stock to be ripped is fed *against* the rotation of the saw blade.

• Be sure that the stock being ripped has a straight edge.

• Saws powered by universal motors run much faster than induction motors and are by nature particularly noisy. Induction motor-powered models are nearly as noisy when cutting, but quieter when idling. Anyone who operates a saw with a universal motor for more than an hour or so should take steps to protect hearing. Wax earplugs are reasonably effective. They sell in drug stores for less than a dollar a pair. Earmuff-type protectors sold in sporting-goods stores that cater to marksmen can also be used, but they are more expensive.

• Always wear safety goggles, particularly when rip cutting. Sharp chips hurled off a high-speed blade can be dangerous to your eyes.

• Saws have an exhaust port on the blade guard, and most have a rubber sleeve inserted in that port. These sleeves can be swiveled to direct chips in a given direction, but they do little to reduce the problem of fine, airborne sawdust. It is best to attach a shop vacuum to the saw, via the sleeve.

RADIAL-ARM SAW MAINTENANCE

The saw blade should occasionally be checked for proper alignment to determine if the blade is square with the table surface. This is done by placing one edge of a steel carpenter's square against the edge of the blade and the other edge of the square on the table. Misalignment can be corrected by loosening the motor bracket and squaring the blade manually. The miter scale should then read zero. If it doesn't, the indicator found on most saws can be loosened and reset to zero. The blade must move evenly across the table as it travels toward the rip fence. A steel square placed on the table and pressed against the rip fence serves as a straightedge to provide a reference line. The blade should track from start to finish. Tracking compensation adjustments are usually provided on the saw.

Radial-arm saws otherwise require very little maintenance, especially those fitted with an induction motor, for there are no brushes to wear out. Always follow the manufacturer's maintenance instructions. On some saws, the track (in the arm) must never be oiled, but the elevating arm mechanism, miter latch, and bevel clamp do require a little machine oil. The tool generates a lot of sawdust, so keep it clean, for the saw works most efficiently if the arbor flanges (large washers that sandwich the blade), air openings, and various moving surfaces are periodically wiped clean of grease and dirt.

14

Reciprocating Saws

When you consider the arm-tiring, back-wrenching, elbow-bending effort it takes to cut any appreciable size workpiece with a handsaw, it seems entirely natural that someone would get the bright idea to create a motor-

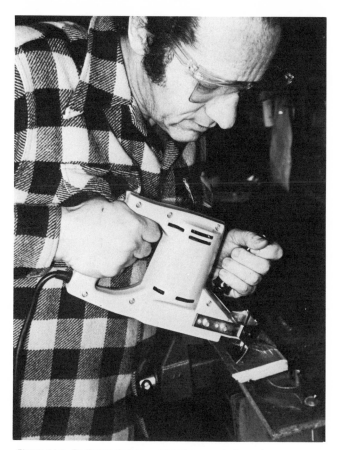

Figure 14-1. Reciprocating saw. GRAF-WHALEN photograph.

powered saw with the same kind of back-and-forth cutting action. That's essentially what a reciprocating saw is, and it is a useful tool for general home and garden use.

A sort of big cousin to the *saber saw,* the reciprocating saw features back-and-forth cutting action, with a stroke of 1 inch and more. It is a two-handed power tool, in which the saw blade extends horizontally from the motor housing, rather like the way the blade of a hedge trimmer is fitted. But in place of the shearing blades of the trimmer, the reciprocating saw sports a toothed saw-blade that ranges from a stubby 4-inch, fine-toothed variety, up through progressively longer and coarser-toothed blades, to a maximum of about 12 inches. Fitted with the right blade, the reciprocating saw can tackle so many wood, metal, and plastic cutting jobs that its versatility alone makes it a handy addition to the tools you keep in your shop.

HOW THEY WORK
The series universal motor of the recip saw has a very high starting torque, and so, the saw starts cutting the instant the switch is closed. The mechanism that converts the motor's rotary action to a linear, reciprocating action is similar to that of the saber saw (in some models) or to the hedge trimmer (in vertical motor models).

While the "recip" saw isn't as fast as a chain saw in cutting firewood or limbing trees, it will do the job with a bit more time; and, although it won't make quite as clean a straight-line cut as a circular saw or as smooth a curve as a saber saw, a recip saw can and will do all these jobs and more. For at-home jobs, such as "roughing-in" cuts in walls, panels, sheathing, plywood, studs, and plasterboard, the recip is a real glutton for cutting. It's especially useful for flush cutting in tight quarters and for making plunge cuts where no other tool can quite fit or handle the job. As a power hacksaw, the recip ranks high, too.

WHAT'S AVAILABLE

Recip saws are offered in a weight range of 4 to 8 pounds, with a variety of handle and housing designs. All, however, share the basic features of a rear handle with trigger switch (or speed control), a front handle (screw-in or molded), a blade ram (the reciprocating shaft that accepts the saw blade), and a soleplate (a rest attached to the front of the housing, through which the blade protrudes and about which the tool can be moved up or down when the blade is in the work). Blade attachment methods differ, but a clamp about the blade tang and the ram is most common, so that blade changing requires just a minute or so of work with a hex wrench or screwdriver. As in the electric drill, universal motors are the motive power of recip saws. Outputs of about 3,300 strokes per minute (spm) are common, although some models feature two and three speeds for selective cutting action on different stocks.

Figure 14-2. SKIL MODEL 474 DOUBLE INSULATED ADJUSTABLE TRIGGER SPEED CONTROL RECIPROSAW®. This reciprocating saw is longer than vertical motor types because its motor is mounted in line with the blade. A molded hand-grip up front and a pistol grip at the rear keep the tool well-balanced in the user's hands. Electronic speed control (like that found in electric drills) sets blade cutting speed in proportion to the finger pressure applied to the trigger. Photograph courtesy of Skil Corporation.

Figure 14-4. Double-insulated construction is a useful safety feature. The plug of a double-insulated saw has no ground pin. GRAF-WHALEN photograph.

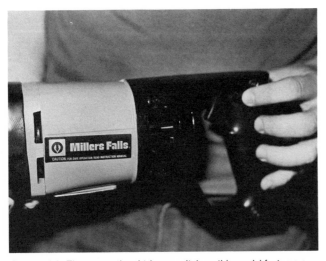

Figure 14-3. The conventional trigger switch on this model features a locking button to hold switch on during sawing, so you can concentrate on the cutting path of the blade. GRAF-WHALEN photograph.

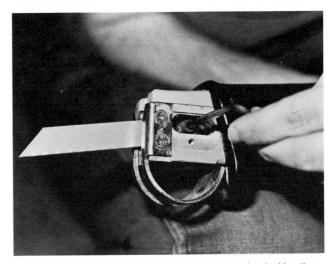

Figure 14-5. The blade attachment for this model requires locking the tang of the blade in ram with a hex wrench. Other manufacturers' models use different methods of blade attachment. GRAF-WHALEN photograph.

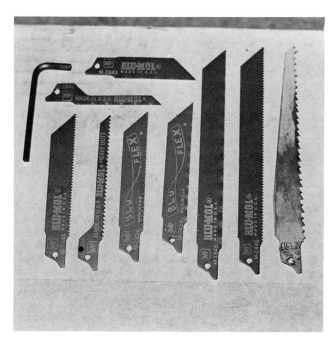

Figure 14-6. The range of blades available for the reciprocating saw is one of the strengths of this versatile tool. The accompanying table describes the selection of a blade to match the sawing job you face. Photograph courtesy of Miller Falls, an Ingersol Rand Tool Company.

For general-purpose cutting and plunge cutting, some models accept a 6-inch blade with 7 teeth per inch (tpi). This whips through 2×4s and 2×6s with ease, and plunges nicely into paneling, plywood, Masonite®, and wallboard. For sheet metal cutting, a 5-inch blade with 14 teeth per inch is a good choice. Brass, copper, or mild steel can be handled with a 5-inch blade with 14 teeth per inch. For coarse cutting (limbing raw wood or rough-cutting large openings, as for doors or windows), a large 12-inch blade, having only 3 teeth per inch, is available. Because blade-mounting arrangements differ, manufacturers' blades are rarely interchangeable. Also, there are some differences in length and tooth count among otherwise equivalent recip-saw blades of different manufacturers' lines.

Selecting a Blade

The following chart will help you to select the proper blade for each job. It is very important that you make certain each blade is straight before using it to avoid breaking the blade or damaging the saw. Use only sharp blades.

Guide to Selecting a Blade

Blade Type	Speed	Type of Cut	Material	Thickness
Approx. 7 tpi	Med.	Rough plunge	Wood	1/4–2 1/4″
	High	General	Wood	1/4–2 1/4″
Approx. 10 tpi	High	Scroll	Wood	1/4–2 1/4″
	Med.	Smooth plunge	Wood	1/4–2 1/4″
	Med.	Scroll	Composition board	1/4–5/8″
Approx. 32 tpi	Med.	General	Metal, thin wall tubing	3/32–1/4″
Approx. 8 tpi	Med.	Smooth	Wood	1/4–2 1/4″
	Med.	Extra smooth	Plastic	1/4–1″
	Med.	Extra smooth	Plywood	1/4–1″
Approx. 14 tpi	High	Straight	Plywood	1/4–1/2″
	Med. high	General	Thin wall	1/8–3/8″
	Med.	General	Ferrous thin wall	3/16–1/4″

Note: Due to variations in material density, hardness, etc., the above information should be used only as a guide.

Selecting a Speed

Some recip saws are capable of only one motor speed. However, others may be operated at either high or low speed. On these models, use "high" for soft materials like pinewood, plastics, or linoleum (some plastics may require "low" to prevent melting) and "low" for harder materials like steel and oak. Still other models are equipped with a "Variable Speed" switch that gives a continuous range of speeds. The same rule applies to these models as to the two-speed ones; the harder the material, the slower the speed.

TIPS FOR USING YOUR RECIPROCATING SAW

Your saw can perform many different cuts, each requiring a different technique and blade-shoe configuration. Here are a few general tips on using your saw, plus some specific cutting techniques.

• Never start or stop the saw while the blade is engaging the material. This places undue stress on mechanical and electrical components.

• Start cuts at an angle for an easier, cleaner start.

• Cut thick materials with a rocking motion. This allows the blade to cut less material at a time than it would if it were set to make a square cut, so that it works more efficiently.

• When cutting thin sheet metal, clamp the metal between pieces of scrap plywood, and cut the entire "sandwich" to minimize vibrations, which rob cutting efficiency.

• You will find that different materials are best cut with different forward pressures on the saw. Experiment a little. The saw will move forward smoothly and easily when you find the right pressure.

• *Always* grasp both handles firmly.

• The blade cuts only when it is moving on the backstroke, toward the saw housing. As a result, material with a finish on one side should be cut with the finished side away from the housing to minimize splintering. To minimize splintering on the face nearest the saw, clamp a piece of scrap material to it before cutting.

• Clearly mark the line along which you intend to cut.

• *Do not* force or bend the blade. It may break and injure you. If the blade binds, stop the saw (unplug it) and free the blade before proceeding.

• When cutting hard materials, pause periodically to let the blade cool.

• Cut close to the work support to minimize vibrations.

• On long cuts, place wedges at regular intervals along the cut (kerf) to keep the two cut edges from drawing together and binding the blade.

• *Never* cut material that is thicker than the effective blade length. The tip of the blade will bounce in the bottom of the cut, increasing stresses in the saw and hindering your control.

Perpendicular Flush Cutting

Install the blade with teeth in the vertical position and cut with the bottom of the housing facing the obstruction.

Parallel Flush Cutting

Install the blade in the horizontal position and cut with the bottom of the housing against the obstruction. *Important:* The shoe *must* be turned so that it does not interfere with the blade.

Plunge Cutting

Install the blade vertically with the teeth pointing down; install the shoe and its curved end down. Mark the line to be cut and rest the saw on the edge of the shoe with the blade off the work. Start the saw, and slowly pivot it on the shoe until the blade contacts the material. Continue tilting the saw until the blade cuts through the material and the shoe is resting flat on the work. You may now proceed with a regular cut.

RULES FOR SAFE USE

• Keep the work area uncluttered. A crowded bench invites accidents.

• Avoid use in dangerous areas. That includes wet or damp locations, dark areas, or places where explosives or volatile fumes collect.

• Store the saw under lock and key for child safety.

• Wear safety glasses or a face or dust mask where cutting produces dusty material.

• Don't mistreat the power cord.

• Secure your workpiece before cutting. A vise or clamp is much better and safer than your hand, and it leaves both your hands free to handle the saw.

• Don't change blades with the tool plugged in; disconnect the saw from the outlet for safety. Likewise, don't carry a plugged-in tool with your finger on the switch.

• Don't remove the soleplate. It serves as a guard and protects you.

• When using the saw outside, provide power through an extension cord graded for outdoor use. For added safety, consider a portable ground-fault interrupter.

• Use only sharp blades. Dull blades cut poorly and make the saw hard to maneuver.

RECIPROCATING SAW MAINTENANCE

There is a fair amount of variation in recip saw design, and so, some differences in maintenance recommendations exist from model to model.

Generally, most recip saws are powered by universal (brush-type) motors. The carbon brushes used in these motors wear down over a period of time and will probably need replacement after 50 to 100 hours of use. (Those are *saw-running hours*, which could take years to accumulate, considering that the saw is usually operated for only a few minutes for each cut.) In some cases, brush replacement will require disassembly of the saw.

Lubrication requirements vary with different designs. Most recip saws have bronze sleeve bearings, and the life of these will be extended by periodically applying a dab of light grease. Saws with sealed gear packs are generally claimed to require no lubrication during the saw's life.

Figure 14-7. Safety glasses, proper stance, a firm grip on the saw's handles (easy with the well-placed grips of a saw like this Shopmate model), and proper immobilization of the workpiece all add up to a cut that's quick, clean, and free of hazards. GRAF-WHALEN photograph.

15

Saber Saws

Next to electric drills, saber saws (or as they are also called, jigsaws or bayonet saws) are the home craftsman's and professional carpenter's favorite portable electric tool. The reasons? A saber saw is a versatile tool—light, portable, handy, relatively safe, and less expensive than other kinds of power saws. It can be guided with just one hand, as its small, narrow blade rapidly plunges up and down. It zips through planks of any width and up to about 2 inches thick, as well as plywood, hardboard, and even leather, ceramic, linoleum, practically all plastic materials, and light sheet metal. The blades slip vertically into a metal collar and are held in place by tightening one or two screws with a screwdriver or a small hexagonal wrench. When fitted with the proper blade, this lightweight machine can do the job of a ripsaw, crosscut saw, coping saw, jigsaw, keyhole saw, band saw, or hacksaw. The saber saw can also perform an extraordinary feat known as the *plunge cut*. The tool can start its own hole inside the area of a soft wallboard or paneling. It is also ideal for making quick cutouts in ceilings and walls to mount outlets, fixtures, or to run plumbing pipes.

Most light-duty saws with 5/8-inch-long strokes have motors that draw about 2.5 amps and develop up to 1/4 horsepower. Such saws readily cut 1-inch hardwood or 1 1/2-inch softwood. Heavier-duty saws with 1-inch-long strokes have motors drawing up to about 4 amps and develop around 1/2 horsepower. These large tools can rip 2-inch planks twice as fast as smaller models, and with extra-length blades they can cut off or notch 4×4s. A lightweight, light-duty saber saw is perhaps easier to handle, and, if you'll use it only for light woodwork—cutting off 2×4s and sawing plywood—it's just the tool for the work. But, if you'll use your saw in construction work, a larger, faster-cutting model will be worth the extra money. A heavy-duty saw is also preferable if you'll be sawing metal with the tool. Larger models have enough power to gradually hack-saw through mild-steel plate, and, because the longer stroke utilizes more of the blade's teeth, metal-cutting blades give longer service.

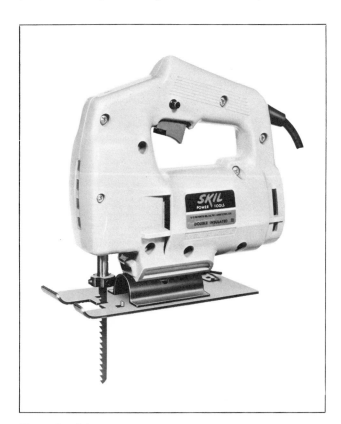

Figure 15-1. Saber saw—SKIL MODEL 497 VARIABLE SPEED JIG SAW®
Photograph courtesy of Skil Corporation.

HOW THEY WORK

When power is applied to the universal motor of a typical saber saw, a small gear at the end of the rotor's shaft starts to drive a husky 1 1/2-inch-diameter helical gear at full speed or at a rotational speed determined by the output voltage from the speed control module.

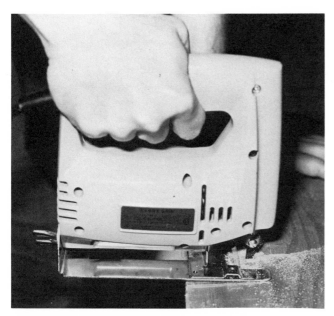

Figure 15-2. Saber saw in use. GRAF-WHALEN photograph.

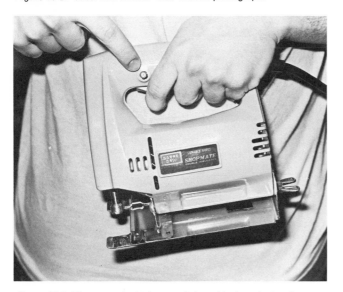

Figure 15-3. The convenient trigger switch and lock-on feature is universal in saber saws marketed today. Some top-of-the-line models offer variable-speed squeeze-control, replacing the trigger switch, for instant change of cutting speed. GRAF-WHALEN photograph.

From the other side of this helical gear extends an eccentric pin. This is fitted with a small roller bearing, which slides snugly inside a 3/4-inch-long channel, attached to a drive shaft that is free to move up and down inside a well-lubricated sleeve bearing. The other end of the drive shaft is fitted with a chuck (also called a locking collar) that holds the saw blade.

The eccentric pin and roller move in a circular path around the axis of the helical gear as it rotates. When the roller reaches the top, it pulls the channel (and subsequently the saw blade) up. For the next 180 degrees of helical gear rotation, it pushes down. Then it pulls the channel up again as it goes through a complete revolution, thereby converting rotation into reciprocating motion. This rotation to push-pull conversion is accomplished at high speed and produces the well-known, rapid, up-down strokes of the blade.

A fan blade attached to the rotor cools the motor, and, at the same time, directs a steady stream of air via a channel in the housing of the saw to the area where the blade meets the work. This jet stream of air disperses sawdust or shards of metal or plastic to provide a clear view of any guideline and to allow a constant check on the progress of the cut.

WHAT'S AVAILABLE

Saws come in single-, two-, or three-speed and variable-speed models. They are turned on and off with thumb-operated slide switches, toggle switches, or forefinger-actuated trigger switches. Slide switches are found mainly on fixed-speed models and they are generally self-locking for continuous operation of the saw. Some slide switches and all trigger switches are spring loaded so they provide "instant-off" action when pressure is released.

Most better saws incorporate an infinitely variable speed control that modulates motor speed and can be comfortably operated with the forefinger or thumb of the hand holding the handle of the saw. The speed-control module (see chapter 1 on electric drills for details) provides continuous variation in motor speed in direct response to trigger-finger pressure, and, thereby, smoothly varies the number of reciprocating cutting strokes from 0 to a maximum of 3,000 or more spm (strokes per minute).

The speed rating of saber saws can be misleading. The number of cutting strokes per minute is actually half the spm rating, because return strokes are counted, as well as cutting strokes. Also, note that the stated speed is the saw's *free-running* speed; as soon as the blade bites into the work, the saw slows down.

Different cutting speeds are needed for best results, depending on the material being cut—fast for softwoods and plastics and slower for metals and other hard materials. So that you don't have to hold the trigger precisely down, a small screw-in knob in the trigger switch of some models can be preset to limit the maximum number of cutting strokes when the trigger switch is fully depressed. If continued operation is desired for lengthy periods of sawing, a push-button lock can hold the switch on at maximum cutting speed on some models. A short squeeze on the trigger instantly releases the lock and stops the saw.

If your work is limited to rough-cutting softwood construction lumber and fir plywood, a speed of 3,200 to 3,400 spm does it most efficiently. You can also cut most hardwoods at this speed. For accuracy in thin plywood or hardboard, or, if you want to follow curves in any thickness, work at a slower speed—1,800 to 2,600 spm—the lower speed of the two-speed saber saws.

All saber-saw blades cut on the "up" stroke, so splintering and feathering will occur on the surface of the work that is in contact with the base plate. Thus, anytime the finish cut is important, work with the good side of the stock down. If this is not possible, work with a blade designed to produce a smooth cut, even though cut speed might be reduced. A little trick that may come in handy is to place a strip of transparent tape over the cut line before you saw. This does the job of holding the wood fibers in place, regardless of the blade action.

Some saws provide a straight up-and-down blade action, while others have a canted blade or one that moves in a small orbit. The last two types back the blade away on the downstroke and move it forward on the up or cutting stroke. This reduces power-wasting drag on the downstroke and frees the kerf of waste, which will reduce friction and heat and prolong blade life.

For sawing thermoplastics, use a slow speed. Otherwise, the blade runs hot and melts the plastic instead of separating it. As the melted plastic cools it closes the kerf behind the saw or it seizes the blade.

A comfortable sure-grip handle is most important so the saw can be held firmly against the work. This is particularly important when the saw is operating at high speed. Saws are equipped with an L-shaped or D-shaped handle, from which the power cord exits. Some models also have an auxiliary handle or knob for convenient two-hand operation. Since personal preferences vary, it is a good idea to handle a saw before you buy it.

All-metal saws are equipped with a grounding-type, three-wire power cord. Thus, a three-prong, grounding-type outlet or a proper grounding adapter are essential for safe operation of the tool. Such a saw is somewhat more durable, though a bit noisier, than the double-insulated saw, which has an all-plastic housing and does not require use of a grounding-type outlet.

Low-friction ball and roller or needle bearings in the motor and gear train are to be preferred over sleeve-type bearings, which are standard on most models. If the saw is to be used extensively for long periods of time, a saw with better bearings is likely to increase its durability.

Selecting the Right Blade

A wide variety of saber-saw blades is available, with each of them optimized to do a particular job best. Because the life of *any* blade is shortened by improper use and to achieve maximum cutting efficiency from your saw, always use the blade best suited for the job at hand. An inexpensive saber saw fitted with a fine-quality blade will generally outperform a more expensive one with a cheap blade. So it pays to always choose your blades with care.

The best saber-saw blades are not at all expensive. You can have an almost all-inclusive assortment of blades for just a few dollars and thus be prepared to cut anything from a thin sheet of wood to a sheet of steel 1/2 inch thick! A *good* assortment of blades can prove a most economical investment in the long run, for you will be less likely to use blades on jobs they were never meant to handle.

One "general-purpose" saw blade is usually supplied with each new saw. However, to use this single blade for *all* jobs would definitely be a mistake. To do so would surely reduce the quality of your work and, at the same time, increase your workload. So let's have a good look at some of the blades that are available.

The most popular blade for most rough-cutting jobs in wood is the *saw-set* blade, sometimes referred to as an *alternate-set* blade, because alternate teeth are spread left and right like those of a crosscut saw. Such a blade produces a relatively rough cut with a wide kerf (slot). A blade with 6 teeth per inch (tpi) is suitable for material more than 1 inch thick, and one with 10 tpi is recommended for material under 1 inch. A blade especially designed to cut plywood can reduce considerably—and sometimes even eliminate—the follow-through sanding necessary to get a good, smooth edge. For fast cuts, where smoothness is not a consideration, use a coarse-toothed, wood-cutting blade with 6 or 7 teeth per inch. Always use the shortest blade that will do the job, and also remember that a saw with less than a full 1-inch stroke—even if fitted with an oversize blade—may still not be powerful enough to cut through thick lumber.

A *hollow-ground* blade has teeth that lie in a straight line (like those of a rip saw), and it has part of the blade ground away to reduce its thickness. Such a blade makes smooth, narrow cuts, but it should not be used on curves.

Normally, you should choose a wide blade (3/8 or 1/2 inch) for straight cuts and a narrow one (1/4 inch) for doing curves. The thickness of the material also influences the

BLADES	MATERIAL TO BE CUT	TYPE OF CUT	SPEED OF CUT	TEETH PER INCH	BLADE LENGTH
	Soft and hardwood	Rough	Fastest	7	3"
	Soft and hardwood, plywood	Medium	Medium	10	3"
	Soft and hardwood, plywood	Smooth	Medium	7	3"
	Soft and hardwood, plywood	Smooth	Medium	10	4 1/4"
	Soft and hardwood, plywood	Smooth	Medium	6	4 1/4"
	Soft and hardwood, plywood	Smooth	Medium	6	4 1/4"
	Plywood and veneers	Fine	Medium	10	3"
	Plywood	Medium-Fine	Medium-Fast	7	3"
	Plywood	Medium	Fast	5	3"
	Plaster, lath	Rough	Fast	9	3 5/8"
	Soft and hardwood, plywood	Smooth	Medium	10	4"
	Soft and hardwood, plywood	Coarse	Fast	6	4"
	Soft and hardwood, plywood	Fine	Medium	10	2 1/2"
	Nonferrous metals	Fine	Slow	14	3"
	Ferrous metals	Fine	Slow	32	3"
	Leather, rubber, compositions	Smooth	Fast	Knife Edge	3"
	Plywood, plastics	Medium	Fast	5	3"
	Most wood and fiber building materials	Rough	Fast	7	3"
		Medium	Medium	10	3"
	Wood and plywood	Rough	Fast	7	3"

Figure 15-4. A wide assortment of blade types for every job and material make the saber saw one of the most versatile tools found in the home shop. Chart courtesy of Black & Decker Mfg. Co.

choice in blade length. Blade lengths can be short (from 2 1/2 to 3 inches) or long (from 4 to 6 inches). Even with hollow-ground blades, the smoothness of the cut depends to some extent on the number of teeth per inch. Thus, a cut produced by a hollow-ground blade with 8 teeth per inch might be rougher than that of a saw-set blade with 10 teeth per inch.

It is also good to remember that high-speed carbon blades cost more than carbon-steel blades, but they do last considerably longer.

Scroll blades have a narrow body, measured from the teeth to the opposite edge. As a consequence, these blades are somewhat more flexible and are, therefore, excellent for cutting intricate curves in plywood and similar material.

By using a blade with *wave-set teeth* (like those on a hacksaw blade), you can use the saber saw like a power hacksaw. These so-called *metal-cutting* blades are made of high-strength steel for durability at high speeds. They differ, one from the other, mainly in the number of teeth per inch. A common size is 32 tpi, with the teeth aligned in an undulating wave set. To cut heavy metal stock, use a blade with about 24 teeth per inch *and* a liberal amount of cutting oil. Always choose a blade with teeth fine enough so that at least two are always in contact with the metal. Cutting sheet metal requires a fine-toothed blade, 24 to 32 teeth per inch. For thicker metal and faster cutting, use a blade with 14 to 18 teeth per inch. Coarse blades are preferable on soft metal, which tends to clog fine blades.

When cutting relatively thin sheet metal, it is best to sandwich it between two sheets of plywood and follow the guidelines marked on the plywood with your saw. This will avoid curling of the thin metal and makes for a much smoother cut. This clamping technique also stops the metal from moving with the oscillating blade, thereby preventing the blade from cutting the material. In *any* metal cutting job, it is best to keep the cutting speed at the lowest practical rate to prevent the blade from overheating.

For cutting jobs in leather, rubber, cardboard, rubber tile, and the like, use a toothless knife blade that fits the saw like any other blade, but cuts like a knife.

A few manufacturers make blades that are intended to fit only their saws. When in doubt about which blade to buy for your saw, take the old blade with you and match the shank end.

Although all blades appear to be quite stiff, they can still twist, bend, or arc during the cut. The main cause of this problem is forcing the cut and thus trying to get the teeth to chew out more material than they are capable of handling. If the cut isn't progressing smoothly (you can tell this easily by sound and feel) and there is a need for ex-

cessive feed pressure, the blade is either dull, being overworked, or the wrong type. Do not, for example, use a wood-cutting blade to cut any metal other than aluminum or any other such soft metal that can be worked with ordinary woodworking tools. However, in a pinch, you can use most metal-cutting blades on hardboard, wood, or similar materials.

Always use low speeds for tough cutting jobs and high speeds for easy ones. Speed control is *always* an advantage, for you can alter the cutting speed in the middle of a job. Thus, you can slow down a bit when you hit a knot or particularly dense area in a piece of wood.

If you have to do much work with green, damp lumber, it pays to use *Teflon®-coated* blades. They're more expensive than conventional blades, but they generate less friction and can also follow sharper curves. Also, foreign matter is less likely to stick to this unique type of blade. For slicing through slatey clay pipe, brick, stainless steel, or ceramic tile, admittedly some of the most difficult of all materials to cut, use a long-life, toothless *tungsten-carbide* blade that will outlast conventional blades by an impressive margin. The cutting edges consist of hundreds of particles of tungsten-carbide granules that are fused to the blade material. These blades advance through the work with an abrasive action and *they can cut almost anything*. Cutting speed is not one of their strong points and they aren't meant to replace comparable toothed blades. Tungsten-carbide blades also work well on wood, where they will leave an almost sanded edge with an absolute minimum of splintering and feathering. Even an occasional nail that would quickly ruin the teeth of a conventional blade, does not present a problem with this blade type.

Fine-grit blades work best in thin, hard material (such as Formica®) where the quality of the cut is relatively important and chipping or delamination is a problem. To get the job done a little faster, use medium-grit blades. Coarse-grit blades cut the fastest, and, since they form a wider kerf, they can be used to make smaller-radius cuts than are possible with finer-grit blades.

TIPS FOR USING YOUR SABER SAW
Saber saws afford a wide variety of cutting options. The following are some.

Cuts to a Vertical Surface
No standard saw can cut flush up to a wall or other vertical surface, except with a special blade. The front edge of the base plate, or shoe, or the front of the motor housing projects ahead of the cutting edge of standard blades. Many saws have movable shoes that can be adjusted rearward, but they still have a gap between the cut and a ver-

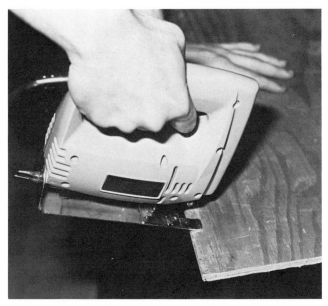

Figure 15-5. To begin a straight cut, grasp handle of saw firmly, so that the front of the saw lines up with the edge of the workpiece and the blade aligns with the section to be cut. Apply power and let the blade enter the piece. Don't force. Concentrate on guiding the tool. Shut off power before removing the tool from the workpiece. GRAF-WHALEN photograph.

Figure 15-6. The plunge cut is begun by grasping handle with the front of saw facing you, then tilting the front down and holding the base plate shoe against the workpiece with firm pressure. Apply power and ease saw back downward, so that the blade gradually sinks into work. Continue until the blade cuts through; then place the saw on its base plate and cut as with any common cut. GRAF-WHALEN photograph.

tical surface. Most saws can cut to within about 1 1/2 inches or less of a wall parallel to the cut.

Special flush-cutting blades are available that permit the saw to cut flush up to a wall. Some models have a movable base plate that slides back and forth—forward for maximum support in starting a cut and all the way back to get the closest possible cut to a vertical surface in front of the saw. A similar problem arises when it is necessary to saw parallel to an adjacent wall. You can get only as close as the saw's width will permit. Some saws solve the problem with a special side-cutting attachment; other models permit you to cut closer to the wall by mounting the blade at right angles to its regular position or by using a special blade that cuts at right angles to the normal cut. Some types have an extra-wide base and a side-mounted motor. These saws can cut closer to a wall than most other models *on one side*, but you can't get it at all close to a wall on the other side.

Scroll Cuts

When fitted with scroll blades, saber saws can easily cut curves in thin stock such as 1/4-inch plywood. But even with careful guidance, the narrow scroll blade may tend to flex or twist out of vertical while cutting heavier stock. The narrow scroll blades recommended for this work do tend to twist or flex, especially in thick wood, so that they're not completely straight in the slot.

The wider the blade, the less it will bend; the narrower the blade, the smaller the curves you can successfully navigate. When cutting curves or cutouts in close-quarter work, there may not be room to swing the saw about. Some saws have a swiveling blade-holder that allows rotation of the blade with a control knob atop the housing while sawing. It's not too easy to steer the blade with one hand and the saw with the other, but it can be done with practice. A thumbscrew generally clamp-locks the blade at any desired point in its rotation.

Plunge Cuts

It's possible to start a cut in the middle of a panel *without* drilling a hole for the blade. Simply tilt the saw forward onto the "ears" in front of the shoe—at an angle of about 80 degrees to the wood—and turn on the power. Then, by using the front of the shoe as pivot point, swing the saw gradually backward toward the work, until the blade bites into, and through, the wood. To make this plunge cut as smoothly as possible and minimize vibration, adjust the shoe to get the most overhang in front. Use the highest speed-setting and the shortest, stiffest blade possible.

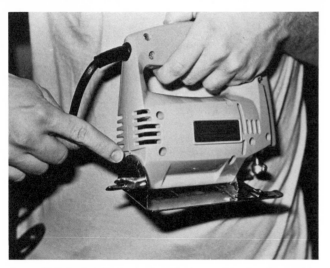

Figure 15-7. For bevel cuts, a nut can be loosened to allow the saw to be turned to the desired angle, as measured on an angle scale on the base plate. GRAF-WHALEN photograph.

Figure 15-8. A rip-guide attachment eases the chore of guiding the saw accurately through a long cut. Photograph courtesy of Black & Decker Mfg. Co.

Bevel Cuts

The shoe (also called sole plate or base plate) of some saber saws can be tilted as much as 45 degrees to the left and right to make bevel cuts. Some models have a convenient wing nut that loosens the base plate; with others, you need a screwdriver. Most have a scale to help set the desired angle, but some of these scales are hard to read. Keep in mind that bevel cuts reduce a saw's maximum depth of cut—by about one-third when the shoe is tilted 45 degrees.

Rip Cuts, Circular Cuts

Long, straight cuts with a saber saw, unaided, require an unusually steady hand. For that type of work, you can clamp on a straight-edged piece of wood as a guide or use a rip guide—an outrigger bracket that attaches to the shoe of the saw and keeps the blade parallel to the straight edge of the board being cut. The rip guide is also useful for cutting circles. A common technique is to drive a nail where the circle's center will be; then, with the guide arm as radius, you can pilot the saw, compass fashion, around the nail. Most rip guides stretch no farther than about 7 inches, nor do most come in closer than the edge of the shoe. But some guides slide under the shoe, making it possible to rip off narrow strips.

RULES FOR SAFE USE

A saber saw is not likely to retaliate for carelessness as savagely as a circular saw, but any power-driven blade can do injury. Except for double-insulated types, you should ground the saw electrically to guard against shock resulting from an electrical breakdown, and any extension cord should be the heavy-duty type. Always unplug the saw before changing blades or making an adjustment. If the saw has an angle adjustment, especially one tightened by hand, make sure it's set tight before you start work. When working outdoors or on a damp basement floor, you might consider the peace of mind that use of a ground-fault interrupter can provide. See chapter 40 for more information about ground-fault interrupters.

SABER SAW MAINTENANCE

The life span of any motor is greatly diminished by excessive heat. Thus, it is most important that the air vents in the saw's housing are not obstructed. Cooling air should circulate freely through the housing to prevent destructive heat buildup inside the saw. Should the vents become clogged with sawdust, they must be cleaned out with a brush, small stick, or cotton swab.

A few drops of light machine oil, placed in the appropriate holes in the housing that leads to the bearings at regular intervals, will assure trouble-free operation.

Some models are equipped with oil-storing felt pads that are accessible when the cover is removed.

Be careful not to change the position of the sleeve bearings that support the shafts of the armature and train drive while the saw is disassembled. Misalignment upon reassembly will result in excessive friction, which, in turn, gives rise to undesirable heat that can cause the saw to fail prematurely.

The motor's carbon brushes should be readily accessible for inspection or replacement. On some saws this simply requires that two small caps be unscrewed, whereas other saws may have to be partially taken apart to gain access to the brushes. They should be at least 1/4 inch long to prevent power loss and avoid possible damage to the motor's commutator.

Figure 15-9. A cooling airflow must be kept passing through the tool during operation or the motor may overheat. Clear dust and debris from vent ports, and don't block airflow with your hands. GRAF-WHALEN photograph.

16

Table Saws

For the really serious woodworker or home carpenter, a good table saw is an investment that pays and repays dividends over and over again, with each precise cross-cut, perfectly mitered joint, accurately grooved cut, or smoothly ripped piece.

A table saw can make crosscuts, rip cuts, miters, bevels, and compound cuts. Equipped with the right accessories,

Figure 16-1. Table saw. Photograph courtesy of Rockwell International.

it can also dado, shape, and sand workpieces. It is a large, stationary power tool, designed for stand-up use, and it has the great virtue of permitting very fine, accurate cuts to be made in large or small workpieces.

WHAT'S AVAILABLE

A table saw consists of a machined-flat metal table surface, supported on a sturdy stand with a slot located in the center, through which the circular saw blade extends. The table provides support as the workpiece is fed into the rotating blade. For high accuracy in cross-cutting, the table is precisely grooved to accept a guide known as a *miter gage*. The workpiece is pressed against the vertical face of this gage to keep it at a perfect, adjustable angle with respect to the rotating blade. Pushing the gage forward advances the workpiece through and past the blade so that each cut is flat and square. For accurate angle cutting, the miter gage can be turned to any angle up to 45 degrees.

The maximum blade diameter that can be used in a table saw establishes the cutting capacity of the tool. Thus, an 8-inch blade can accommodate a 2 1/2-inch-thick workpiece for a straight cut, decreasing to 1 3/4 inches at 45 degrees. A 10-inch blade can accommodate a 3 5/8-inch-thick workpiece for a straight cut, decreasing to 2 1/4-inch at 45 degrees.

The saw blade is typically held by an arbor which is belt driven (at speeds of about 3,400 rpm) by an electric motor of 1 1/2 horsepower rating or more. Two locking adjustments allow you to precisely set the height of the blade and to tilt it by as much as 45 degrees. In table saws meant for the home woodcraft shop, the blade itself is typically a 7 1/2- to 10-inch-diameter type.

For ripping (long cuts with the grain of the workpiece), the table saw comes equipped with a rip guide (or fence). This clamps to the front and rear edges of the table and has rails which allow it to move forward or away from the blade side, always remaining perfectly parallel to the blade. In use, the workpiece rides against the rip guide as it feeds through the blade. This ensures a clean cut, parallel to the guide edge, keeping the blade cutting true despite variations in grain direction. For safe use, the top of the saw blade is covered by a dual-purpose guard and splitter. The guard is a heavy-duty, transparent, plastic cover that makes it hard (but not impossible)

for your fingers to contact the deadly blade. The splitter is the back support of the guard. Made of metal, it is aligned behind the blade so that it slides into the workpiece kerf and holds the cut open. This prevents blade binding and kickbacks.

IMPORTANT FEATURES TO LOOK FOR

Table saws differ in the features they offer, while rarely differing in the basics described above. The basic measurements of a table saw's capability are the size of the table and its blade size. Table size determines how large a workpiece you can handle. Small units are designed for general cross-cutting and light ripping. Larger units can accommodate big 4- by 8-foot plywood sheets.

The rip guide (or rip fence, if you prefer) provides another measure of table saw capacity. Some are limited to the width of the table, while others have extension rails that hold the fence out past the table, giving somewhat greater capacity (24-inch capacity is typical). In practice, unless the fence is sturdily supported by heavy rails that resist vibration and sagging, some of the apparent extra capacity may not be usable.

The stand, which supports the table saw, is as important as the table. It must be heavy, well balanced, sturdily braced, and designed to prevent movement and creeping while a workpiece is being fed in. Open-frame, box panel, and cast stands are offered. Heavy-duty saws weigh in at upwards of 250 pounds. Light-duty hobby saws fall in the 50- to 125-pound class. General-purpose intermediates lie in between.

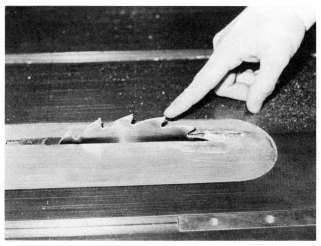

Figure 16-2. The table-saw blade protrudes through a slot in the flat-ground table. Blade height can be adjusted for stocks of varying thickness, and the blade can be changed to meet most cutting requirements. GRAF-WHALEN photograph.

Figure 16-3. Where a precise cut is required, the miter gage is used. The gage locks at any angle between 30 and 90 degrees and moves within a slot cut into the table. The work is pushed against the gage, which keeps the work at the preset angle as it addresses the blade. GRAF-WHALEN photograph.

Figure 16-4. The rip guide (foreground left) keeps the workpiece moving along a straight path as it passes through the blade. Here, a push stick is used to move the workpiece, keeping the operator's hands away from the blade. GRAF-WHALEN photograph.

The miter guide, rip guide, and adjustments should all adjust easily, but lock securely, in the desired position. This will give you a positive control over cutting operations, without the loss of accuracy through "slop" in the adjustment or creepage of settings.

The power switch should be located where it is immediately accessible for shutoff—up front on the table. It should also be positioned or mechanically guarded so that it cannot be turned on by accident. A three-wire, grounding-type plug is an essential safety feature.

A see-through blade guard/splitter is an indispensable safety feature. It should be sturdily made, able to resist normal wear and tear, and should give an unobstructed clear view of the blade and where it will enter the workpiece. Antikickback pawls are additional safety items that will prevent the workpiece from being thrown back at you during ripping jobs.

Every table saw will eventually need adjustment to preserve its cutting accuracy. This includes the blade perpendicularity; rip-guide parallelism to blade; miter gage setting; and accuracy and repeatability of bevel gage setting, rip scale setting, and blade height. Also, in belt-and-pulley drive systems, expect to tighten or replace the belt after many hours of use. Have your dealer go over each of these points with you before settling on a final choice.

For versatility, choose a table saw that can accommodate a wide range of attachments and accessories; for example: dado-head sets, sanding disc-attachments, tenoning attachments, molding inserts, cutter-head sets, cutter-head knives, taper jigs, etc.

Blades

The blades used on table saws are essentially the same as those used on radial-arm saws, differing only in the method of use. Here is a brief rundown on the five principal blade types:

Combination blade: This is an all-purpose blade, useful for cross-cutting, ripping, mitering, and beveling. It works well in soft or hard woods as a crosscut or mitering blade, and it rips furniture stock with ease. Its teeth are set for fast, precise, and smooth cutting, and expansion slots are provided to keep the blade cutting free. The blade is ground flat and usually has two or more *cutting teeth* followed by a *cleaner tooth.* (A *planer combination blade* differs in that it is ground hollow on both sides to keep the blade from binding in the kerf and in that it cuts smoothly, eliminating the need for sanding to a great extent.)

Free-cutting rip blade: This blade is an excellent choice for with-the-grain sawing in all woods. It is also a good choice for resawing. The teeth are like a series of chisels, and the blade has extra-deep gullets to sweep out sawdust, so that each tooth gets a clear path for cutting. Expansion slots are provided to keep the blade cutting free.

Crosscut blade: For sawing across the grain of a workpiece, this blade is equipped with alternate bevel teeth that shear and sever wood fibers cleanly. Where the bulk of the work is cross-cutting, this blade should be chosen over the combination type. (A special, flat-ground, crosscut plywood blade is also available where work involves much cutting of plywood, fiberboard, veneers, and other sensitive materials. The blade's fine teeth produce no splinters and leave a smooth surface on the cut plywood, requiring no sanding in most cases.)

Carbide-tipped blade: Where durability of the cutting edge is a big factor, the extra expense of these tough blades is well justified. With a life of ten times that of chrome-nickel-molybdenum steel blades, these heavy-duty wonders can easily handle any job of cutting in hard or soft woods, laminates, plywood, plastics, and other hard-to-cut materials. They can even be used on soft aluminum, asbestos, and brass. However, they're not intended for use on ferrous (iron-based) metals or on masonry.

Plywood and veneer blade: Where the cutting must be extra fine, without chipping or splintering, this blade will do the trick. It's meant for use in sensitive materials like paneling, veneers, and furniture-grade finishing. The blade has a taper-ground rim for smooth cutting, and its fine teeth require no setting.

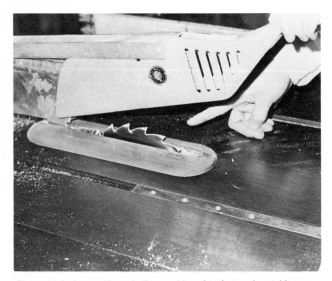

Figure 16-5. A guard is an indispensable safety feature in a table saw. This lift-up guard hugs the workpiece to keep your hands away from the dangerous blade. Don't thwart the sound safety engineering of your table saw by removing the guard. It's there for your protection. GRAF-WHALEN photograph.

COMBINATION
For cross-cutting, rip work, and general carpentry.

RIP
For quick cutting with grain. Has better chip clearance and less binding than combination blade.

HARD/CHISEL TOOTH COMBINATION
For cross-cutting and rip work. Teeth stay sharp longer. Good for tempered laminates, exterior plywood, and other materials that tend to dull blades. Resharpen by grinding.

CROSS-CUT
For smoother cross-grain cuts. Also for use as rip and cut-off blade on very hard woods.

MITER OR "PLANER"
For smoothest cut cross-grain or rip. Can cut soft aluminum or copper with lubricant.

FINE-TOOTH
For fine cut-off work. Can cut soft wallboard or thin plastic materials.

FLOORING
For repairing old floors; cutting crating or used lumber where nails might be hit.

PANELING
For smooth, splinter-free cutting or plywood and other laminates. The smooth cut often eliminates the need for further finishing.

PERMA-GRIT BLADES
Five tools in one that saw, sand, shape, dado, and plough. Can be used on thin veneers, plywood, hardwood, fiberglass, and plastics.

KNIFE BLADES
For cotton sampling and for cutting rubber (up to 1/4" thick), Neoprene, rugs, fabrics, and similar materials.

CARBIDE-TIPPED BLADES
Stay sharp up to thirty times longer in cutting lumber. Good for cutting hard-to-cut materials, such as asbestos sheets and asphalt siding, but should not be used for stone, masonry, metal, or wood where nails may be hit.

METAL-CUTTING BLADES

COARSE TOOTH (NONFERROUS METALS)
For 3/8" and thicker aluminum, magnesium, or lead. Must be used with lubricant.

FINE TOOTH (NONFERROUS METALS)
For copper, brass, 3/8" or thinner aluminum and magnesium, 1/16" or thinner aluminum and magnesium, 1/16" and thicker plastics. Must be used with lubricant.

FRICTION (FERROUS METALS)
For cutting light-gauge flat or corrugated steel sheets, such as metal roofing.

Figure 16-6. Blades for table saws.

Heads

Dado head: A dado head can be used to cut *dadoes* (grooves across the grain of a workpiece), *ploughs* (grooves which follow the grain of a workpiece), and *rabbets* (grooves cut in the edge of a workpiece to receive another piece to form a joint).

Two types of dado heads are available—the *adjustable* and the *blade-and-chipper set.* The adjustable type can be set to cut from 1/4-inch to 13/16-inch-wide dadoes, increasing in 1/16-inch steps. It has carbide-tipped teeth for long life. The blade-and-chipper set consists of a "sandwich" of two combination blades (the outermost blades) plus a selection of 1/8-inch chippers or a 1/16-inch chipper. In use, the sandwich is assembled to obtain the desired width (range: 1/8-inch to 13/16-inch). Paper washers are used to take up slack on the arbor. The process of setting up is time-consuming, and the blades must be adjusted for correct rotation and synchronism of cut.

Molding (shaping) heads: Decorative surfaces and moldings can be created on a workpiece with the use of a molding head. The head accepts one or more sets of cutters, which, in rotating, cut away the material from the workpiece to leave the molding shape. Coves, beads, rounds, flutes, sashes, thumbs, lips, V-grooves, drawer-joints, and ogee shapes are but a few of the possibilities with this attachment, which mounts on the table saw arbor, replacing the blade.

TIPS FOR USING YOUR TABLE SAW

The table saw has four basic cutting capabilities—crosscutting, ripping, beveling (or chamfering), and cutting a compound angle. Beyond these lie the more artistic efforts, such as mortises, pattern sawing, resawing, and cove cutting. But, just as every jockey must learn to ride before racing, so must you master the basic cuts before running ahead to the virtuoso jobs.

Because the table-saw blade cuts from behind and beneath the workpiece, the possibilities of error are greater than with other power cutting tools. A little extra time spent in setting up will minimize mistakes. You may want to pencil-mark the workpiece for aid in adjusting the saw for correct cutting. Alternatively, you can try the cutting maneuver on scrap wood, and then duplicate it on the workpiece.

Crosscuts

Sawing across the grain at an angle of 90 degrees is considered a crosscut. (Any other cross-grain cut at a greater or lesser angle is known as a miter cut.) To make an accurate crosscut, place the miter gage in the table groove and set it so that the head is perpendicular to the blade. (On

some gages, this will be a 90-degree setting; on others, it will be a 0-degree setting.) Adjust the blade height (about 1/8 to 1/4 inch higher than the stock you're cutting). Now, set the blade angle for a straight square cut or to the bevel angle required. If the rip guide will be in your way, remove it for the time being.

The "good" surface of the workpiece should be faced up and squarely against the miter gage. Apply power and guide the work to the blade with the miter head. On large pieces, where your hands are far from the blade, reverse the miter gage and feed *against* it, until the cut has progressed to the point where the saw can be turned off, the miter gage reversed and moved behind the piece, and the cut completed in the normal manner.

Rip Cuts

Sawing with the grain of the wood is a rip cut. For accuracy, the rip guide should be preset and locked at the correct position. The blade height should be adjusted for correct clearance, and the blade angle set for a square cut or the desired bevel angle. Feed the workpiece (good side up), using one hand to hold the piece down on the table and against the rip guide; the other hand should move the piece along the rip guide. Keep your body to one side of the workpiece and blade; if the piece snags and kicks back, you'll avoid a nasty blow. Feed slowly and keep your hands clear of the blade at all times.

Miter Cuts

A miter cut is a crosscut made at other than a 90-degree angle. Set the miter gage to the desired angle and cut as described in the crosscut section. Table extensions will be helpful where a long piece is being miter-cut. A firm grip is needed to prevent the piece from creeping as it is being sawed at an angle.

Bevel Cuts

A bevel cut (sometimes called a chamfer cut) is treated as a crosscut, but the blade angle is adjusted for the desired bevel angle. Be sure to compensate blade height for the angle at which you're sawing.

Compound Cuts

A compound angle cut combines both a miter *and* a bevel. It can be tricky, and you'd do well to try a scrap piece first to test your settings.

Dado Cuts

The kinds of cuts made by a single blade can also be made using a dado head. However, you should be adept at the basic cuts before graduating to dado cuts. The object in dadoing is to cut grooves in the major workpiece surface.

(Dado cuts in the edges of a piece are usually referred to as rabbet cuts.) Replace the standard blade and standard insert in the table with the dado head and insert. Select the width of the cut with the head and the depth of the cut with the saw's adjustments.

Try all cuts on scrap wood first. Dadoing takes practice and careful setup, so a few passes with scrap wood won't be wasting time.

Rabbeting

Using the dado head to rabbet the edge of a piece is treated as a rip cut, if along the grain, or as a crosscut, if across the grain. If a narrow piece is to be rabbeted, start with wider stock that will keep your hands clear of the dado head. Make the required rabbet cut, then rip to the desired width as a finishing operation.

Special rip guides are available for simplified rabbeting. One of these may be a worthwhile investment to round out your table saw's repertoire of capabilities.

RULES FOR SAFE USE

• A table saw can inflict serious wounds or sever fingers or a hand through your momentary inattention. Concentrate *completely* on the job you are doing, always putting your personal safety above *everything* else.

• Before changing blades or doing any other setup work, disconnect the plug of the saw from the outlet. Don't rely on the power switch alone.

• Keep the blade guard in place. Even though you may be tempted to remove it for more convenient maneuvering of a workpiece, the blade guard is the only shield against the ruthless, ripping teeth of the whirling blade. If you remove it, your accident potential soars.

• Know where your hands are at every instant! Never place them in front of the blade. Also, even if you are cutting a groove that shouldn't come through the workpiece, play safe and never place your hand on the workpiece over the blade. You *could* have made a faulty measurement, and a spoiled piece is nothing compared to the awful consequences of contacting the blade!

• Stop the saw before you make adjustments or when removing a cut piece or dust from the table. Pros do. They make safety a habit.

• Hold the workpiece solidly against the miter gage to preserve precision in cutting. (Watch those fingers!) Be sure that the rip guide is solidly locked when cutting with the grain.

• Size up the cut beforehand. Watch out for knots, nails, or any obstruction which might bind the blade. Be sure that you can maneuver the piece fully through the cut without losing your balance or losing sight of the blade's path. Also, before you begin cutting, plan your cuts so that you can make the same type of cuts on one or more pieces at the same time.

• Safety glasses or goggles aren't kid stuff when you're working with a table saw. Wear them to give you an edge against being momentarily blinded by unexpected sawdust blow-back.

• Take your time. In planning, setup, and feeding the work to the cutters, there's no substitute for giving yourself (and the saw) the time it takes to produce an accurate craftsmanlike job. Unhurried craftsmanship is the way to quality work with consistent safety. Never force-feed the workpiece. Feel the rhythm and pace of the blade's progress and time your actions to it. Together, you'll do a great job!

• If you tire, take a break. No artist ever turned out a masterpiece by working past his (or her) peak. A few minutes away from the job will give you new perspectives and renewed enthusiasm for what you're doing. What's more, you'll work with greater emphasis on safety.

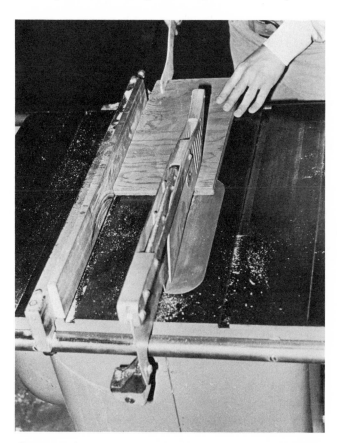

Figure 16-7. At all times, your hands should be well clear of the table saw's blade. A push stick is a handy way to guide material against a rip guide for accurate straight cutting. GRAF-WHALEN photograph.

99

• If you have small children, secure your work area after you've finished working to be sure that they don't try to imitate your efforts at the table saw. Pulling out the plug will help. Locking the area is even better. Best yet is to switch off power at a main switch or circuit breaker that feeds shop outlets.

TABLE SAW MAINTENANCE

Ruggedly constructed, table saws need little maintenance. Proper cleanup after each use will prevent sawdust accumulations. Periodically, it may also be necessary to adjust drive-belt tension to compensate for stretching. More often, the accuracy of adjustments will need to be checked and realignment made, if necessary. The miter gage should produce a perfect square cut when set to 90 degrees (0 degrees on some models). If not, move the gage face until a perfect right-angle cut is obtained, then adjust the gage pointer to the right spot. To check alignment of the rip guide and ensure that it is perfectly parallel to the blade at all settings, lock it in place; then measure from its inner face to a tooth on the rear of the blade. Rotate the blade until this same tooth is at the front, then measure from it to the rip-guide face. Both measurements should be exactly equal. If not, the rip guide should be adjusted until equality is obtained.

To be sure that the blade-angle adjustment is accurate, place a square on the table surface, against one side of the blade. Now set the indicator to 90 degrees. The blade and square should be flush against each other. If not, adjust so that they are, and reset the indicator to 90 degrees.

17

Electric Soldering Tools

Soldering is a metallurgical process that results in the bonding together of two similar (or dissimilar) metals, by means of a third metal that has a much lower melting point than the metals to be united. The third metal, called *solder* (from the Latin word *soldare,* meaning "to make solid"), usually consists of an alloy of tin and lead. When the solder is melted, it flows and adheres securely to the other metals; and, when cooled, it makes a good mechanical and excellent electrical connection between them as a result of the creation of a newly formed alloy.

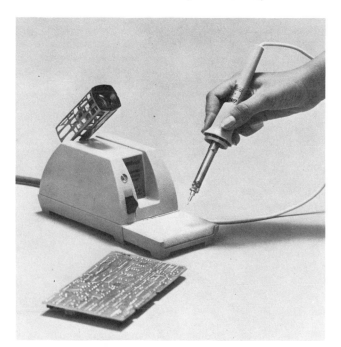

Figure 17-1. Soldering tool. Photograph courtesy of Ungar Division of Eldon Industries, Inc.

The function of an electric soldering tool is simply to heat the work to be soldered to a solder-alloying temperature. The metal must be kept hot enough to maintain the solder in a molten condition long enough for the alloying process to take place. It is not enough for a soldering tool to simply get hot enough to exceed the melting point of the solder. It must be capable of producing a sufficient output of heat to bring the joint up to the correct temperature, and it must be able to transfer the heat efficiently and rapidly from the soldering-iron tip to the metal. Ideally, the temperature of the soldering tool tip should be about 100°F higher than the melting temperature of the solder alloy, both before *and* during the soldering operation. At the same time, the size of the components being soldered and the proximity of other components or conductors place mechanical limits on the size of the soldering tool.

WHAT'S AVAILABLE

There are many kinds of soldering tools designed for general-purpose work. There are soldering irons, including soldering pencils, soldering guns, and soldering pistols. Most tools must be continuously connected to the AC line, but some contain small rechargeable batteries that make the tool completely portable. All are rated in *watts,* according to their electrical power consumption. The wattage rating tells the amount of electrical power converted by the tool into heat. A light-duty soldering tool has a range of about 10 to 50 watts. This is sufficient for most electronic work and for soldering small jewelry items with low melting-point solder. Ratings for medium-duty irons are 50 to 150 watts. This is the best compromise for the occasional solderer who needs a general-purpose tool. At this power it is easy to solder heavy numbers 14 and 12 solid copper wires found in household wiring and appliances, and there is enough heat for working stained-glass projects. Irons in this group also provide sufficient heat to repair small metal toys or other items fabricated of light solderable sheet metal.

Jobs such as "sweating" together larger pieces of metal, particularly copper, require a heavy-duty gun. Bigger jobs—some plumbing work and jobs involving larger areas of metal—call for a propane torch, MAPP gas torch, or a large industrial iron of enormous wattage rating.

Basic Soldering Irons

Within the shank of the basic soldering iron is a resistance-wire heating element, to which the 117-volt AC household power is applied. Current flow through the wire causes it to heat, and this heat is then transferred to the tip by conduction. The tip is electrically isolated from, though thermally coupled to, the heating element. Some irons have a heat baffle which minimizes heat transfer from the tip back to the handle—and the user's hand. This is an important consideration in buying a tool that's comfortable to use. An iron requires several minutes to warm up to operating temperature and must be placed on a stand or holder to keep the tip from burning or melting the work surface.

Soldering irons are generally available in sizes from about 60 to 500 watts or more. An iron is most useful for continuous service. There's no need for as much wattage in an iron (compared to a transformer-type gun), because the tip has more mass and stores heat more readily than a gun's thin tip.

The size of an iron, its tip, and its operating temperature are all related to the size of the work. After the iron has heated up and remained idle for a half hour or so, the tip stabilizes its idling temperature. This must be high enough so that rapid and frequent applications to the cold workpiece won't immediately drop tip temperature below the solder melting point. A small tip, which loses heat rapidly when applied to the work, should idle at a proportionally higher temperature than a large tip, which has more mass and, therefore, greater heat-storage capacity.

To solder heavy sheet metal may require the use of an extra large iron of 500 to 700 watts rating with a tip from 1 1/2 to 1 3/4 inches. For plumbing, where soldering is done on copper pipes and fittings that soak up great amounts of heat, a torch is vastly more effective.

Pencil Irons

Soldering pencils are low-power soldering tools with nominal power ratings that range from 10 to 50 watts. They operate just like a standard iron in that they must be plugged directly into the electrical outlet to start them heating. Pencil irons weigh only a few ounces and reach

proper working temperature in about 3 minutes. Interchangeable heating elements in some models produce a number of tip temperatures or accept a wide variety of different tips. For general electrical work, a wattage of about 25 to 50 watts and a chisel-type tip are best choices. For very fine work on TV and electronic circuits and microminiature components, a 10-watt iron is sufficient.

Soldering Guns

In the 1930s, Carl Weller, a radio technician, invented a new concept in solder-melting equipment—the *soldering gun.* The heating element of this tool, which also serves as its soldering tip, consists of a specially formed copper conductor whose maximum resistance is at its wedge-shaped tip. This special conductor, which looks somewhat like an oversize hairpin, is connected across the secondary winding of a transformer that is housed in a pistol-shaped plastic case. A finger-actuated trigger switch turns the gun on and off.

Unlike the soldering iron, which relies on a slow-heating resistance element, the soldering gun heats up almost instantly. The built-in transformer's primary has many turns and is connected across the AC line only when the switch is actuated. The secondary winding consists of a single turn, so the secondary *voltage* is low, but the *current* is enormous. This heavy current flow heats the tip.

Guns are available from 100 to several hundred watts. Some have a dual-position switch, which connects the AC line to all, or only part, of the primary winding, thereby providing more or less secondary current.

A soldering gun heats rapidly and is most useful for intermittent work. It can melt solder about 5 seconds after the trigger is pulled; it also cools quickly and requires no stand to rest on. Almost all soldering guns have one or two small lamps designed so that they throw some light on the work area when the gun is turned on.

After being used for a while, soldering guns begin to suffer a heat loss. This is almost always due to a loosening of the nuts or screws that hold the tip. After a number of heating cycles, the hardware loses its grip or corrosion sets in. Because solder-tip connections must have extremely low resistance, it is advisable to occasionally loosen and then retighten the mounting hardware. This will renew the solid electrical connections at these points so as to get maximum heat from the gun.

The advantages of the solder gun are its quick heating and cooling; its small, easily maneuverable tip; the fact that is has no expensive element to burn out; and its ability to control the temperature with its trigger. Disadvantages include its weight and bulk and the necessity to operate its

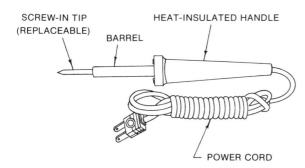

SCREW-IN TIP (REPLACEABLE) BARREL HEAT-INSULATED HANDLE

POWER CORD

Figure 17-2. The principal parts of soldering pencil.

Figure 17-3. Heating elements and tips on soldering pencils are generally easily interchanged. In this design, an element is simply screwed into the handle socket. GRAF-WHALEN photograph.

Figure 17-4. This temperature-controlled soldering tool remains at a preselected, even temperature determined by the nickel-iron disc included in the base of the interchangeable tip. A few wipes of the tip on the moistened sponge in the base of the stand quickly cleans the tip. Photograph courtesy of Ungar Division of Eldon Industries, Inc.

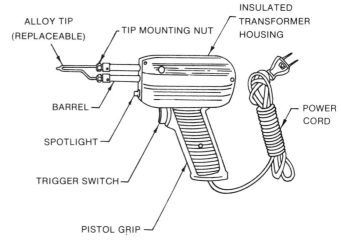

ALLOY TIP (REPLACEABLE) TIP MOUNTING NUT INSULATED TRANSFORMER HOUSING

BARREL

SPOTLIGHT

TRIGGER SWITCH

PISTOL GRIP

POWER CORD

Figure 17-5. The principal parts of a soldering gun.

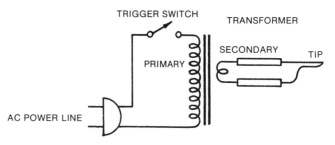

TRIGGER SWITCH TRANSFORMER

PRIMARY SECONDARY TIP

AC POWER LINE

Figure 17-6. The basic circuit of the common transformer-type soldering gun. High current flows through the secondary winding of the transformer, and heats the soldering tip.

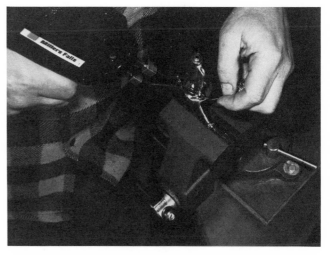

Figure 17-7. The soldering gun is trigger-finger activated and reaches operating temperature in just a few seconds. Usually there are one or two small lamps that throw some light on the work area when the tool is turned on. GRAF-WHALEN photograph.

small tip at a high temperature to compensate for the lack of a heat reservoir.

Soldering Pistols

The soldering pistol has about the same shape as the soldering gun. The pistol combines the features of both the soldering iron and the soldering gun. It employs both a heating element and a step-down transformer, and its soldering tip resembles those found on soldering irons.

The built-in, step-down transformer serves the same basic function as in the soldering gun: It provides a low-voltage–high-current source for almost instantaneous heat. Soldering pistols can be obtained in either light-medium-, or heavy-duty units. By inserting the proper heating tube, heat ranges from 25 to 450 watts are possible. Another advantage of the soldering pistol, in addition to nearly instant heat, is its narrow tip that can easily be manipulated into tight corners that the larger solder-gun tip cannot reach.

Automatic Temperature-Controlled Irons

An ingenious temperature-controlled soldering tool makes use of the *Curie point* of iron alloys. The base of this soldering iron's interchangeable tip is fitted with a temperature-sensing disc of a nickel-iron alloy. A permanent magnet attached to a spring-loaded, "normally off" switch, contained within the soldering iron, is attracted to this nickel-iron disc, because it is normally magnetic. When the magnet is attracted to the disc, it pulls the switch on and closes the transformer secondary circuit, allowing current to flow through the heater.

However, a ferromagnetic nickel-iron alloy loses its magnetism when its temperature reaches the Curie-point temperature. When this happens, the permanent magnet is no longer attracted to the nickel-iron disc and the

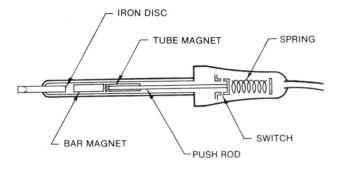

Figure 17-8. Mechanism of a heat-controlled soldering tool using the Curie effect.

switch snaps off, thereby opening the secondary and stopping current flow through the heating element. When the tip cools down slightly, the disc's temperature drops below the critical Curie point and the magnet is again attracted to it, closing the switch and reapplying current to the heating element.

The temperature of the tip is thus held fairly close to whatever temperature is determined by the particular alloy used in the disc. Each tip has its own iron disc, which can be made with different Curie points, and, therefore, its own temperature setting. By simply inserting tips with different Curie points, the working temperature of the iron can be maintained at 500, 600, 700, or 800° F. This particular iron has a very rapid warm-up time, good heat recovery, and does not overheat.

Cordless Irons

For occasional light-duty soldering jobs that must be done far from a plug-in electrical source, cordless soldering tools, operated from internal, rechargeable nickel-cadmium batteries, are a true boon. Also, since these cordless irons generate no electromagnetic fields, they're just about perfect for soldering sensitive electronic parts, which could otherwise be damaged by AC-operated soldering tools. Most cordless irons weigh about 6 ounces—slightly more than a conventional iron and cord. They heat up in 5 to 6 seconds to a tip temperature of about 700° F. On an average they can make about 100 joints per charge and are good for about 500 to 1,000 battery charge/discharge cycles before their built-in batteries need to be replaced. Cordless irons have one or more built-in bulbs to illuminate the work as you solder. The tool is brought to working temperature and kept there by finger pressure on a button in the handle. Releasing the button turns off the heat and the light.

Irons are rated from 10 to 50 watts and most of them take overnight for a complete recharge of their batteries. Some models come equipped with a stand that contains the charger and accepts the iron when it isn't in use; so, the batteries get a "boost" every time the tool is placed into the stand. Some models have the charging circuit built into an oversize wall plug—like those used to recharge calculator or transistor-radio batteries. The charger's cord must be plugged into the tool to recharge the batteries.

To get the most joints per charge, start soldering as soon as the iron is hot enough to melt the solder. Also try to solder several joints each time the iron is turned on. Discharge the batteries most of the way before recharging, and use the iron frequently; the more nickel-cadmium batteries used, the greater the amount of charge these batteries will hold.

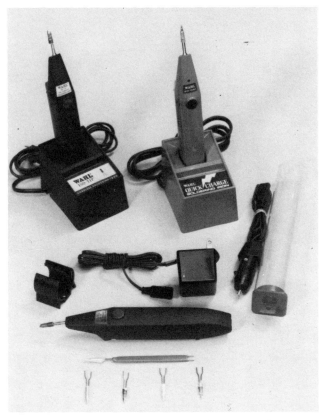

Figure 17-9. Cordless irons charge their batteries in stands, from a plug-in charger, or from a car cigarette lighter. They're good for about 100 connections per charge. Photograph courtesy of Wahl Clipper Corporation.

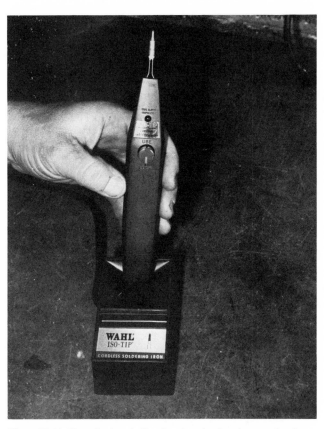

Figure 17-11. Place the iron in the charging stand and connection is automatically made between the built-in battery and the charger. Overnight, power is stored up and replenished. GRAF-WHALEN photograph.

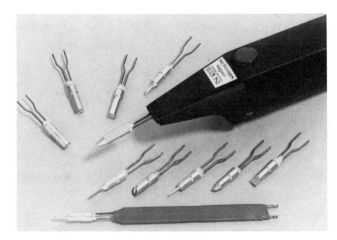

Figure 17-10. This cordless soldering tool accepts a number of interchangeable tips. The push-button switch can be locked in an "off" position to prevent accidental battery drain when the tool is stored. Photograph courtesy of Wahl Clipper Corporation.

Figure 17-12. A small light bulb spotlights the work area whenever the push-button switch is turned on to provide battery power to the tip's heating element. GRAF-WHALEN photograph.

TIPS FOR USING YOUR SOLDERING TOOL
Solder, Oxidation, and Flux

Solder is a homogenous mixture (an alloy) of two or more elemental metals. The most popular solder is made of lead and tin in varying proportions. Other elements may be present, such as cadmium, zinc, bismuth, or antimony, but generally in very low percentages. Pure lead has a melting point of approximately 621°F and tin's melting point is 450°F. The two metals blended together result in an alloy with a melting point *lower than* that of *either* metal alone. The exact melting point of this alloy depends on the ratio of tin to lead; generally, the more tin, the lower the melting point. The lowest temperature at which this solder will melt—361°F—can be attained only when the alloy contains 63 percent tin and 37 percent lead. This combination is known as a *eutectic* alloy (from the Greek word meaning "easily melted"). If the alloy contains a greater percentage of either tin or lead, it passes through an intermediate semimolten, or plastic, state as it is heated, becoming a liquid at a higher temperature.

Most solders are identified by their tin-to-lead combination. A solder alloy that contains 60 percent tin and 40 percent lead is described as 60/40 solder, with the percentage of tin always shown as the first number in the ratio.

When solder is applied to a metal for which it has an affinity—such as copper—the molten solder actually dissolves some of the surface metal. A new alloy forms between the metal and the solder, producing a direct metallic-chemical bond between the solder and the base metal. It is this characteristic of solder that makes it so valuable in electronic work, for such a bond has a very low electrical resistance, while at the same time it is quite resistant to mechanical shock stress and vibration. The strength of the solder joint depends on the ratio of the solder's tin-lead content, with maximum strength occurring when the tin content is between 40 and 65 percent.

Certain metals, such as tin-plated metals and gold, are readily solderable with low or medium temperature solder alloys. Silver, copper, and cadmium-plated metals are fairly easy to solder, but require a somewhat harder (higher temperature) solder. Other metals, such as brass, steel, stainless steel, and nickel or chromium-plated metals, and aluminum cannot be easily soldered and require special techniques. Hard and silver solders are used for jewelry and for electrical connections that must operate in high ambient temperatures without melting, such as in motors and projector lamps. Hard solders have greater mechanical strength than do tin/lead solders. Silver solder (which contains about 1 percent or 2 percent silver) is useful where corrosion is a problem. The most popular solder for electronic work is 1/16 inch or 1/32 inch in diameter and furnished in a coil or on a spool. Its small cross-sectional area allows it to be fed conveniently to a joint and melted easily with low-heat soldering tools.

In order for the all-important metallic bond to be formed, it is essential that the solder alloy contact the surface of the base metal. Dirt, grease, or paint prevent such contact and result in an improperly soldered joint. For a good job the metal surfaces to be soldered must be clean. Another impediment to good solder-to-base contact is caused by oxygen in the air. Metals usually *oxidize* when they are exposed to the atmosphere. The base metal combines with oxygen and, in so doing, a surface film forms on the metal. This oxide film has high electrical resistance and is a poor conductor of heat. It keeps the molten solder away from the base metal and, therefore, must be removed or a good bond cannot be established. This is accomplished by using any of the various substances called "flux" that by their chemical action serve to prevent oxidation of metal surfaces.

A commonly used flux is made of a dark-brown paste called *rosin.* It works very well with the tin- or solder-dipped metals used for wire, lugs, or connectors in electrical and electronic equipment. Although flux is necessary, it is easy to apply too much or too little. If too little is applied, a poorly soldered connection will result. Too much flux may result in excessive spreading of the solder and an excessive residue. In order that the proper amount of flux may always be used, solders with self-contained fluxes have been developed. The flux is held

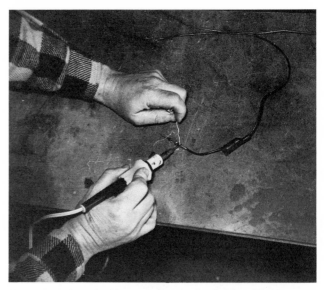

Figure 17-13. A good solder connection requires that the soldering tool apply sufficient heat to the workpiece, heating it to the point where it readily melts the applied solder. GRAF-WHALEN photograph.

within a hollow core in the solder wire, so there is no need to use an external flux during the soldering process. As the metals to be joined are heated, the flux is automatically released. It flows on the surfaces and removes the oxide film. Then, if there is sufficient heat, the solder flows and displaces the flux. If the joint isn't heated sufficiently, the solder never replaces the flux, which then results in an unsatisfactory connection, commonly called a "rosin joint." Too much heat, on the other hand, is also undesirable, because the flux oxidizes and loses effectiveness. Bronze, cadmium-plated brass, phosphor-bronze, solder-plated surfaces, or copper solder well with rosin flux, providing they are not corroded or tarnished.

In some soldering operations, such as gutter and downspout installations, a liquid flux is brushed on the galvanized first, and then solid-wire or bar solder is applied. Soldering nickel plate, galvanized steel, beryllium copper, silicon bronze, zinc and zinc plate, monel, nichrome, and stainless steel requires the use of *aniline phosphate* or *zinc chloride* fluxes. Unfortunately, these are *acid fluxes* that leave a corrosive residue, which can cause damages to the soldered joints, conductors, and insulation. Acid fluxes should *never* be used in electronics work.

Soldering-Iron Tips

The part of the soldering iron that requires the most attention is the tip. Soldering tips come in a variety of sizes and shapes for specific applications.

Before use, soldering tips must be "tinned"; that is, coated evenly on all faces with a thin film of solder. During use they should be cleaned frequently by wiping them with a damp cloth or sponge. From time to time, tips require retinning and, as hardened flux or oxide accumulates, abrasive or wire-brush cleaning.

Prolonged operation at high temperatures causes oxidation and flaking of the metal tip. In addition, at the tip face, where the solder is melted, cavities form due to the chemical affinity of solder for copper (the best all-around, heat-conductive tip material), which absorbs it each time the tip is used. Little can be done to stop the flaking other than running the iron at a lower temperature during standby periods.

Other types of tips are made from alloys, or are nickel- or chromium-plated to achieve longer life. One method used by some manufacturers is to clad the copper tip with iron, which is harder and more durable than copper, even though the copper core is retained for its thermal properties. A disadvantage with all these tips is that they cannot be filed without ruining them; once the plating or cladding has gone, the tip must be discarded. Unlike these, a copper tip can be filed flat at its face many times before

filing and flaking has reduced the tip size to unserviceable proportions. No soldering tool's tip should need replacement very often if it is properly cared for, unless the tool is used almost continuously.

Specialized tips are available for such chores as cutting plastic or asphalt tiles, removing putty, burning patterns in wood, removing scratches and dents from furniture, or for sealing plastic bags. These extra features of a soldering tool may carry weight in your decision to buy, but don't always have a bearing on the tool's principal soldering function or its usefulness in that capacity.

How to Solder

To make a good solder connection, the cardinal rule is to "keep it clean." That goes for the soldering tool as well as for the work to be soldered. In electrical work, wires and terminals are usually clean and dirt isn't a major problem. Sheet metal, however, may need cleaning with a wire brush or sandpaper to get rid of dirt or corrosion. Solder makes a good connection only with clean, bare metal. If the metal is dirty or grimy, clean it with a wire brush, steel wool, or sandpaper. Manicurists' emery boards (sandpaper on narrow, stiff cardboard) are inexpensive and they make excellent throw-away cleaning tools. If the wire or connection is new, it may not be necessary to clean it mechanically. A flux of rosin should be applied to remove the film of oxide that any metal has on its surface. Since most solder today has a rosin flux core, this step can often be omitted. Heat the work where you want to apply solder. It's very important to heat the work first, before applying solder. If the temperature of the joint never goes higher than the liquid point of the solder, the result will be a *cold solder joint*—a crystallized connection, which has undesirable electrical resistance or which is mechanically faulty. To prevent this, apply the tip of the soldering tool underneath the joint, if possible, as heat rises. If it's not possible for the tip to contact all wires and terminals in the joint, make sure it touches and heats the largest piece of metal involved. (But don't overheat the joint or the solder itself will oxidize and make a poor connection.) Then, apply solder, letting it flow by gravity and capillary action between the parts to be joined. If the joint won't melt solder, wait until it will or use a hotter iron. Use enough, but only enough, solder to make a smooth, globular joint, with the solder filling all spaces and crevices. Too much solder is bad, but it is also bad practice if the solder doesn't flow freely on all elements of the joint. Ideally, when solder is applied to a hot joint, the solder should shrink inward toward the center of mass of the joint by capillary action. *Remove the solder first, then the heat,* and do not allow the newly soldered connection to move while the solder is in a fluid, mobile state.

Allow the joint to cool without disturbing it. A lumpy or pitted appearance shows the solder was not hot enough. It should also appear as a "mound" rather than a blob. It may be necessary to heat sink the leads of heat-sensitive electronic components. The heat sink can be a commercially available item, the jaws of long-nose pliers, an alligator clip, or even a paper clip in a pinch. The heat sink serves as a heat absorber and radiator and should be placed as close to the component as possible.

A final word: Be sure that the tool you choose can furnish enough heat to the workpiece for effective soldering. No single tool can match the demands of every soldering job, and it may be necessary to have several tools for small, medium, and large jobs. In the use of each type, some measure of skill is required, and practice in joining parts with each type of tool will soon make you a skilled artisan in the very useful craft of soldering.

RULES FOR SAFE USE

The use of any soldering tool poses some degree of hazard due to the extreme temperatures of the molten solder and the tool, which generates the heat. Respect for the heat of the soldering tool should come early, for it can easily inflict third-degree burns if improperly handled. Also, it is well to remember that an unwatched iron should be kept in a safe holder or stand, whenever it is plugged in. The heat of the iron can scorch wood and cause low-grade smoldering of combustibles, if left unattended.

But more than the risk of fire is the risk of personal, bodily injury from the molten solder heated by the tool. A great hazard is the application of hot, fluid solder to a wet surface, which can cause the fiery metal to sputter and fly. This makes eye and skin protection a very sensible precaution when soldering.

Handle hot solder with care. Extreme care should be exercised with hot solder in its molten state. Molten solder can cause severe burns if it comes in contact with the skin. In the event that skin contact with hot solder should occur, physicians advise that you 1) immerse contacted area in cold, clean water immediately; 2) do not attempt to remove the set solder from the skin; 3) cover contacted areas with clean, wet compresses, and see a physician at once.

18

Electric Arc Welders

Welding is the process of fusing two metal surfaces together so that they join with great strength. It takes tremendous heat to do this (about 6,000° F), and that heat can be supplied by an *electric arc welder*. Unlike torch welding, an electric arc welder gives a great degree of control over the position and size of the junction formed during the welding process; and arc welding is a skill that can be learned by most homeowners who perform occasional small welding jobs around the home or shop.

The basic idea in arc welding is to use the high-temperature arc struck between a hand-held (with gloves) electrode and the workpiece (both of which are connected by heavy-gauge, insulated wires to the welder) to create the fused joint. The arc is so hot that it cuts into the workpiece, forming either a crater or a molten-metal pool, depending upon the arc's temperature. (This, in turn, is dependent upon the current rating of the welding tool.) The electrode can be either of two types—*consumable* or *refractory*. The consumable type supplies filler metal to the weld to ensure that there are no voids in the junction formed. Refractory electrodes are usually made of tungsten or carbon, both of which have melting points in excess of the arc temperature. These supply no filler metal to the work, but are used to position molten metal formed on the workpiece by the arc.

The welder itself is simply a device that converts the power line AC voltage to a much lower voltage, but with the capacity to supply much higher current. It also allows the voltage, and, therefore, the current, to be adjusted to suit small or large jobs.

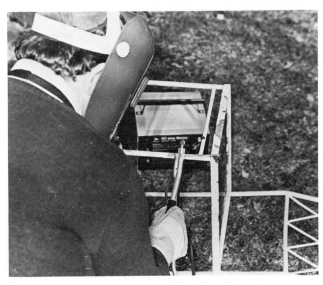

Figure 18-1. Electric arc welder. GRAF-WHALEN photograph.

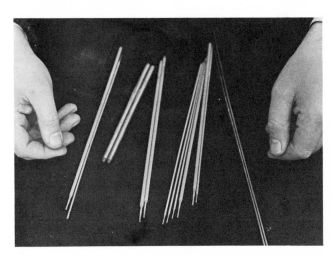

Figure 18-2. Electrodes come in many lengths, diameters, and materials. Consumable electrodes provide filler metal to the weld. Refractory electrodes are used for heating the surface, without adding filler. GRAF-WHALEN photograph.

HOW THEY WORK

An electric arc is a source of intense, concentrated heat created by current flow between two conductive surfaces. In arc welding, the current source is a hefty step-down transformer, plugged into the 120-volt AC line. The transformer safely isolates you and the workpiece from the hazardous power line, while it also steps up the amount of current that can be delivered. This is done by stepping down the primary line voltage to about 40 volts on the secondary of the transformer. As a crude approximation, if the primary line voltage is 120 volts and the maximum current it can supply is 20 amperes, the power line can provide 2,400 watts (volts × amps = watts). However, on the transformer's secondary winding, if the output voltage is 40 volts, up to *60 amperes* can be furnished to the welding circuit, still totaling 2,400 watts. Of course, this doesn't count losses and inefficiencies, but the idea is that output current can be juggled by altering voltage, so long as input and output wattage remain about the same.

The 2,400 watts that a welder can put into a small arc creates heat. This heat causes the base metal of the workpiece to revert to almost liquid state at the point at which the arc is directed. This heat also melts the electrode metal, causing it to mix with the base metal and fuse. As the electrode melts and is moved along, it forms a uniform pile of metal along the base metal, called a "bead." This bead joins the workpiece surfaces and, when cooled and solidified, forms a tough, resilient junction that makes the welded surfaces, for all practical purposes, one piece.

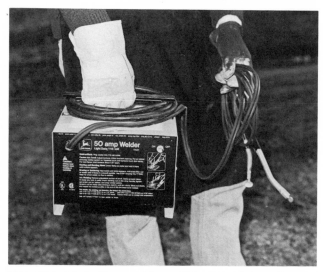

Figure 18-3. A typical home-welding outfit for light-duty jobs. Note the leather welding glove and leather apron worn by the welder. GRAF-WHALEN photograph.

WHAT'S AVAILABLE

Many different types and sizes of electric arc welders are offered today, but the type usually encountered by the homeowner is the plug-in, AC-powered welder. And, although professional models deliver up to several hundred amperes of current for heavy-duty welding operations, the homeowner models are generally limited to a maximum output of 100 amperes or less. This means that the kind of joining jobs you can tackle will be limited to comparatively small surface areas, such as repairing metal lawn furniture, fences, cracks in sheet metal surfaces, tools, and general light-duty fusing.

Typically, a homeowner electric arc-welding outfit includes a multipurpose welding and carbon-arc torch, cables, sample electrodes, carbons, and helmet with eye shield. (Not included, but an essential investment for hand protection against showers of hot sparks and molten metal, are a pair of good-quality welder's gloves.)

TIPS FOR USING YOUR ELECTRIC ARC WELDER

The power of the arc welder depends upon the efficient flow of current to the circuit created between the hand-held electrode torch and the workpiece. This requires that all connections be kept clean and tight, with no evidence of rust, scale, or loose contact. Any of these will cause power to be needlessly wasted in the parts where poor contact increases resistance. (You'll be able to tell where the problem is because heat will be generated there. In a good, clean welding circuit, only the arc gets hot.)

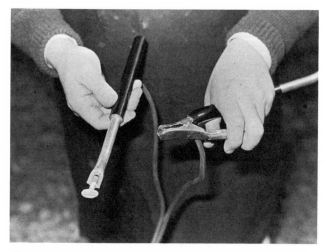

Figure 18-4. The electrode holder has an insulated handle and a thumbscrew to securely contact electrode. The clamp (right) is attached to workpiece. On this welder, the clamp is part of a second electrode holder used for carbon-arc torch work. GRAF-WHALEN photograph.

The protective clothing you choose should include a cap you can wear to cover your hair beneath the helmet, heavy leather welder's gloves, leather pull-on sleeves, and a leather or asbestos apron to cover your clothing. Heavy shoes are recommended, and it is wise to never roll your pants legs as a precaution against molten metal falling into the cuff and burning the skin. The helmet headband should be sized and snugly fitted to your head, so that you can easily flip it up or down, as required.

Preparation

The surfaces to be welded must be free of rust, scale, oil, and paint. Welding on metals not properly cleaned will cause a brittle and porous weld. In some cases, where edge-to-edge joining is required, beveling may be necessary on one plate or on the edges of both plates, depending on the thickness of the metal. Angle of bevel is usually 60 degrees between the two plates.

Attach the ground clamp of the welding machine to the workpiece, ensuring that it makes clean electrical contact (no rust, paint, grease, or other material should come between the metal-to-metal contact). Select the proper electrode for the job and fit it to the holder. Be sure that it is snugly secured in the holder.

Striking the Arc

Warning: Never strike an arc unless your eyes and body are protected. Wear helmet, gloves, and protective apron to prevent burns from sparks or molten metal.

Inspect electrode end to be sure it is clean and shiny so that it will make good contact with the base metal. Flip down your helmet to protect your eyes. With a short stroke, rather like striking a match, move the electrode across the surface to be welded. You will hear a sputter and see an arc. As soon as the arc has been struck, raise the electrode about 1/8 inch to prevent it from sticking to the base metal. This will probably happen the first few times you try welding.

It is a good idea for the beginning welder to practice striking arcs over and over again until it becomes second nature. Some users will strike a satisfactory arc after three tries, while others may take a dozen tries before they catch on to the method. Knowing you have a good arc is a matter of experience. A good, crisp, cracking sound (like eggs frying) accompanies a good arc.

Laying the Bead

Hold the electrode at a 15-degree angle. It is good practice to "lead" the weld a little so you can watch the puddle behind the arc. As the electrode melts away, move the holder down closer to the base metal, or the arc will break before the welding has been completed. When lifting the

Figure 18-5. Old paint, rust, or any other material that interferes with metal-to-metal contact must be removed before the ground clamp is attached. GRAF-WHALEN photograph.

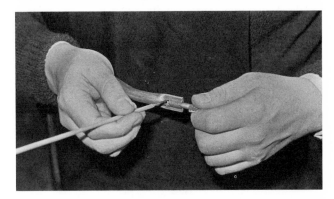

Figure 18-6. The electrode is held in place in the holder by clamping down a thumbscrew on its metal end. GRAF-WHALEN photograph.

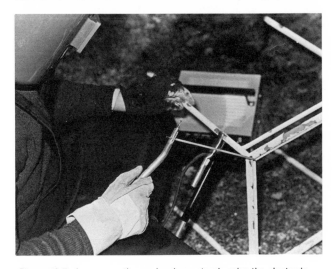

Figure 18-7. As soon as the arc has been struck, raise the electrode slightly to keep it from sticking to the workpiece. GRAF-WHALEN photograph.

electrode from the base metal, never move it too far or the arc will break, as the arc cannot jump more than a limited distance.

The length of the arc determines the amount of penetration—the depth to which the heat goes into the metal. A short arc, created by holding the electrode tip close to the base metal, gives more heat and deeper penetration. For most purposes, this is the best arc.

Moving the electrode holder too rapidly will not allow the electrode to melt down and fuse properly with the molten base metal. For a good weld, don't work too fast; move the arc very slowly. To ensure proper penetration and evenness of the weld, watch the molten pool of metal forming just behind the arc. The "bead" is created as the molten metal from the electrode falls into the base metal puddle.

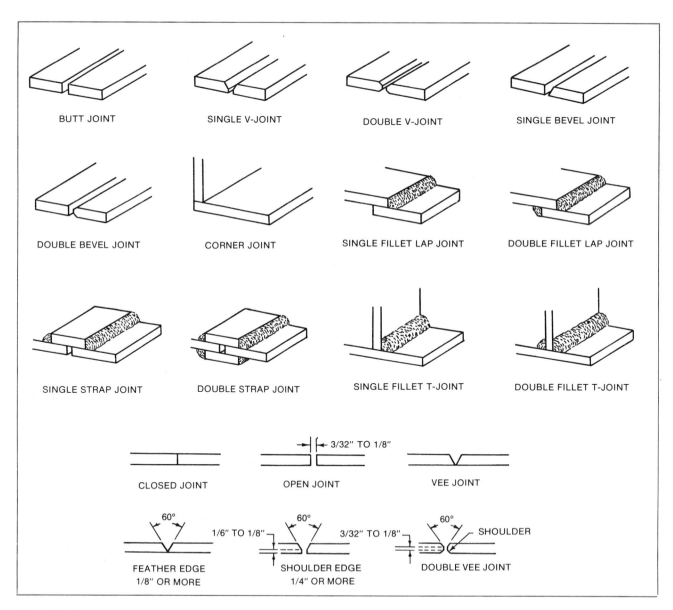

Figure 18-8. There are many possible ways of joining metals by welding. These are the most common methods.

The coating on the outside of the electrode provides protection and insulation for the arc. As the coating burns off, it forms protective gases which envelop the space around the weld. This space prevents the air from reaching the molten metal and creating undesirable chemical reactions.

Slag formation, which is the accumulation of dirty metal scale on the finished weld, may be removed with a hammer or chisel after it has cooled. Peening a weld with a hammer is accepted practice, because it relieves the strains set up by intense heat. This is especially true of cast iron.

Types of Beads

Stringer bead: A stringer bead is made by one continuous passage of the electrode, without weaving or oscillating. To lay a stringer bead, first strike an arc and hold it at the starting point for a short period to ensure fusion and to allow the bead to build up slightly. Use a short arc about 1/8 inch long. Move the electrode forward at a steady rate. As forward movement continues, move the electrode down at a uniform rate to compensate for the metal melted away.

If you are right-handed, move from left to right. If you are left-handed, reverse the process. The top of the electrode in the holder should be slightly ahead of the arc. This position will throw the molten metal behind the arc and ensure good penetration. The bead will be about 1/8 inch high, using a 1/8-inch electrode. A good weld will be of consistent width and height and will have uniform ripples.

Weave bead: The weave bead will deposit metal in a wider space than would normally be possible with the stringer bead. The weave bead is accomplished by weaving from one edge of the space that is to be filled to the other edge. Continue this motion as well as forward speed of travel. Pause momentarily at each edge of the weave. This will provide the same heat at the edge of the weave as in the middle.

Burning Holes

When burning holes, hold the electrode perpendicular to the base metal, and rotate the arc in a small circle, until the base metal becomes soft. Pushing or jabbing the electrode firmly through the base metal starts the hole. Its size and shape are determined by directing the arc in larger circles. Do not attempt to burn holes in material heavier than sheet metal.

Cutting

The procedure used in cutting is simple. The heat of the arc is used to melt away the base metal along the side of the cut. The cut should be started at the edge of the base metal with the electrode pointed in at the cut. If the metal is fairly thick, the electrode should be worked up and down during the cutting operation, from the top to the bottom of the cut. Less electrode will be consumed if it is soaked in water a moment before use. Again, do not attempt to cut any metal heavier than sheet metal.

Carbon Arc Torch

The carbon arc torch greatly facilitates preheating for bending and shaping. It enables the user to solder, braze, and weld metals such as aluminum, brass, bronze, cast iron, malleable iron, malleable steel, and monel metal by the flame method.

When using the torch, it is not necessary to ground the base metal, since the arc is created by the transfer of energy from one carbon to the other, instead of from the electrode to the base metal. Because of its very hot flame (approximately 10,000°F at the arc), the carbon arc torch is highly suitable for bending, shaping, welding, and brazing operations.

Bending and Shaping

Before heating for bending or shaping, the metal should be placed in a vise, where it can be held firmly. Heat the metal with the torch to a temperature at which it will bend easily. Iron and steel, when heated to a cherry red color, will bend freely. Apply bending pressure with a clamp, wrench, or hammer.

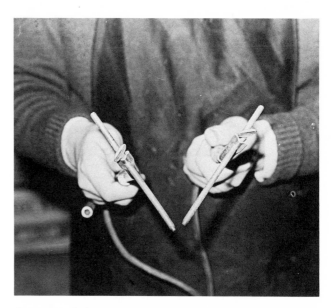

Figure 18-9. Carbon electrodes are fitted to the two electrode holders to produce a carbon-arc torch. GRAF-WHALEN photograph.

113

Brazing

Brazing is the process of joining two metals, often of a different type, by means of a third metal. Brazing differs from welding in that the parts being joined are not brought to a fluid or plastic state. The strength of the brazed joints is limited to the strength of the third metal.

Brazing copper or brass: To braze copper or brass, a good grade of commercial bronze filler rod (used in the same manner as ordinary solder with the arc torch) is all that is required. Either of two methods may be used to join the base metal and the filler rod: 1) *fusion method* or 2) *bonding method.* In the fusion method, the melting temperature of the base metal and the filler rod are about the same. The base metal and the filler rod are heated to the same degree of plasticity and mixed during brazing. In the bonding method, the base metal requires more heat than the filler rod. The base metal must, therefore, be heated to a temperature greater than that required to melt the filler rod. When the base metal reaches the proper temperature, the filler rod is held under the torch where it melts and flows into the porous surface of the base metal. As the difference between the melting temperature of the base metal and the melting temperature of the filler rod determines which method is to be used, heat either the base metal or the base metal and filler rod, as necessary. The base metal should be a dull red color before filler rod is added.

Brazing galvanized iron: Brazing, rather than welding, is suggested when working on galvanized iron, because brazing is done at a lower temperature. This protects the zinc coating on galvanized iron. Use the bonding method described above. Hold the flame close to the base metal and add brazing flux and a good grade of commercial bronze filler rod.

Brazing cast iron: Light iron castings may be brazed by the same method used for brazing galvanized iron. The casting should be heated to a cherry red color before adding metal from the filler rod.

Arc Welding Terms You Should Know

Arc: The high temperature plasma produced by flow of electric current through a gaseous space or air gap. In arc welding, this flow of electricity through the air produces temperatures in the range of 6,000°F.

Arc welding: Fusing two metals together using an electric arc as the source of heat.

Base metal: The metal to be welded, cut, or brazed. Also called the "workpiece."

Bead: The junction produced by the finished weld. Describes neatness of the ripples formed by the metal in a semiliquid state.

Vertical position: A type of weld where welding is done on a vertical plane and on a vertical surface.

Bevel: Angling the metal edge where welding is to take place.

Bond: The junction between the weld metal and the base metal.

Braze welding: Making an adhesion groove, fillet, or plug connection with a brazing alloy.

Brazing: Making an adhesion connection with a minimum of alloy, which melts above 800°F and which flows by capillary between close-fitting parts.

Butt joint: An assembly in which the two pieces joined are in the same plane, with the edge of one piece touching the edge of the other.

Carbon electrode: Carbon in solid form used for arc heating of materials for welding, brazing, bending, and shaping.

Electrode: A conductor which brings electricity up to the point where the arc is to be formed. In electric arc welding, the electrode is usually melted and becomes a part of the weld.

Face: The external surface of the weld bead.

Filler rod: Metal wire that is melted and added to the welding puddle to produce the necessary increase in bead thickness.

Fillet weld: Metal fused into a corner, formed by two pieces of metal whose welded surfaces are at approximately 90 degrees with respect to each other.

Flux: A chemical used to promote fusion of metals during the welding process.

Fusion: The mixing of molten metals.

Horizontal position: A weld performed on a horizontal seam at least partially on a vertical surface.

Joint: Where two pieces meet when a structure is made of smaller pieces.

Lead wire: Electric wire from the power source to the electrode holder or to the ground clamp.

Overhead position: A weld made on the underside of the joint, with the face of the weld in a horizontal plane.

Penetration: Depth of fusion into the base metal, as measured from the surface of the base metal.

Puddle: The portion of a weld that is molten at the place the heat is supplied.

Soldering: Means of fastening metals together by adhering another metal to the two pieces of these metals. Only the joining metal is melted during this process.

Tack weld: A small weld used to temporarily hold together components of an assembly.

Toe: The junction between the face of the weld and the base metal.

Undercut: A depression at the toe of the weld which is below the surface of the base metal.·

Welding: The art of fastening metal together by means of interfusing metals.

Welding rod: The wire or rod which is melted into the weld metal.

RULES FOR SAFE USE

The high-intensity arc of even a small welding machine can inflict devastating skin burns. Moreover, the hot sparks and molten metal, which erupt from the workpiece when the arc is struck, pose serious risk to the welder who has not taken precautions to cover head, face, hands, and body with protective, nonflammable clothing. Secondarily, but just as important, hot shards can ignite flammable fumes, materials, and surfaces in the area, making it imperative that you *choose carefully* the place where you carry on any welding operation. Finally, use of an eye-protecting vision shield is absolutely mandatory! The brilliant arc releases great amounts of ultraviolet, visible, and infrared energy. These can permanently damage the retina and cause blindness. Neither you nor anyone within hailing distance should ever look upon the arc without eye protection. The welder's helmet incorporates protection in the form of a near opaque shield that covers the eye area completely.

Although a transformer-operated arc welder is inherently isolated from the AC power line, the possibility of electrical shock does exist should an internal failure occur. It is recommended that a ground-fault interrupter be used between the arc welder and power line as an additional safety precaution.

Common Welding Problems and Their Solutions

Trouble	Possible Cause	Possible Remedy
Arc hard to strike.	Wrong type of electrode.	Check to be sure electrode is not a DC type. DC electrodes require higher voltage and will not operate on alternating current welders successfully.
	Electrode too large.	Try an electrode with a smaller diameter.
	Base metal not grounded properly.	Check ground carefully.
	Voltage from power line low due to heavy loads.	Try to strike arc at a time when less current is being used.
Bead too thin in places.	Uneven speed of moving electrode across base metal.	Slow down and try to maintain a steady rate of travel over the surface to be welded.
Bead too thick in places.	Holding the electrode too long in one place or moving it too slowly across base metal.	Speed up and maintain a uniform rate of speed along the length of the bead.
Excessive spatter.	Holding too long an arc.	Hold a short arc and feed the electrode down as the electrode burns off.
Ragged depressions at edge of weld.	Moving the arc too rapidly or too short an arc.	Slow down. If that doesn't help, try a longer arc.
Overlapping beads.	Arc too long or rate of travel too fast.	Try a shorter arc or slower electrode movement.
Electrode sticks to work.	Electrode in direct contact with base metal while arc is being struck.	Move electrode slightly away from the base metal immediately after the arc is struck. Practice is required to do this and maintain the arc.

19

Shop Vacuum Cleaners

In Grandma's day, the dust mop was the only answer to the incessant encroachment of dirt into the living areas of the home. But, the early 1900s saw the invention of the vacuum cleaner, providing the homemaker with a more efficient tool for removal of dust and dirt from floors, rugs, and other parts of the house. Through the years, vacuum cleaners have gained in importance to the point where nearly every household in the country has at least one.

Yet, the home shop has been, until recently, a holdout against the vacuum cleaner. Perhaps that's because most shops produce so much dirt, dust, chips, and other residue that the household vacuum cleaner is a poor match for its cleanup demands. But the introduction of the shop vacuum has changed all that.

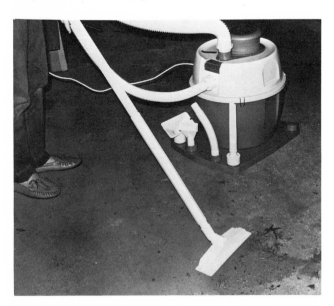

Figure 19-1. Shop vacuum cleaner. GRAF-WHALEN photograph.

Shop vacuums are tough, brawny suction machines that are the equal of any messy cleanup chore. They are, most commonly, canister-type machines, in which suction is created by a 1-horsepower motor. Pickup hoses of 1 1/4- to 2 1/2-inch diameter are provided, so that the shop vacuum can pick up leaves, shavings, wood chips, sawdust, dirt, debris, and, generally, any crude material you wouldn't want to suck up with the vacuum cleaner that's used on your expensive living room rug or drapes. What's more, these vacuums aren't limited to dry dirt pickup. Many can be used to suck up liquids, as well. These latter types are called "wet-dry" vacuums. They are just the thing for bailing out a rain-filled boat from dockside or for clearing the home, garage, patio, car, trailer, workshop, basement, fireplace, or rain gutters of disagreeable wet or dry residue.

WHAT'S AVAILABLE

Shop vacuum is a generic term. Other terms commonly used are *wet-dry vacuum, indoor/outdoor vacuum, heavy-duty vacuum,* and *utility vacuum.* Most shop vacuums are made of injection-molded plastic or epoxy-coated steel (coated to prevent rusting). The container sizes of current models range from a modest (but serviceable) 5 gallons to a huge, industrial-capacity, 55-gallon size. However, the best-selling sizes for homeowner use range from 5 to 12 gallons. The canister is supported on a roll-around dolly, and some models even provide stowage for accessories, right on the machine.

For most applications, a 1 1/4-inch hose and accessories provides adequate suction and versatility. However, where large debris must be picked up or where it is possible that the smaller hose could be blocked by stuck debris, large 2 1/2-inch hose and accessories are recommended. The most common accessories are listed here.

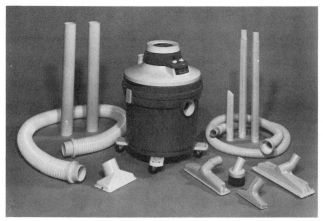

Figure 19-2. A shop vacuum, like this Douglas model, features strong suction, tough plastic construction throughout, a wide range of accessories, mobility, and the capability to deal with wet or dry debris that no household vacuum can match. Photograph courtesy of Douglas Division, The Scott & Fetzer Company.

Figure 19-4. Large wheels and a good-sized canister make this Black & Decker model an easy-to-maneuver companion for cleanup chores outdoors. Photograph courtesy of Black & Decker Mfg. Co.

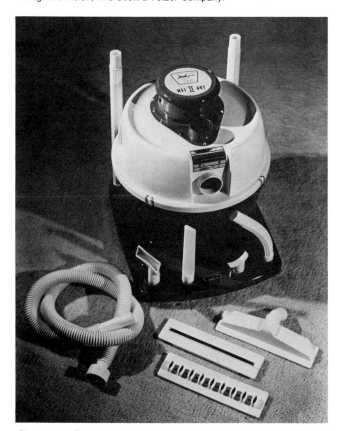

Figure 19-3. This Maxi-Vac wet/dry vacuum carries its accessories on a caster-based platform, minimizing storage space problems. Photograph courtesy of Maxi-Vac Manufacturing Company, Inc.

Figure 19-5. The exhaust port faces straight up on most models. The suction port is on the side. Hose can be connected to the exhaust port when a high-powered blow stream of air is needed. GRAF-WHALEN photograph.

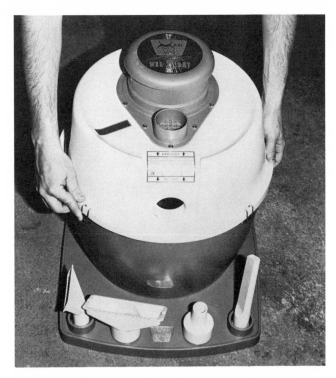

Figure 19-6. The canister top removes by opening snap closures on side of the housing. GRAF-WHALEN photograph.

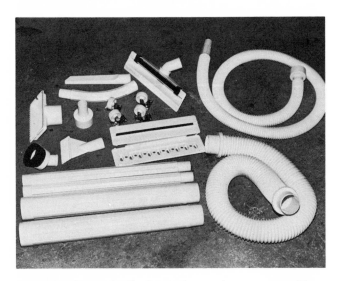

Figure 19-7. Accessories like these make your shop vacuum capable of tackling just about any cleanup job. Clockwise from the bottom left are straight wands of 2 1/2-inch and 1 1/4-inch diameter, oval floor brush and upholstery nozzle, utility floor tool, curved wand, crevice tool, carpet tool, and 1 1/4-inch flexible hose and 2 1/2-inch flexible hose. At center are squeegee and shag inserts and casters, which provide easy mobility. GRAF-WHALEN photograph.

Straight wand: Used between flexible hose and other accessories for long reaching or stand-up operation.

Carpet tool: A wide, flat suction head with a "floating" brush and swivel neck. It combs out dirt from carpet pile for easy pickup with push-pull action.

Squeegee insert: A flexible snap-in insert for a carpet tool that converts it into a wet pickup tool for use on large floor areas. It leaves the floor bone dry with just one pass.

Shag insert: Another snap-in accessory that adds a number of rakelike tubes to the carpet tool. These rake and shape the shag pile, while breaking up suction into a number of smaller airways, rather than just one.

Crevice tool: Adapts hose or wand end to a narrow flattened tube that is easily worked into cracks, corners, and tight spots where no other accessory tool can fit. Useful in car and fireplace cleanup.

Upholstery nozzle: A flared nozzle that directs flat suction on yielding surfaces, such as upholstery.

Utility floor tool: A large (3 by 6 inches) flared nozzle meant for picking up bulky material (wood shavings, leaves, chips, etc.) from the shop floor or patio.

Oval floor-brush: A 9-inch-wide nozzle surrounded by a brush on all sides. Combines push-broom action with suction for general flat-surface dust cleanup.

Brush nozzle: A round, angle-head nozzle surrounded by a brush on all sides. Used for small-area brushing and tight-spot cleanup. It is very useful for rough surfaces with clinging dust or dirt.

Shop vacuums of homeowner-size typically employ universal (brush-type) motors that draw about 8 amps in operation. (Brush life is approximately 600 hours of operation.) The motor is sealed away from the collection container, although the impeller communicates with the container interior, generally, through a metal or plastic housing equipped with many fine holes. For dry pickup, a paper filter may be placed over the impeller housing to permit unrestricted airflow, but to trap dirt particles that might foul the impeller. For wet pickup, a nylon mesh filter is the typical route. No vacuum should be operated without a filter, since particles may be expelled at high speed, posing a hazard.

Many wet-dry vacuums have built-in, shut-off valves that stop water flow when the canister is full. Some also have removable drain plugs, so you can let water flush into a floor drain without lugging the water-filled container to a drainage point.

Virtually all models allow switch-over of the hose from an intake port to an exhaust port, so that the vacuum can be used to blow as well as suck. This can be handy in blowing leaves or light debris into a more accessible area for pickup.

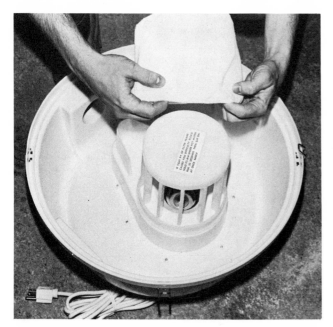

Figure 19-8. A filter is placed over impeller housing to keep particles and debris out of impeller. GRAF-WHALEN photograph.

Figure 19-9. Canister capacity is determined by its diameter and height. Wet capacity of this model is 7 1/2 gallons, while it can hold up to 12 gallons of dry debris. GRAF-WHALEN photograph.

IMPORTANT FEATURES TO LOOK FOR

Safety Features

Insulated construction is an important electrical safety feature, not only in a shop vacuum, but in any tool likely to be used in wet or damp surroundings where it is likely that your body will be grounded. Machines that are of all-metal construction (and many plastic-cased models, too) have a three-wire, grounding-type plug. A ground-fault interrupter is a prudent extra precaution for powering any shop vacuum safely.

Stowage Attachments

The convenience of having the right cleanup tools at hand is significant. Attachments that stow right on the machine are a help, but parts that store easily in a closet, on a shelf, or in a drawer also rate high in convenience.

Stability

The vacuum dolly should keep the center of gravity low, so that it isn't easily tipped over. This is especially important in wet-dry models, where an accidental spill means a tedious redo of the cleanup chore.

Capacity

If you're buying a wet-dry type for its wet pickup capability, don't immediately rush for the largest size you can find. Three gallons of water (a usual rating) add about 24 pounds to the machine's weight, for a gross of about 40 to 50 pounds. That can be quite a load if you have to lug the full container up a flight of basement stairs to dump it outside. Try to base your requirements on realistic needs and your own physical strength.

Pickup Power

Ask for a demonstration under conditions that at least approximate your use. Static tests, like holding a hose to a ceiling to show how the machine's suction supports the hose weight, are not a realistic measure of debris pickup. Try picking up sand or small gravel off a flat, hard floor for a good idea of the machine's suction.

Matching Your Real Needs

Discuss the jobs you want to do with your dealer. The range of machines offered is broad, and many features may not be needed in the work you'll be doing. Why pay for them if you'll never use them?

TIPS FOR USING YOUR SHOP VACUUM
Dry Pickup
Select the right hose size and the correct accessory for the job you're doing. Fine materials will be most easily removed with brush-fitted accessories that coax dirt particles away from the surface where suction can get at them. Fleecy or lintlike materials need suction only and will foul brushes. For shavings, chips, etc., one of the nozzle-type accessories should prove best. If shavings are large or ragged, use the large-diameter hose to minimize the chances of plugging. Ditto for leaves or other fibrous material of appreciable size.

Be sure that the filter is in place within the unit so that fine particles will not be blown out through the exhaust. This can be an eye-hazard. Also, never attempt to suck up hot, ignited, or smoking materials.

Wet Pickup
Don't submerge the vacuum or place it precariously near the spill area. You could accidentally pull it into the wet spot, and, though it would survive, why take chances with electricity? The right kind of filter element (one that won't be ruined by getting wet) should be in place.

The hose or one of the nozzles (usually a general-purpose floor tool with a wide, flat, flaring mouth) can be used for wet or sudsy pickup. Never use your vacuum to pick up flammable liquids nor operate the machine in an atmosphere of flammable vapors.

SHOP VACUUM CLEANER MAINTENANCE
Shop vacuums require minimal maintenance; mostly, it's a matter of cleaning the accessories to remove incidental debris. Brush-type accessories should be rinsed in a mild-detergent-and-water solution to wash out dirt or caked mud caught in the bristles. Occasionally, you may also want to blow out any trapped residue in the hose by connecting to the positive pressure outlet of the vacuum and directing the air blast toward a safe area.

Don't allow wet or damp material to remain in the container, as this may lead to mildew. Clean the interior thoroughly and store with the lid open. This will also promote longer life of the filter element.

20

Power Pumps

Figure 20-1. Power pump. GRAF-WHALEN photograph.

Water always seems to wind up in the wrong place at the wrong time. It may be in the bottom of a boat hull after a season's storage, in your basement or garage after a sudden cloudburst, or in the water heater that won't drain out completely by gravity, just when you need to replace a heating element. At times like these and for countless other fluid-transfer jobs, a powered pump is an indispensable power tool. Available for both fixed and portable use, pumps are the handy alternative to messy hand bailing when you're facing a tough fluid-removal problem.

Pumps offered to homeowners are usually of the *rotary positive-displacement, impeller type*, or of the *centrifugal type*. The former type is usually small. It is suitable for removing up to several inches of water from a basement or garage, for operating a decorative water fountain from a recirculated reservoir, to bail a beached boat

Figure 20-2. Rotary positive-displacement, impeller-type pumps are typically compact, easy to set up, and easy to use. They must not be run dry, however. GRAF-WHALEN photograph.

Figure 20-3. The centrifugal pump meant for larger draining jobs requires very little attention. It can be run dry without damage. GRAF-WHALEN photograph.

(where a bilge pump isn't available or its use isn't convenient), or to drain or fill tanks on a camper or trailer (not for gas tanks or for handling dangerous, volatile fluids). Generally, this class of pumps operates from the 120-volt power line, can handle from 30 to 360 gallons per hour, and has enough pushing power to move a 5/8-inch hoseful of water up to a 40-foot height. However, the motors of this pump type are not suited for submersion, and, since most have brush-type universal motors, these pumps shouldn't be operated where explosive fumes are in the air or hazardous materials are in the water.

For big jobs, the centrifugal pump is favored. These usually have quiet induction-type (AC only) motors. What's more, they are generally available in sealed metal or epoxy plastic housings, so that they can be safely submerged.

HOW THEY WORK

Rotary Positive-Displacement, Flexible-Impeller Pumps

This type pump has a flexible, molded-rubber impeller, fitted into a chamber that has inlet and outlet hose fittings. The impeller has as many as six vanes, rounded off at their tips so that the vanes can slide and seal against the chamber surface. When the impeller turns, the rotating vanes create a self-priming suction that gulps water through the inlet, and then pushes it out the outlet. The process is repeated endlessly. Because the impeller seals so tightly in the chamber, friction is great. And so, the pump must never be used dry. If it is, heat will build up and the impeller will be ruined or will weld itself to the chamber wall. Similarly, although this pump type can handle dirty water, it's not meant to pump mud, wet sand, or abrasive slurry. Too much of such material will quickly wear out the impeller or the polished metal plates between which it rotates, eventually stalling the pump.

Centrifugal Pumps

The impeller of a centrifugal-type pump isn't flexible; it's often made of rigid plastic or metal. The vanes extend radially from the center of a disc-shaped plate that whirls at high speed within a chamber when motor power is applied. Water is drawn to the center of the plate, where it is flung outward by the vanes into the chamber and expelled from the outlet port. Sealed types, meant for direct immersion, have a screen or grillwork opening, through which water enters the chamber. These pumps are self-priming. However, on other types which are fed through piping, the chamber must contain some water (priming) before the pump will operate efficiently. To make such a pump self-priming will require installation of a one-way valve, called a *foot valve*, in the intake line.

A foot valve will allow water to be drawn into the line, but not let it flow out when the pump is turned off. This means that water will remain in the chamber to prime the pump the next time it's turned on.

Generally, a centrifugal pump can be run dry without damage, because its vanes do not rub and pound on the chamber surfaces, as do those of a flexible-vane, rotary-displacement type. This also makes these pumps more capable in handling silt and muck in the water, although a steady diet of abrasives still isn't recommended.

SOME PUMP TERMS YOU SHOULD KNOW

Getting the best pump for the job you have in mind means knowing what to ask for in the terminology of the field. Get to know these words and their meanings and you'll get the best pump for your money.

Discharge head: The altitude measured from the pump outlet port to the point at which water is discharged. Generally, water in an outlet hose means that the pump must push against gravity to do its job. Where the discharge head is too great, the pump's pushing power may be insufficient to move water. As head increases, pump efficiency decreases.

Flow rate: The quantity of water moved in a given period of time, usually measured in gallons per minute (gpm) or gallons per hour (gph). It varies considerably with discharge head and suction head.

gph: Gallons per hour. The flow rate of a pump (usually a small pump), based on its ability to move water over a comparatively long time. It is not a useful measure unless the discharge head is known and stated.

gpm: Gallons per minute. The flow rate of a pump (usually a large pump), based on its ability to move water over a comparatively short time. It is not a useful measure unless the discharge head is known and stated.

Lift: An alternative term for suction head.

Ports: The inlet and outlet of the pump, through which water enters under suction and leaves under pressure.

Prime: The infusion of water into the pump chamber to commence pumping action. Once primed, the pump action continues, so long as there is a flow.

Self-priming: The ability of the pump to commence pumping without requiring assistance. (See prime, above.)

Suction head: The altitude of the water column, measured from the source to the inlet port of the pump. Generally, water in an inlet hose means that the pump must draw up, working against gravity and the fluid friction of the water column. Where the suction head is too great, the pump may lose its prime and run dry.

Sump pump: A specialized, fixed pump that installs within a pit, dug into the lowest point where water accumulates. This pit (sump) fills with water before your basement or garage does. The pump's job is to drain the pit before water can accumulate.

Thermal protection: An electrical circuit-breaker built into the motor. It senses the motor's temperature and snaps open if the motor runs too hot. This protection prevents electrical fires, but is far too late to shut down a pump motor in a flexible-vane pump that has been allowed to operate dry. In most cases, allowing the motor to cool will automatically reset the thermal protector.

IMPORTANT FEATURES TO LOOK FOR

Selection of the right kind of pump calls for an accurate size-up of your individual needs. No single pump can handle every job. (What's more, there are some jobs, such as handling gasoline, fuel oil, other explosives, and corrosive materials, that only experts with specialized pumping equipment should handle.) Following are some guidelines that will help you make a choice.

Do You Need a Fixed or Portable Pump?

Are you doing a "one-time" job or can it be expected to happen again? If it's a one-time job, you may be able to arrange time to work with a low-cost, low-capacity, portable pump. There isn't sufficient need to warrant a big investment in a large-capacity pump you might not use again for years. Alternatively, you may want to rent, rather than buy. However, if a sudden storm has left you with a basement full of water, it's likely that this will happen again. You'll be better off installing a fixed pump or at least equipping yourself with a portable submersible type of at least 1,000 gph rating. On the other hand, if portability and light-duty "puddle draining" is your usual chore, you may be better off with a positive-displacement, rotary-vane type. They're inexpensive, easy to set up, and store in minimum space.

Will You Be Around to Turn the Pump On and Off?

Most sump pumps and other fixed-type drainers feature automatic switches that sense water level and turn the pump on when it's needed and off when its job is done. This is not true of most portable pumps. So, if you choose a portable, plan on being around when it's used. This is especially true of the rotary positive-displacement types. If these run dry, you can ruin the vanes on the impeller in under 2 minutes. Most fixed pumps for sump-draining jobs use float- or diaphragm-operated switches. Of the two, the diaphragm-type is considered least trouble.

Can the Pump Handle Dirty Water?

Regardless of your choice, it should include some form of screen or strainer on the inlet side of the pump to guard against leaves, paper, or other floating debris being

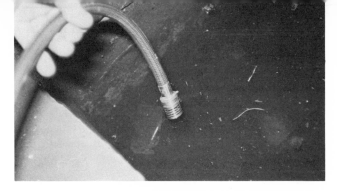

Figure 20-4. A strainer placed on the inlet hose will prevent jam-ups caused by leaves or dirt being sucked into the line. This will protect positive-displacement, impeller-type pumps from running dry and being damaged. GRAF-WHALEN photograph.

sucked into the pump. Also, the strainer should not be easily blocked by a "dam" of debris. This can cause the pump to lose its prime (if centrifugal) or to be damaged by dry running (if rotary type). All pumps can handle some content of dissolved dirt and floating sand. But, don't consistently use a pump for moving muddy water or you'll shorten its life by making it work harder and subjecting it to harsh abrasion.

How High Must You Pump?

The discharge head that the pump's outlet port "looks into" represents quite a load of water. That's because it is a column of water confined in a hose or pipe, subject to the earth's gravity. Remember that until the water is expelled from the hose, it affects the pump's pushing ability. And so, when you shop for a pump, consider how high above the pump's location the discharge will take place. This will give you a good idea of the "head" the pump will be pushing. Anything below this rating won't do. Everything above it will do the job faster.

Read the Fine Print About "Priming"

The flexible-vane, rotary-displacement types are offered as self-priming (as are the sealed, submersible, centrifugal types). But, in many pumps, this action holds good only at a suction head of less than 10 feet, in most cases. If the pump is much more than this above the source, it will need to be primed. And, if a block-up occurs, the pump will lose its prime. If the pump is advertised as self-priming, read the statistics and get answers to your questions before deciding to buy.

Examine the Fittings

Most portables are equipped to accept the screw-on fittings of a garden hose on the inlet and outlet ports. Most durable are the brass insert fittings. Least durable are the plastic fittings molded on to low-cost pumps. The latter can be damaged by a fall or by cross-threading. Once the threads are destroyed, the pump is of little value.

Be Aware of Electrical Safety

As with all power-line operated devices used near damp or wet ground surfaces, the possibility of electrical shock exists. Conscientious design and good materials minimize this possibility. However, it is a sensible precaution to use every means at hand to give yourself the safest possible conditions. Pumps not specifically marked *submersible* should never be used in water. Keep them high and dry. And, if the pump is equipped with a three-prong, grounding-type plug, be sure that the ground pin is solidly grounded by the AC outlet. Don't use "cheater adaptors" or improper extension cords that leave the ground pin "floating." An accidental short to the ungrounded motor case could make it "hot" with respect to damp basement or garage floors. For best safety, use a portable ground-fault interrupter between the pump and power line.

TIPS FOR USING YOUR POWER PUMP
Rotary Positive-Displacement, Flexible-Impeller Pumps

Place the pump on a dry surface as near as possible to the location to be drained. Attach hoses to the inlet and outlet ports of the pump. (These are usually marked to show which is which.) Lay out hoses, using the minimum length, and avoid kinks and sharp bends that might strangle pumping action. Arrange a discharge location so that water flows away from the area to be drained. Most pumps of this type will self-prime to 10 feet when the impeller is dry or to 20 feet if it is wet. Attach the strainer to the inlet suction hose and place in the water. Adjust its height to prevent debris pickup or mud-sucking, which might block the pump circuit. Plug the pump into a grounding-type outlet or into a portable ground-fault

Figure 20-5. A positive-displacement, impeller-type pump will quickly remove standing water from this garage sump pit. Note the discharge line in drain. GRAF-WHALEN photograph.

interrupter that is plugged into the line outlet. During operation, the pump's sound will help you know what's happening. When pumping, a steady, mechanical, whirring noise will be heard. If a blockage reduces flow rate, the pump's note will change. Should it run dry, the whirring will be entirely different in character, signaling that the pump is laboring. Be alert to these changes and switch off power when action is needed to keep the pump from running dry.

If dirt or mud should block the inlet, shut down power and back-flush to wash out the offending debris. Be sure that hoses are airtight in their connection to the inlet and outlet fittings to gain greatest efficiency.

Centrifugal Pumps

These pumps handle large-volume water removal chores easier and with less attention than their rotary positive-displacement cousins. However, the submersible types must be lowered into the water they are to pump. This can create quite a discharge head if you are pumping out a deep location, such as a flooded basement. Remember that flow rate decreases as head increases. So, find the nearest, practical drain location at a reasonable height above the pump and you'll get fastest drainage. For example, with one popular type, delivery is only 5 gpm with a discharge head of 20 feet. This rises to 20 gpm with a 3-foot head.

To use a submersible, simply attach a hose to the outlet port, lower the submersible into the water, and lead the discharge hose to a suitable drain location. Then, plug into an AC outlet or into a portable ground-fault interrupter that's plugged into the AC outlet. Keep any electrical connections high and dry. Only the pump unit is submersible. This type pump can be run dry without damage, but keep your ears tuned to its sound for indications that debris is reducing flow.

POWER PUMP MAINTENANCE

Most pumps require little or no maintenance throughout their operating lives. However, in rotary positive-displacement, flexible-vane types, the motor will require new carbon brushes after about 300 operating hours. Brush replacement requires unscrewing holder caps on either side of the motor, removing the old set of brushes and springs, installing a new set, and reinstalling the cap screws. The operation shouldn't take more than 10 minutes.

General cleaning is all that's needed by most pumps. Flush out the impeller chamber before storage to wash away debris before it can cake and harden in the chamber. Most pump motors are factory lubricated for their operating lives and require no user care.

21

Sump Pumps

Sump pumps are small, self-priming pumps driven by fractional horsepower motors, with electrical switching devices that control the pump cycle automatically with rising and falling water levels.

The submersible pump is powered by an oil-filled motor that never needs lubrication. This motor is housed within a waterproof cast-iron or bronze housing that will not be damaged by flooding or condensation while the pump is operated in a wet sump. Typically, a sump pump is installed in a pit about 2 feet below the lowest point in the house.

The power switch is actuated by water pressure on a diaphragm, and operation is completely automatic. When the rising water level reaches 8 inches, then the water, which has entered through a rectangular opening on the bottom of the switch housing, exerts sufficient pressure on the diaphragm/gasket assembly to activate a snap-action switch, which turns on the motor.

When the water level drops to 3 inches or below, pressure on the diaphragm is reduced. This relaxes pressure on the switch, allows it to open, and shuts off the motor.

A vent (or breather) tube is contained within the power cord. This allows air trapped within the switch housing to escape and assures proper operation due to diaphragm pressure only.

The abrasion-resistant impeller blade's rapid rotation within the pump housing forces the water (plus any solids small enough to pass through the strainer base) through the discharge port into the discharge pipe. Pump capacity depends on water level. The higher the water, the lower the pump's capacity. A typical pump that can lift 2,700 gph at a 10-foot head can only lift 1,500 gph when the water level is 20 feet above the pump.

See chapter 20 for information about power pumps.

22

Electric Screwdrivers

Until you've used one, you might just think that this is merely an electrified hand tool that's more luxury than necessity. But try one and be convinced. The human hand and arm are sort of poorly designed for the job of twisting-while-keeping-steady-pressure-and-holding-a-straight-line. It's rather like a rub-your-tummy, pat-your-head task. The experiences you've probably had with marred screw heads, gouged workpieces, and cockeyed screws bear mute testimony to the fact that there *are* some jobs where manual skills and muscle can be augmented by a well-designed power tool. (After all, if we hadn't already accepted this hypothesis, we'd still be using hand drills and long, muscle-powered hand saws!)

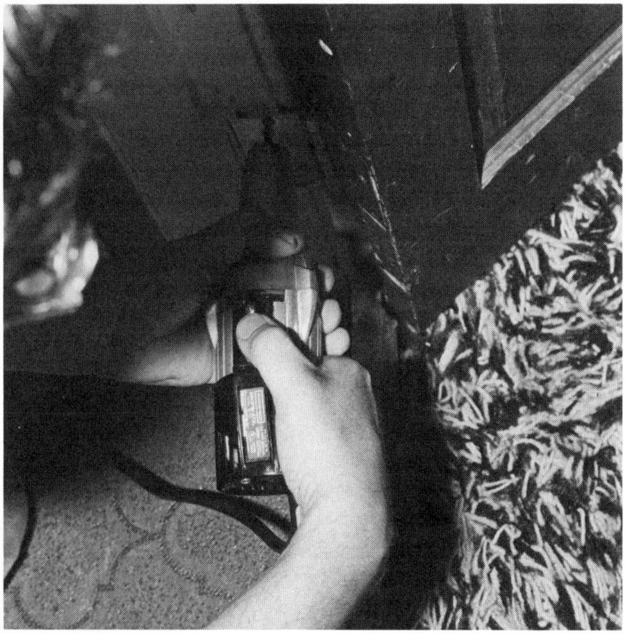

The electric screwdriver is that kind of auxiliary tool. It's designed to supply the screw-driving effort, while your hand supplies the pressure and guidance to seat the screw squarely in its destined place. The secret lies in the genuinely great amount of torque (twisting effort) that a small motor can exert through a system of meshed gears. The motor spins along at moderately high speed, driving gears of radically different diameters. Speed of rotation is slowed through each such reduction, but with each reduction, the slower-turning output-shaft exerts greater and greater turning force. It's virtually impossible to stop the shaft of an electric screwdriver from rotating with just your bare hands. And that's what gives it the power to sink screws with such inexorable force: It twists harder than your hands can.

WHAT'S AVAILABLE

Electric screwdrivers come in AC-powered and cordless battery-powered models, and each type features an output chuck that accepts slip-in, straight-blade bits, as well as Phillips-head bits. Most also accept drilling bits, which are used to produce starter holes for screws of different diameter. What's more, the electric screwdriver has the ability to operate either clockwise or counterclockwise. This makes it just as adept at backing-out bound screws as it is in sinking screw fasteners for the first time.

AC-powered models are compact and easy to hold. Their small size, which stems from the absence of any self-contained power supply, is offset by their need to be near an AC power outlet or extension cord. This dependency, however, is balanced by their somewhat greater torque, which gives them a decided edge in screw-driving jobs around the home and shop.

Cordless models are larger and a bit bulkier than AC-

Figure 22-1. Electric screwdriver. GRAF-WHALEN photograph.

powered types, and their driving power isn't as great or as long-winded as line-powered models. But they are free to roam where you do, and they put real power in your hands, without the clumsy handling problems of a trailing extension cord. Some even go so far as to convert into electric drills, using snap-in Jacobs chucks. And so, there is versatility in the cordless models that makes them worthy of consideration.

IMPORTANT FEATURES TO LOOK FOR
AC-Powered Models
A sturdy housing that fits your mitt comfortably, a power switch you can work with one hand, a tough power cord (fitted with a three-wire, grounding-type plug, if the housing of the unit is metal), and a fair assortment of straight and Phillips-head bits are key features. Look also for a positive-grip head that won't allow a bit to fall out just because you tilt the tool down. The direction of rotation should be reversible with a switch, and it should be possible for you to work the tool with one hand for use in tight locations.

Cordless Models
Most have tough housings of high-impact plastic, with metal components in the driving parts. A clever snap-in power pack (as in the Disston model) is a positive plus, for it means that you can power other cordless power tools with the same pack or keep extra packs on charge for uninterrupted use in long jobs. (Few are quite so ingenious as the Disston's, which plugs into the outlet for charging and then delivers power to the tool through the same prongs used for AC charging.) A momentary on/off reversing switch is a plus, because it snaps to the off position when the tool isn't needed, saving battery power.

TIPS FOR USING YOUR ELECTRIC SCREWDRIVER
Depending upon the job to be done, the proper bit must be selected. You will find packed with your screwdriver an assortment of bits. After selecting the bit to be used, insert the shank portion of the bit into the chuck. To do this, grasp the end of the bit with the fingers and push the bit into the chuck until it snaps into place. You may need to turn the bit slightly to cause it to fit into the hex-shaped grooves. To remove the bit, press the chuck release, while at the same time pulling outward on the bit.

When working with wood, it is always advisable to drill a pilot hole for the screw to be sunk. This avoids splitting of the workpiece. Depending upon the screwdriver type you have, you may be able to use one of the drilling bits provided. Alternatively, if your model offers a drill chuck, snap it in and use a twist drill of about two-thirds the diameter of the screw to be sunk.

Figure 22-2. The compact AC-powered screwdriver is adaptable to any screw-driving chore, requiring only the proper bit to drive any screw. GRAF-WHALEN photograph.

Figure 22-3. Metal-body, AC-powered models have three-wire, grounding-type plugs for safety's sake. GRAF-WHALEN photograph.

Figure 22-4. A reversing switch sets the screwdriver for in or out rotation. GRAF-WHALEN photograph.

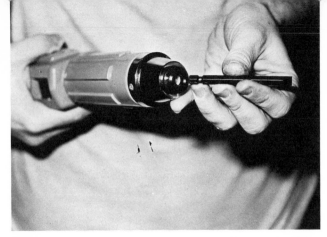

Figure 22-5. The chuck of the screwdriver accepts bits properly cut for driving by its mechanism. GRAF-WHALEN photograph.

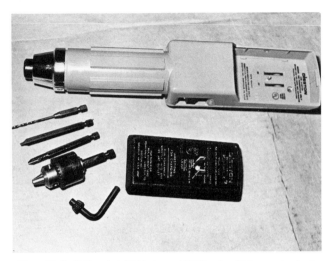

Figure 22-6. Drills, straight blade, and Phillips-head bits are standard accessories. The Jacobs chuck accepts other driven items. The battery pack is at the rear. Photograph courtesy of Disston, Inc.

Figure 22-7. The battery pack of this cordless model has built-in plug prongs that fit a standard AC wall outlet. Some prongs furnish DC power to the tool when the pack is engaged in the recessed end of tool. GRAF-WHALEN photograph.

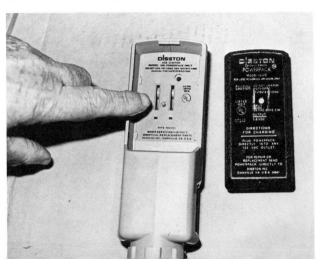

Figure 22-8. The battery pack simply snaps into place to furnish operating power for tools. To keep "little helpers" from operating tool the pack should be removed and stored where tots can't reach it. GRAF-WHALEN photograph.

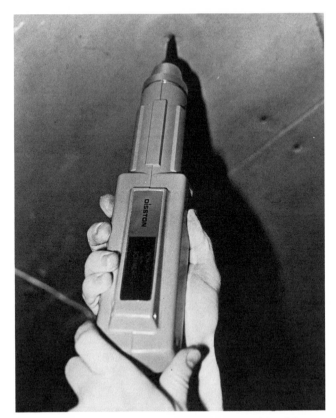

Figure 22-9. Overhead drilling or screw-setting is a specialty of the cordless screwdriver. There's no dangling power cord to get in your way, and the tool can be used in locations far removed from an AC outlet. GRAF-WHALEN photograph.

Once the pilot hole has been made, change bits (matching to the screw to be fitted). The "right" bit is the one that provides maximum edge-to-edge contact with the screw's driving faces. Start the screw by hand, then place the bit in contact and apply power, guiding the sinking action by keeping your hand moving in a straight line. Continue power application until you feel the screw "bottom," but stop immediately—excessive tightening may shear the head on soft fasteners of brass or aluminum construction.

Cordless models can, typically, drive up to fifty 1-inch-long, number 8 screws in soft wood without predrilling. Pilot holes will increase drilling time, because less power is needed to seat each screw. The amount of drilling time increases for smaller or shorter screws, but decreases for harder woods. Experience is the best teacher.

To back out a seated screw, reverse the tool's direction of rotation after seating it in the screw head. You may have to clear paint or other matter from the head, which might cause the tool's bit to lose its "bite." If a Phillips-head bit starts spinning in the screw head, try a different size bit that gives greater edge contact.

RULES FOR SAFE USE
• Keep hands clear of bits at all times.
• Keep children away. All visitors should be kept a safe distance from the work area.
• In cordless models, use only the proper battery power-pack with your screwdriver. Use of any other power source may lead to problems or void the manufacturer's warranty.
• Dress properly. Do not wear loose clothing or jewelry that can be caught in moving parts.
• Hold the screwdriver firmly to avoid slipping from the work surface.
• Use the right tool. Never use a tool to perform a job for which it was not intended.
• Don't force the tool. It will do the job better and safer at the rate for which it was designed.
• Don't overreach. Keep proper footing and balance at all times.
• Store idle tools indoors. When not in use tools should be stored in a dry, high or locked-up place, out of the reach of children. In cordless models, it's wise to remove and separately store the power pack, if possible.

• Maintain the tool with care. Inspect bits for wear and keep the unit clean for safest performance. Follow instructions in the manual for proper service.
• Secure the work. Use clamps or a vise to hold work. It's safer than using your hand and it frees both hands to operate the tool.
• Keep work area clean and well lighted. Cluttered, dark areas and benches invite accidents.
• With cordless models, for safety before servicing or when changing bits, remove the power pack.

ELECTRIC SCREWDRIVER MAINTENANCE
All electric screwdrivers, whether line or cordless types, use universal (brush-type) motors. After hundreds of operating hours, the brushes will require replacement. However, it may take many years to accumulate the degree of wear that necessitates brush replacement. If the tool loses power and cannot properly seat a screw without stalling, brush inspection and replacement are probably in order.

In cordless models, the battery pack is the chief determinant of the tool's power. The pack should be recharged after use and kept in a location that is cool and dry, away from furnace pipes or heat ducts. Excessive storage temperatures sap the life of all battery types.

One other thing: The batteries of the cordless electric screwdriver have a "memory" quality that reduces their power storage capacity. If you habitually use your tool for a few minutes and then place the pack on charge, the batteries will "remember" that you only needed a fraction of their capacity. Gradually, they will lose capacity to a point where you get much less operating time from them than would otherwise be expected. The "cure-all" for this peculiar phenomenon is to "treat 'em rough." Run the tool to the point where the batteries are *totally* exhausted. Recharge for at least 16 hours. Then run the batteries down again, all the way. Recharge, again. If necessary, repeat the deep discharge and recharge again. By cycling the batteries between the wide extremes of total discharge and recharge, you will gradually increase their power capacity, until they're fully able to hold a maximum charge again. It sounds rough, but it's the way to keep cordless tool batteries delivering all the energy they were designed to deliver.

23

Electric Impact Tools

Anyone who has ever strained back and arm muscles to the limit trying to change a flat, knows exactly how tough a job it can be to free a nut that is seemingly "frozen" to a wheel stud. The problem isn't solved by strength alone. Rather, it takes a succession of sharp tugs to overcome the binding friction that has locked the nut in place. Once it can be moved, the nut is as good as off. That bit of wisdom is embodied in mechanical form in the electric impact tool—an increasingly popular power tool for use in the home, workshop, garage, or around the farm. Looking like an oversize electric drill, the impact tool has a "business end" (called an anvil), which mates with square-drive sockets. Snapped in place on the anvil, the socket becomes a power-driven (rather than a muscle-driven) tool, capable of loosening or tightening nuts and hex bolts, driving wood screws, and more. Fitted with a snap-on chuck, the impact tool can accept drills, reamers, taps, and small hole saws.

If this all sounds like the impact tool is just a large-scale drill, you're right and you're wrong. Unlike a drill, which applies *continuous torque* (twisting effort), the rotary hammer of the impact tool delivers sharp, staccato blows to the anvil, at the rate of 2,000 to 3,000 blows per minute. Sure, the anvil rotates, but as a result of the hammer-like blows from the mechanism inside, rather than from a steady twisting effort from the motor (such as in the case of a drill). Get the picture? Each impact delivers a concentrated torque force—stronger, by far, than a steady twisting force. By applying these impacts in either the clockwise or counterclockwise direction of rotation, a nut can be snubbed up as tight as you wish or loosened with next to no effort on your part.

WHAT'S AVAILABLE
Electric impact tools are offered in light-duty 3/8-inch and heavy-duty 1/2-inch drive sizes, thus roughly corresponding to the functional capabilities of their hand-driven socket tool counterparts. The 3/8-inch-size impact tool has a typical motor rating of about 1/5 horsepower, and can deliver up to 40 foot pounds of torque in 5 seconds of operation. The 1/2-inch-size impact tool has a typical motor rating of 1/3 horsepower and delivers up to 100 foot pounds of torque in 5 seconds of operation.

Light-duty models have the advantage of getting into tight spots where the bulkier 1/2-inch models can't fit. They're generally useful on fasteners up to 3/8 inch, and, weighing only about 4 1/2 pounds, they are not fatiguing to use. However, the light-duty models aren't meant to handle brawny jobs like removal of auto wheel lug nuts. For that kind of service, you need a 1/2-inch, heavy-duty

Figure 23-1. Electric impact tool. GRAF-WHALEN photograph.

model. Generally larger (about 12 inches in length), heavier (about 7 pounds), and somewhat less maneuverable than the light-duty types, the half-inchers trade agility for truly muscular performance. Their motors turn more slowly, but their rotary hammer mechanisms are heavier, delivering more force-per-impact to the anvil.

Many impact tools of both sizes are offered in double-insulated designs, with unbreakable plastic housings or with vinyl-clad aluminum housings. Models provided in bare metal housings come equipped with a three-wire, grounding-type plug and must be grounded to ensure safety against accidental shock.

Accessories for electric impact tools include special heavy six-point socket sets of forged steel (standard sockets for hand wrench use *should not be used with impact tools*), available in sets or individually. For heavy-duty half-inchers, sockets range in size from 7/16 to 1 inch, in 1/16-inch increments. Lighter-duty 3/8-inch tools take sockets from 5/16 to 11/16 inch, in 1/16-inch increments. Extensions, universal joints, angle-head attachments, and screwdriver chucks and bits (flat and Phillips) are also offered.

For drilling or boring tough or thick materials, a snap-on chuck is offered for the 1/2-inch models. This accepts bits with shanks of 1/8- to 1/2-inch diameter and can accommodate extra-long bits for doing jobs an ordinary drill couldn't handle. Small hole saws can also be chucked to the impact tool where its extra power is needed for tough cutting jobs.

TIPS FOR USING YOUR IMPACT TOOL
Because the impact tool owes its effectiveness to a rapid succession of light, rotary impacts, it is important for you to determine just how much "hammering" is enough to tighten bolts and nuts without producing excessive stress in the attaching parts. This is a practice that must be guided by your "feel" for the tool. Excessive torquing with the impact tool can lead to sheared bolts.

Make a trial setting on one or two fastenings by holding the tool on impact for less than the required tightening time—say, 2 seconds on a 3/8-inch bolt or 1 second on a 4/16-inch bolt. Adjust tightening time to fit conditions, but do not go beyond reasonable running time or you may over-torque and damage the fasteners. Where torque is critical, finish up with a hand torque-wrench. Gradually, you will learn how long to tighten fasteners with the impact tool. Bear in mind that the loosening torque will average only 75 to 80 percent of the tightening torque. This will help you to minimize the tightening effort you apply to any bolt-seating task.

For drilling jobs, attach the chuck accessory and fit the appropriate drill bit into the chuck's jaws. The action of

Figure 23-2. A reversing ring-switch at the rear of the impact tool sets the motor for clockwise or counterclockwise operation. The socket fitted to the anvil is a special type, able to withstand sharp blows produced by tool operation. GRAF-WHALEN photograph.

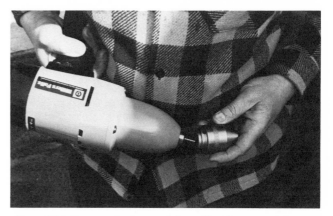

Figure 23-3. Snap-on chuck converts impact tool from wrench to drilling and boring use. GRAF-WHALEN photograph.

Figure 23-4. Useful in so many ways, the impact tool can loosen or torque down nuts and bolts in many tight spots. Where torque is critical, you may wish to tighten fasteners almost all the way by the tool, finishing manually. GRAF-WHALEN photograph.

the impact tool is somewhat rougher than that of a drill, so expect holes that are not quite as smooth, especially in thin material. In heavy jobs, though, the impact tool will drill to greater depths than a conventional 1/2-inch drill with much less binding. The bit can be backed out of a deep hole by switching off power, reversing the tool's direction of rotation, and reapplying power.

RULES FOR SAFE USE
• For personal safety, wear eye-protecting goggles or safety glasses when using an impact tool.
• Keep your working area uncluttered, so that there's less chance of tripping or fumbling. These are often the main ingredients of accidents.
• Shoo children and pets away from the work area, so that there's no risk to them and so that you can work without distractions.
• Don't force the tool to take on a job bigger than its rating qualifies it to handle. A 3/8-inch, light-duty impact tool isn't meant to do the work of a larger model.
• Don't use standard (hand) sockets or drive parts with an impact tool. They're not meant to withstand the sharp blows the tool delivers. A broken part can injure you.
• Secure your work with clamps, vise, or other immobilizing methods. Keep your balance and proper footing. Use both hands to operate the tool.
• When working outdoors or in damp areas where ground contact is likely, be sure that the tool is grounded (if required). Even if the tool is double-insulated, use of a portable ground-fault interrupter is recommended for added safety.
• Avoid use in areas where there are dangerous explosive or combustible fumes. Universal motors used in these tools create sparks that can ignite vapors.
• Don't damage the motor of your impact tool by reversing direction of rotation while the trigger switch is depressed. Severe arcing will result, possibly burning out a commutator section.

IMPACT TOOL MAINTENANCE
The inlet and outlet air passages of the motor housing must be kept open to allow free passage of ventilating, cooling air. Blow out any accumulated dust periodically.

Motor armature bearings should be lubricated periodically with SAE 10 or 20 oil. (If the tool is used frequently, oil every three months; otherwise, oil semi-annually.) The anvil, hammer assembly, and case require about 1 ounce of grease annually. Too much grease applied to these parts will cause the impact tool motor to run hot, so apply sparingly. See manufacturer's recommendations for specific details.

24

Electric Power-Tool Brakes

Inertia is a property of matter that sometimes works for us (it keeps flywheels spinning and holds rotational speeds constant), but also works against us when we want a tool to stop working *now*, rather than a minute after power has been shut off. Table saws, grinders, large drill

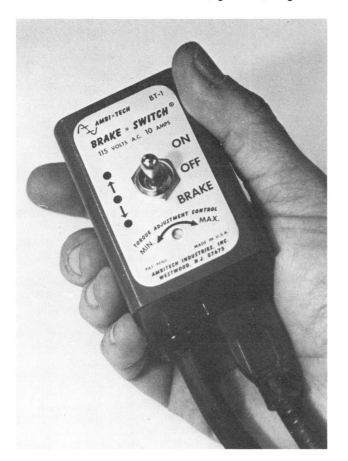

presses, and similar power tools that are run by brawny induction motors (AC only) have the inertial tendency to "store up" rotational energy, so that they keep on running even after the power switch has been opened. That's a nuisance if you have to wait for a blade to coast to a halt before changing it, but it can also be a downright hazard if a tool has to be shut down immediately because something's gone wrong.

A *power-tool brake* is a good investment as a control device if you want instantaneous stopping of an induction motor-powered tool. The tool plugs into the brake and the brake plugs into the AC outlet. To start the tool, you flip a switch on the brake to the "on" position. To stop the tool, you press the switch to a spring-loaded brake position—and the tool miraculously stops in a second or so (rather than the minute or more it would take if its inertia had to be overcome by friction). The safety possibilities are obvious and immediate.

HOW THEY WORK

The bit of magic performed by the power brake is really quite simple. The induction motor that powers tools, such as big saws, runs on *alternating current*. When power is removed, its shaft will be spun by the mechanical inertia of the wheel or blade it was driving. But, if *direct current* is applied to the motor for a brief period, it will stop dead in its tracks, because the magnetic forces set up in the motor resist rotation. This means that the motor will "soak up" the inertial forces applied to its shaft, braking any tool linked to the motor. Disarmingly simple, but effective, the power brake is a worthwhile addition to the home shop equipped with large power tools.

Figure 24-1. Electric power-tool brake. Photograph courtesy of Ambi-Tech Industries, Inc.

Figure 24-2. The brake is installed between the AC outlet (into which its cord plugs) and the tool (which plugs into the outlet on the brake's case). The switch is set to "on" to pass normal AC power to the tool. When flipped to "brake," DC is applied to the tool's motor to stop it dead in its tracks. GRAF-WHALEN photograph.

TIPS FOR USING YOUR POWER BRAKE

The brake is installed between the power outlet and plug of the tool to be controlled. Be sure that the tool's motor is a brushless induction-type (not a universal motor of the type used in drills). Tool power switches can be turned on and power or braking applied through the power brake's switch.

It is imperative that devices driven by the tool's motor (blades or wheels) are tightly fitted. Sudden stops can loosen parts and create hazards. Recognizing this, the power brake features a *torque adjustment*, which allows you to set the slowdown braking rate to a level that recognizes the stresses created by sudden braking of a power tool.

Typical current ratings of power brakes for home shop use are 7.5 amperes at 120 volts AC.

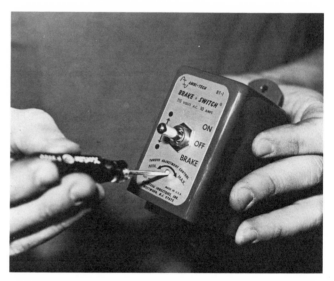

Figure 24-3. Torque adjustment on brake is screwdriver-set. It lets you program the rate at which the tool's motor is braked, to prevent sudden stops that can be dangerous. GRAF-WHALEN photograph.

25

Chain Saws

Not long ago, the chain saw was strictly a professional's lumbering tool. Like the woodsmen who used them, chain saws were heavy, burly, and hard-as-nails machines that needed firm, muscular hands to keep them in line. But, nowadays, scaled-down modern versions of these tough foresting tools have become important helpers to today's suburban homeowner, farmer, and camper. Armed with a chain saw, any adult can fell a tree, limb it, "buck" the tree into fireplace-size logs, and quarter the logs into easy-burning firewood in just a fraction of the time and with far

Figure 25-1a and b. Chain saw and chain saw in action. Photographs courtesy of Allis Chalmers Corp.

less work than would be needed with a hand ax and saw. What's more, a chain saw is a handy aid in pruning trees and in clearing brush, ski trails, and campsites. It's also a construction aid in making shelters, floats and docks, rustic furniture, check dams, fences, and even log buildings.

WHAT'S AVAILABLE

Chain saws come in heavy, medium, and lightweight models. You can get either gasoline- or electric-powered saws, although the gas types are most popular because their power source is completely portable. Generally, the power output of a gas-powered chain saw is measured in cubic inches of its piston's displacement, rather than in horsepower. Heavyweight models, which are suitable for logging chores rivaling a timberjack's work, feature hefty engines of up to 8 cubic inches displacement. Lightweight types meant for casual cutting may sport engines of as little as 1.4 cubic inches displacement. For most jobs, though, a medium-weight model that packs a 4.5- to 5-cubic-inch engine delivers just about the right cutting power.

The power of the engine isn't the only consideration, however, because it's the guide bar and cutting chain of the saw that do the work. And so, you should choose the "business end" of the chain saw with special care. Considering the average size of what you will be cutting, choose the minimum length bar and chain. Remember that you can cut a tree at any point around its circumference, so a bar just 15 inches long can actually cut through

a tree trunk that's 30 inches in diameter. Also, if you plan to do a wide variety of cutting chores, consider purchasing a saw that accepts bars and chains of various sizes. This way, you can reduce the bulk and handling problems of a big saw to the easy handling of a small saw with just a quick change of chain and guide bar.

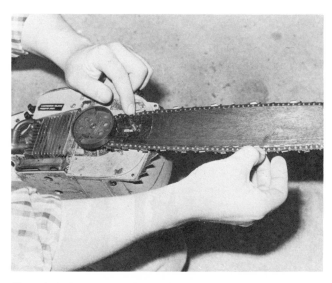

Figure 25-3. The saw chain forms a continuous loop of metal cutting parts, which ride in a groove in the guide bar. You need a solid understanding of saw chains to get the very best performance and chain life. GRAF-WHALEN photograph.

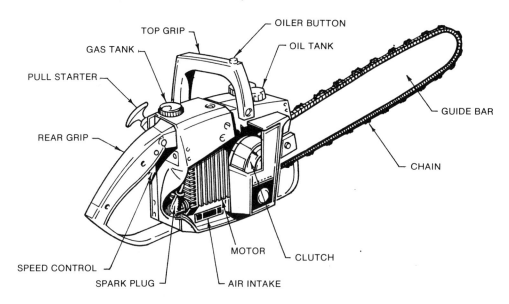

Figure 25-2. Common parts of a gasoline-powered chain saw.

Saw Chain and Guide Bar

Like a bicycle chain, the saw chain forms a continuous loop of metal parts which are pinned together by rivets. The chain can flex lengthwise, but side-to-side motion is not possible. The chain loops around the engine-driven sprocket inside the saw housing and fits into a groove around the guide bar. In most saws, the saw chain simply slips around the nose of the guide bar. However, in others there is a roller or sprocket in the nose end of the bar to reduce friction, wear, and drag on the engine.

Cutters

Saw chains have two types of cutters—left-hand and right-hand. The cutters are shaped so that the inner top edges of each left- and right-hand cutter overlap. The cutters do not cut wood in slices, but remove it as small chips or "bites." Each cutter has a top plate and a side plate, which are sharpened to a fine edge and which regularly need resharpening to keep the chain at top performance. The outside surface of each top and side plate is given a hard chrome finish to keep the edges sharper longer. The edges of the top plate and side plate are angled to pull the cutter into the wood. The edge of the top plate makes the bottom of the cut in the wood. The edges of the side plates make the width of the cut. When these edges are properly angled, the cutters are said to be "self-feeding" and incise into the wood automatically as they are pulled by the chain.

To control the amount of wood the top plate can cut in one bite, each cutter has a fingerlike projection at the front called a *depth gauge*. The vertical distance between the top plate and the depth gauge is called the *depth-gauge setting*. The depth-gauge setting can be regulated to cut thicker chips, as is required for softer woods, or thinner chips, as is required for harder woods. Some cutters have offset depth gauges. These promote smoother cutting by helping to control the side plate width-of-cut, thus lessening cutter chatter and chain wobble. Cutter chatter occurs when the top plate tries to grab too big a bite and breaks the chip out, rather than cutting it free. Wobble occurs when the side plates pull too far into the wood and make the chain lean from side to side. Chatter and wobble are conditions damaging to a saw chain.

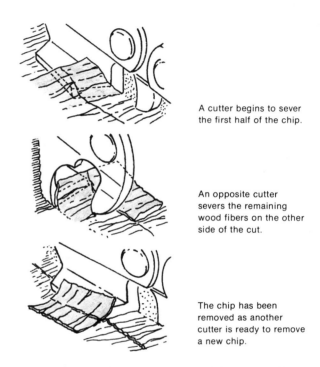

A cutter begins to sever the first half of the chip.

An opposite cutter severs the remaining wood fibers on the other side of the cut.

The chip has been removed as another cutter is ready to remove a new chip.

Figure 25-4. The opposing cutters remove a chip in two steps. The action alternates from one side of the cut to the other.

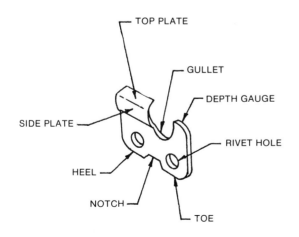

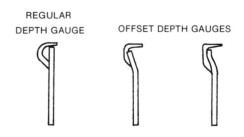

Figure 25-5. A fingerlike projection at the front of the cutter blade, called a depth gauge, controls the amount of wood that the top plate can cut in one bite. Some cutters have offset depth gauges to promote smoother cutting by lessening cutter chatter and chain wobble.

The base of each cutter has three working areas—the toe, the heel, and the notch. The toe at the front and the heel at the rear slide on the guide bar. The notch provides clearance to allow the center link to properly nest between the teeth of a spur sprocket.

Most cutters are made of metal of the same thickness throughout their entire shape. Some cutters have top plates which diminish in thickness toward the inner overlapping edge. These are known as "coined top-plate" cutters. Coining allows more cutter chip clearance between the adjacent inner surfaces of the cutters.

Kerf

There are two types of kerf—*wood kerf* and *mechanical kerf.* Wood kerf is the width of the cut made in the wood by the cutters. Mechanical kerf is the distance between the outside edge of the side plate of a left-hand cutter and the outside edge of the side plate of a right-hand cutter. Cutters have a tendency to pull outward, away from each other, so that the wood kerf is always a little wider than the mechanical kerf. This is necessary for free movement of the bar and chain during the cut.

Chip Clearance

Chip clearance is the action of removing the chip after it has been cut. There are two types of chip clearance—*cutter chip clearance* and *chain chip clearance.* Cutter chip clearance is the ability of the cutter to release the chip after it has been severed from the wood. Chain chip clearance is the ability of the chain to clear the released severed chips out of the kerf without recutting them.

Center Links

The *center links* are the drive links of the chain. The *tang* is the part of the center link that is pushed against by the sprocket to move the chain. The tang also rides in the bar groove and keeps the chain on the bar. The front of the tang is shaped to form a hook or scraper, which helps to keep the bar groove clean. The thickness of the tang is used to denote the gauge of the chain.

Some center links have the same thickness of metal throughout. Other center links are made with a thinner tang section and a thicker rivet section. These coined center links create a stronger chain for use on smaller-gauge bars. The thicker upper section provides more rivet-bearing area and reduces "chain stretch," because it takes longer to wear the rivet holes. The rivet holes of the center link are manufactured to act as bearing races for the rivets, which pivot in the center-link rivet holes.

Side Links

The side links are the connecting links between the cutters and center links, as well as a spacing link between the cutters. Like the cutters, side links have a toe, a heel,

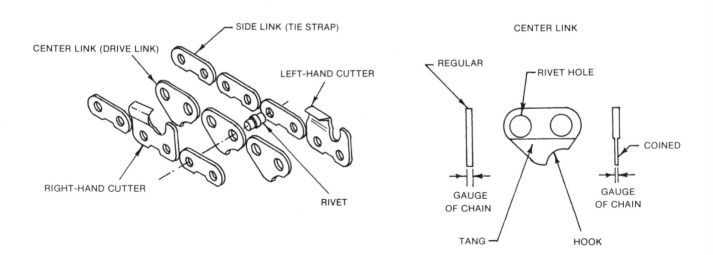

Figure 25-6. The center links drive the chain. For small gauge bars they are "coined." The center links are connected to the side links and cutters by rivets.

and a notch. The toe and heel slide on the bar rails and help support the chain. The notch permits proper nesting of the center-link tang when used with spur sprockets.

Some chains make use of a special side link or center link called a G-link. Its special shape acts as a guard and helps to prevent small limbs or brush from being hit by the depth gauges. It is especially effective in reducing chain grabbing and kickback. Grabbing occurs when the depth gauge is caught by the wood and jams against other pieces of wood. Kickback occurs when the grabbing action suddenly "kicks" loose.

Rivets

The rivets hold the chain together and act as bearings, around which the center links can turn. Rivets are manufactured with a thicker-diameter center section, called the *shoulder*, or *flange*, and two smaller-diameter ends. The shoulder is wider than the thickness of the center link, to prevent the cutters and side links from being clamped against the center links when the rivets are headed, allowing the chain to be flexible. The two smaller-diameter ends of the rivet are called *hubs*, or *shanks*. They are long enough to provide sufficient material for strong and effective rivet heads.

Some side links come with the rivets already installed. These are called preset side links and are used when shortening or repairing chain.

Chain Pitch

The term chain pitch describes the size of the chain. It gets its name in this way: Pitch is a sprocket term and refers to the distance between the tips of the sprocket teeth. It is used as the size of the chain because the center-link tangs must fit between the sprocket teeth. If the tangs won't fit, the chain is "out of pitch" and will be damaged by the sprocket. Thus, chain size is directly related to the sprocket, and sprocket pitch and chain pitch must always match.

A common method of determining chain pitch is by measuring the distance between any three consecutive rivets in a straight line and dividing this distance by two. However, the greater the amount of use and wear a chain has had, the less accurate this method becomes. This is particularly true when measuring .354-inch pitch chain against 3/8-inch (.375-inch) pitch chain.

Chain Gauge

Chain gauge is the thickness of the center-link tang. It is one of the important "sizes" of chain. There are four major chain gauges in use today—.050 inch, .058 inch, .063 inch, and .122 inch.

In most cases, the gauge of the chain to be used depends on the diameter of the wood being cut. Trimming and cutting small branches and trees can be done with narrower-gauge chains on lower-powered saws with short, thin bars. As the diameter of the wood increases, longer bars are necessary. Longer bars must be thicker to support the longer bar length. Thicker bars require a wider wood kerf to prevent the chain and bar from binding or pinching in the cut. A wider wood kerf means a wider mechanical kerf, and as a result, bigger chains, which must be made from bigger parts. Bigger parts mean thicker parts, including a thicker tang to support and drive the chain, and the tang thickness determines the gauge.

Types of Chain

The saw chain can be assembled in many ways. There are three different assembly patterns in general use. They are *standard*, *skip-tooth*, and *semi-skip tooth*. Standard chain is assembled with one side link between each cutter. This is the most common assembly pattern. In large-diameter timber, standard chain has a tendency to "hang up" in the cut. This is because of the large number of chips that have to be carried out of the cut by the chain due to the many cutters that are in the wood at the same time. To provide extra space between the cutters for additional chain chip clearance, chain is assembled in skip-tooth and semi-skip tooth patterns.

In the early days of chain saws, the cutting surfaces of the cutter were called "the teeth" and the cutter was often referred to as the "tooth." This is where these two chains got their names. Skip-tooth chain skips every other tooth, or cutter, and semi-skip tooth chain skips one out of every three teeth, or cutters.

Skip-tooth chain has two side links between each cutter. The extra space allows chips to be carried out of the cut much more easily because the chances of recutting chips by close-following cutters is reduced. Skip-tooth chain permits the use of longer bars on saws of the same power because only half as many cutters are in the wood at the same time. Because of the fewer teeth, skip-tooth chain is rougher cutting than standard sequence or regular chain, and it is not recommended for limbing.

Semi-skip tooth chain has an alternating pattern of side links between the cutters. It is a combination of skip-tooth and standard chain; that is, two side links between cutters followed by one side link between cutters and then repeated. It is smoother cutting than skip-tooth, but not as smooth as standard chain. It does, however, provide almost as much chain-chip clearance as skip-tooth chain and it makes limbing easier.

	FAILURE	CAUSE	REMEDY		FAILURE	CAUSE	REMEDY
	Concave side link and cutter bottoms.	Chain running too tight; insufficient lubrication; dull cutters.	Decrease chain tension; check oiler; file cutters.		Side wear.	Abrasive cutting condition.	Check for gut in timber; lubricate well.
	Heel wear on cutters and side links.	Chain too loose; too much joint; dull cutters.	Increase chain tension; maintain .025" joint. File cutters.		Back nicked.	Chain running too loose.	Increase tension.
	Slight heel wear on cutters and side links.	Back slope on cutters; chain was slightly tight; dull cutters.	Remove back slope; decrease chain tension; file cutters.		Back rounded to bottom.	Worn sprocket; chain running too loose.	Increase tension; renew sprocket.
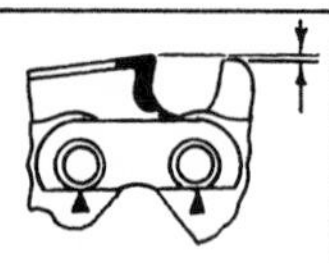	Excessive bottom wear on cutters and side links.	Insufficient joint—chain running tight, filing blunt—no undercut; dull cutters.	Increase joint to .025", decrease tension; file cutters.		Back and front of link peened.	Worn or wrong pitch sprocket.	Renew sprocket; increase tension.
	Severe wear on side and excessive damage.	Stone or nail was struck; dull cutters.	Remove all visible abrasion by filing cutters.		Back peened.	Worn sprocket; dull cutters.	Renew sprocket; file cutters.
	Crack under rear rivet.	Dull or hooked cutters.	Special filing.		Bottom peened and worn.	Link riding on bottom of bar groove; bar rails worn; dull cutters.	Renew bar; file cutters
	Crack under front rivet.	Insufficient joint.	Increase joint to .025"		Bottom point rolled up.	Link bottoming in worn sprocket; dull cutters.	Renew sprocket; file cutters.
	Cracks under both rivets.	Chain running dull and tight—insufficient joint.	Special filing.		Bottom rough and broken off.	Chain run too tight—causes stretch and climbs up on sprocket teeth.	Renew worn chain or sprocket; run chain with less tension.
	Bottom peened and burred.	Hooked cutters—dull—no undercut causes chain to pound on rails.	Eliminate hook; special filing.		Drive lugs worn on one side.	Excessive face angle of cutters—causes side thrust.	Special filing.
	Front peened.	Chain running too slack—crowds at bar entry.	Increase tension.		Drive lugs worn on one side.	Excessive face angle of cutters on one side.	Cutters must have equal face angles.
	Clearance notch peened.	Sprocket teeth worn.	Renew sprocket.		Chain jumps out of bar groove.	Uneven filing; chain run too loose.	Increase chain tension; special filing.

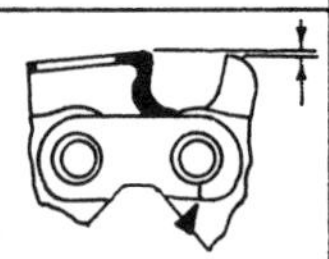

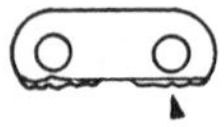

Figure 25-7. Common problems with cutters and links.

TIPS FOR USING YOUR CHAIN SAW
Felling

"Felling" is the term used for cutting down a tree. A number of different techniques are used, depending on the size and condition of the tree and such physical factors as the lean of the tree, other trees in the area, the slope of the ground etc. Strong wind conditions are hazardous to topping and felling. Generally, inexperienced chain saw operators should not attempt to top or fell large trees, trees in bad condition, or trees that are difficult because of other reasons. Chain saw users should first gain experience in felling small trees, while at the same time carefully adhering to the following practices.

Decide beforehand which retreat path to follow when the tree begins to fall. The retreat path should be away from the tree's fall. It is even better if there is another tree to hide behind. While you're at it, check the ground for slippery spots, roots, or debris that could trip you as you try to retreat. Next, check the tree to be felled to see if there are dead branches or loose bark that might fall. Dislodge them with a long pole, if possible. When this has been done, determine the "lean" of the tree by using a plumb bob. A string with anything tied to the end for a weight will do. The line is held out at arm's length and the tree sighted. The plumb line will be vertical. If the line of the tree varies from that of the string, that is the direction of the lean. Sighting should be made from several places to determine the exact direction of the lean. If possible, the tree should be felled in the direction of the lean.

Now, start the saw, make sure you have good footing, and hold the saw firmly with both hands. Stand directly behind the saw and make your undercut. The undercut is made on the side upon which the tree will fall, and it helps control the direction of the fall. When the undercut is started, the engine end of the saw should be held firmly against the tree trunk and the bar swung into the cut. The undercut should be approximately one-third the diameter of the tree. The cutout wedge-shaped section should be wide enough to permit the tree to lean 45 degrees from upright before the two faces close together.

After the undercut is made and the wedge section removed, stop the engine and move around to the back of the tree for the back cut. Then start the engine again. The back cut should be slightly higher than the undercut. After it is started, swing the saw around and cut a short distance into the two sides of the tree. This is "cornering" and prevents the bark and the sides from tearing when the tree falls. If the tree is too wide for the cutter bar to reach across, cut notches in the sides of the tree. If necessary, wedges should be driven into the back cut if the tree tends to lean back and bind the cutting bar.

The engine should be stopped when the wedges are being hammered in. Be sure that the chain or cutter bar do not contact the set wedge when cutting. The back cut should not go through to the undercut. A small "hinge" should be left to guide the fall of the tree. If the back cut goes completely through, the tree may swivel on the stump, slide off erratically, or bind on the bar and chain. Any of these can be deadly! The fall of the tree can be varied from its natural lean by leaving the hinge thicker at one end than the other.

Call out a warning before the tree begins to fall. As soon as the tree starts to go over, stop the saw, set it quickly on the ground, and leave the area by the predetermined retreat path.

Limbing and Pruning

Limbing is the removal of branches from a tree that has been cut down. Pruning is the removal of branches from an upright tree. Individual limbing cuts should be started at the crotch or top side of the branch. It is easier and safer to start limbing from the base of the trunk and work toward the top. Cut as close to the trunk as possible, and take extra care with underneath branches on which the tree rests. The tree may settle when they are removed.

Begin on the bottom side of the branch when pruning small branches. This prevents the peeling of the bark on the trunk. When pruning large branches, notch the underside of the branch first. Complete the cut from the upper side. The second, or back, cut should be made a few inches further out on the limb to keep the trunk bark from peeling. It is safer to stand opposite the side of the trunk being cut.

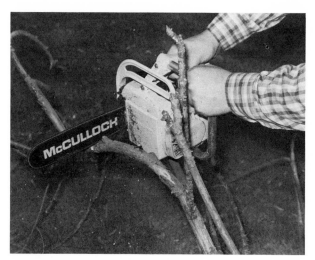

Figure 25-8. Compact saws are especially handy for limbing. GRAF-WHALEN photograph.

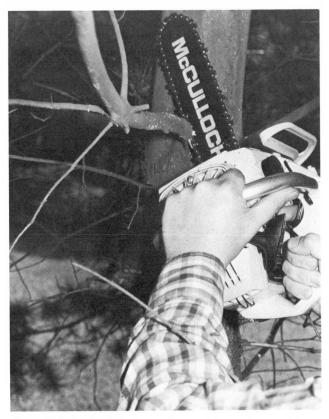

Figure 25-9. Overhead pruning requires special care. A compact saw is easy to handle in tight spots. GRAF-WHALEN photograph.

Figure 25-10. When bucking, be sure that you have safe, sure footing, and stand to one side of the saw—not behind it. GRAF-WHALEN photograph.

Bucking

"Bucking" is the term used for cutting felled trees or logs into shorter lengths. The situation should be studied carefully before a bucking cut is begun, so that you'll know just how the log will move when the cut is completed.

To begin, hold the running saw firmly in both hands. Be sure you have safe, sure footing, and stand to one side of the saw—not behind it. If it is necessary to stand behind the saw, keep legs well apart. Begin cutting only when you have a clear idea which way the cut log will roll or drop. Cut steadily, using manual oiling to ease the chain's bite. Do not allow the saw to bite into the dirt. If necessary, stop the saw and clear away stones, earth, and bark from the area so the chain will not kick them up. Avoid "traps," where the two sections of the log may come together and bind or pinch the chain and cutting bar when the cut is completed. There are numerous traps, depending on how the log is resting. Plan carefully before making a bucking cut.

Cutting Firewood

Cutting firewood is the number-one use for a chain saw among homeowners, suburbanites, campers, and others. There are several things to keep in mind while undertaking this wood-cutting activity.

First, determine your needs and how much firewood you wish to cut on each expedition. Have a suitable vehicle for transportation. You will save time and money by gathering as much firewood as possible on each trip. Also, be sure to request permission of the landowner prior to approaching any property to cut wood. Select cull and other wood that is not growing. Confine cutting to dead trees, fallen limbs, broken branches, and so forth. You will actually help the timber owner by "cleaning up" his land for him, while getting some very valuable firewood for yourself.

Cut your firewood into lengths that can be conveniently carried and stored in your vehicle. Firewood cut to the dimensions of your fireplace in the first place will save your having to cut it a second time. Observe "good neighbor" practices when cutting firewood, and leave the area as neat as possible. Limbs and branches taken off while trimming the trees around your yard make excellent firewood. Think of this in advance before trimming, so that your initial cuts are planned for firewood lengths. High stumps can be cut into firewood by first quartering the standing stump vertically with your saw and then cutting horizontally to the desired lengths until reaching ground level; multiple firewood chunks will result.

The following woods make the following types of fires:
Oak: Long-burning, hot fire. One-quarter split pieces are best.
Maple: Long-burning, hot fire. One-quarter split pieces are best.
Elm: Fast-burning, hot fire with lots of flame.
Birch: Medium-burning fire with medium flame.
Walnut: Medium-burning, easy-to-start fire. It's the only firewood with aroma; it's an "atmosphere type" of fire.
Pine: Fast-burning, easy-to-start, "atmosphere-type" of fire.

Clothing and Protective Gear

The clothing you wear when sawing should be selected to meet two requirements—safety and comfort. Clothes should fit well, but not tightly. Loose garments may catch on branches or other projections and throw you off balance. Tight clothing may hamper movement and agility, with harmful consequences. Clothing should be suitable for weather. Warm—but not bulky—clothes are best for winter; lightweight clothing is preferable in hot weather. Regardless of the weather, though, protect your head with a hard hat when felling trees or working in the woods. These hats, similar to those worn by construction workers, protect against falling bark, dead branches, and other debris, which may be dislodged from the tree overhead.

Snug-fitting work gloves are recommended and you should wear work shoes or boots—preferably with metal-toe reinforcing. Low shoes or soft shoes provide no protection against the vicious saw chain teeth and should not be worn. Calked or hobnailed boots are excellent for working in the woods, on rough ground, or on top of logs. Shoes with nonskid soles should be worn when the footing is slippery.

RULES FOR SAFE USE

Good chain sawing practices should be followed regardless of the type of cutting being done.
• Clear away brush, rocks, or anything else in the working area that might hinder your movements.
• Check to make sure there is no one in the vicinity who might be endangered by a falling tree or a rolling log.
• Stop the engine whenever you have doubts about safety. Use good judgment as to whether the engine should be stopped or running at idle speed when you transfer from one cutting operation to another or when you work in hazardous conditions (slippery surfaces, heavy underbrush, etc.).
• Do not touch the end of an electric saw blade when the saw is in operation.

• When taking a saw from one place to another, turn it off, grasp it firmly in one hand, and carry it at your side with the guide bar facing backward.
• Be especially alert when the chain saw engine is running. The sound of the saw can drown out warning voices or audible signals.
• Look out for metal in logs such as anvils, wire, metal taps, and the like.
• Keep cutting speed under careful control. Modern chain saws cut rapidly; it is very easy to cut too deep or at a wrong angle.
• Select a saw with a bar no longer than the average-size tree or log to be cut. The occasional oversize tree or log can be notched on the sides to allow use of the shorter bar.
• Be especially cautious when operating a saw in wet, slippery weather or where the footing is unsure.
• Do not operate a chain saw when the weather is extremely dry and where there is a fire hazard.

Figure 25-11. The only safe way to carry a chain saw. The saw *must* be turned off and held so that the wicked teeth face away from you. Should you stumble, you will not fall on the teeth and be injured. GRAF-WHALEN photograph.

• Have a second person within calling distance whenever you are working with a chain saw.

• Handle the cutting chain carefully at all times. Wear gloves, if possible. Exercise extreme caution when it is moving.

• Cover your bar and chain with a fitted protective sleeve when transporting the chain saw or storing it for a lengthy period.

• Store and carry gasoline in a safe, shatterproof container—preferably red and marked "gasoline."

• Use a funnel or a flexible pour-hose fitted to the container when fueling the saw.

• Be careful not to spill gasoline.

• Do not fuel the saw when the engine is running or start the engine in the same spot at which it was fueled.

• Keep a fire extinguisher nearby when fueling, if possible or practical.

• Do not wrap the starter cord around your hand when manually starting the saw.

• Be sure you have firm footing and balance when starting.

• Place the saw on the ground or other firm surface before starting. Make sure the chain and bar do not touch anything.

• Grasp the saw firmly when starting. Pull quickly and evenly on the starter cord.

• After starting, guide the starter cord back onto the take-up reel. Do not let go and allow the starter cord to snap back.

Figure 25-12. The proper method of starting a chain saw. Grasp handle firmly on solid, level surface. Keep body well away from the saw while pulling starter-rope. GRAF-WHALEN photograph.

Chain Saw Maintenance

Proper use and maintenance of both the saw engine and chain greatly increase useful life and reduce the cost of operation. A properly cared for chain saw cuts quicker and more easily and gives more hours of trouble-free use.

The first rule with any chain saw, whether gasoline-powered or electric, is to follow the recommendations of the manufacturer. But some rules are common to all power saws.

• Keep chain saw well lubricated. Fuel for the gasoline-powered chain saw is usually sixteen parts gasoline to one part nondetergent oil mixed together. Chain and guide bars need frequent lubrication, and many saws have a built-in oil reservoir and dispensing system. Some work automatically. On some models a thumb button allows the user to lubricate the saw additionally.

• Keep the engine in good operating condition. If it is difficult to start or lacks cutting power, take the engine to your dealer for servicing and adjustment, unless you're able to handle maintenance yourself.

• Keep chain saw sharp. Chains should last a long time but they will become dull eventually. The time to sharpen a saw is when it first begins to get dull. Sharpening kits are a good accessory suggestion. Professionals charge more for sharpening chain saw blades.

• Know when to replace chain. When a new chain is needed, the user will find no difficulty in changing it—if he follows manufacturer's instructions. A new chain may "stretch" slightly when first used, so it should be operated initially at partial throttle and then adjusted.

• Adhere to chain saw safety rules. This will protect both the user and the saw.

• Make sure the chain is sharp and in good condition. Many chain saws have automatic chain oilers, but the manual oiler should also be used in heavy cutting conditions. Maintain proper tension in the cutting chain. It should fit snugly on the cutter bar, with just enough looseness to allow it to be pulled around the bar by hand. Make certain that the engine is turned off when adjusting chain tension. New chain should be checked frequently for proper tension, as it tends to stretch until it is "broken in." Be sure the chain does not move, or "travel," when the engine is at idling speed.

• Do not run the engine at full throttle unless actually cutting wood.

• Do not use the saw with the air filter or muffler removed. This is dangerous to your hearing, the saw engine, and—if sparks fly—the forest too.

• Empty the fuel tank before storing for a long period of time. Empty the tank and remove the chain and bar when storing. Soak the chain in oil and oil the bar groove.

Also, check for loose wires, worn insulation, and loose nuts and bolts. Do not allow dirt, sawdust, or debris to build up on the cooling fins or clog the exhaust ports, and be sure to check the starter pull-rope for signs of fraying. Replace if necessary.

• Keep the chain oil tank full, and fill oil tank each time the fuel tank is filled.

LOGGER'S LINGO

Back cut: The cut made opposite the undercut when felling the tree; the second cut.

Bow: An elliptical, hollow chain saw cutter-bar generally used for felling and bucking small timber.

Bucking: Cutting a tree into logs or sections of desired length.

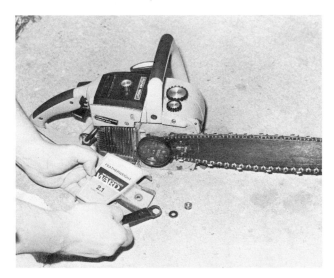

Figure 25-13. Chain maintenance is easy. In most cases, removing just one nut exposes the sprocket and clutch mechanism for easy care. GRAF-WHALEN photograph.

Figure 25-15. Use only good-quality chain-saw oil as a lubricant for the chain. Cheap oils may leave wax residues that foul up automatic oiler operations. GRAF-WHALEN photograph.

Figure 25-14. After a saw has passed its "break-in" period, it may be necessary to readjust idle and operating speeds. GRAF-WHALEN photograph.

Figure 25-16. Be sure to wipe any oil or fuel spills from the machine before using. A slippery handle can cause you to lose your grip and be injured. Spilled fuel invites ignition from the hot exhaust or sparks from anything your whirring chain may strike. GRAF-WHALEN photograph.

Calked boots: High-topped logging shoes with sharp steel spikes protruding from the soles to prevent slipping.

Corner: To cut through a small amount of wood on each side of the tree before completing the back cut.

Falling (or felling): Cutting down a tree.

Hard hat: A hat made of metal or other strong material to protect the head from falling objects.

Hinge: The narrow strip of uncut wood between the back cut and undercut that prevents the tree from twisting as it falls.

Hobnailed boots: High-topped boots with the heads of nails protruding from the heel and sole to prevent slipping.

Holding wood: Same as hinge.

Kerf: The cut made in the wood by the saw.

Lean: The inclination of a tree away from the perpendicular.

Leaner: A tree with a pronounced lean.

Limbing: Removing the branches from a felled tree.

Make your shot: To fell a tree exactly in the direction intended.

Plumb bob: A string with a weight attached, used to determine the lean of a tree.

Pruning: Removing selected branches, or parts of branches, from an upright tree.

School marms: Two trees grown together at the base or a single tree with a prominent fork in the trunk.

Snag: A dead tree with most or all of the branches gone.

Topping: To cut off the upper part of a tree while it is still standing. This is a difficult procedure to be attempted only by highly experienced lumbermen.

Trunk: The main body of a tree.

Undercut: The notch cut in a tree to govern the direction in which the tree is to fall and to prevent splitting.

Wedge: A wedge-shaped piece of metal, plastic, or wood driven into the kerf to control the direction of fall or to keep the kerf from closing and binding on the bar and chain.

26

Battery-Powered Cordless Tools

Battery-powered cordless shop and garden tools offer added safety, greater convenience, and quieter operation than their AC-powered counterparts, whose effectiveness is limited to the length of the extension cord.

Figure 26-1. Battery-powered lawn mower. Photograph courtesy of The Toro Company, Consumer Products Div.

What's more, battery-powered tools offer you the convenience of working in the backyard, on the patio, in the attic, or in the basement without the need for unwrapping and recoiling long extension cords—a chore that often takes longer than the job for which the tool is needed. Also, with any plug-in electric tool, there is an ever-present risk of electrical shock (particularly if the unit is improperly grounded or lacks double insulation). In a low-voltage cordless tool, the current is self-contained. There is no wired circuit to be completed, so grounding is unnecessary, and a cordless tool (unplugged from its AC charger) can be used even while you are standing on wet ground with no fear of getting a shock.

Miniature nickel-cadmium batteries pretty much monopolize the rechargable applications in cordless tools. And a well-charged, nickel-cadmium battery is a very good battery indeed. It's light, rugged, can take high discharge rates (though with severe reduction of power and capacity, if drained critically at low temperatures), holds its voltage fairly constant in use (though the shelf life of its charge is only moderate), and can be used over a wide voltage range.

The charger is frequently a stationary and separate item, connected to the battery only when recharging. Typically, cordless electric tools are used for relatively short periods of time and require a moderately high discharge current. In between these use periods, the battery can be recharged in 14 to 16 hours and can also safely be left on extended overcharge. This extended overcharge feature has value in standby applications where a tool must be instantly ready to operate. Some manufacturers offer special high-rate chargers that provide up to 80 percent of full operating time with only a 1 hour charge. Nickel-cadmium batteries usually need to be recharged about five times before they come up to full power. Thereafter, most require an overnight charge (of 14 to 16 hours) at a cost equivalent to that of burning a 60-watt bulb for about 10 minutes. Unplugged after a full charge, an idle nickel-cadmium battery will lose up to 35 percent of its power in the first month and 50 percent by the end of the second.

Nickel-cadmium batteries can deliver energy at a very rapid rate. Repeated cycles of very high discharge rates do not degrade the performance or life of the battery. High-rate discharge capability makes nickel-cadmium batteries ideal for use in tools where a moderately large amount of energy is desired quickly. This is true in most motor-powered tools and leads to small size, light weight, and economy in the battery and performance of the battery-powered tool.

WHAT'S AVAILABLE
Rotary Lawn Mowers
These are especially suited for small yards or for trimming edges on large lawns, where a riding mower is used for the open lawn spaces. A typical battery-operated mower, powered by a fully enclosed 12-volt, four-pole permanent-magnet motor, with top operating speed of 3,350 rpm, will operate 45 minutes on a single charge. A key is required to activate the power circuit, and a switch must be turned before the motor can be started. Starting occurs by gripping the handle. The mower stops automatically in less than a second when the handle is released. The husky power source for this tool is a lead-acid storage battery. See chapter 31 for more details about lawn mowers.

Cultivators
These have a three-pronged, clawlike blade that uses a reciprocating action to loosen lightly compacted soil for easy weeding and soil aerating. See chapter 28 for more details about cultivators.

Sprayers
Operated by motor-driven pumps, battery-powered sprayers do away with the nuisance of hooking up the garden hose or the need for working a hand pump. Capacities of 1 quart and 1 gallon are available, with nozzle arrangements that provide a fine mist for flowers or a coarse spray with a 12-foot range for large shrubs and small trees. Sprayers with a nozzle that adjusts from jet stream to fine spray can hold a quart of liquid insecti-

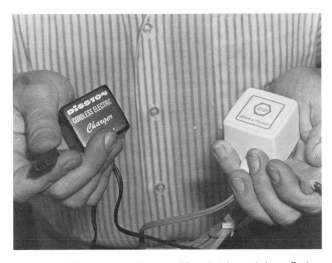

Figure 26-2. Chargers come in many different styles and sizes. Each has been designed for the job of stepping down and rectifying AC power to low-voltage DC for one specific battery. That's why you should never try to use a charger meant for one tool with another tool. You risk ruining the battery. To keep this from happening, manufacturers use different connectors on chargers. Use only the charger recommended by your tool's manufacturer. GRAF-WHALEN photograph.

Figure 26-3. The "heavyweight" battery of this cordless electric rotary mower stores enough amperage to keep the mower blade chomping grass for about three-quarters of an hour. That's enough power for about 7,000 square feet of grass trimming on a single charge. Photograph courtesy of The Toro Company, Consumer Products Div.

Figure 26-4. BLACK & DECKER MOD 4 CORDLESS ONE QUART SPRAYER®. Where close-in spraying is a requirement, this cordless 1-quart sprayer will meet your needs. Its power source—the batteries—are in its slip-on handle, which can be used with an assortment of other tools, as well. Photograph courtesy of Black & Decker Mfg. Co.

Figure 26-5. BLACK & DECKER MOD 4 CORDLESS ONE GALLON SPRAYER®. Where long-reach spraying is your job, this 1-gallon model with spray wand is a good choice. The battery pack is in the slip-on handle, and it can power other tools of the line, as well. Photograph courtesy of Black & Decker Mfg. Co.

cide, fertilizer, or herbicide at a time and dispense up to 4 quarts of fluid on one battery charge. See chapter 35 for more information about sprayers.

Grass, Shrub, and Hedge Trimmers

These offer distinct advantages over corded versions for ground maintenance. They are totally free of stationary power sources, providing the greatest mobility for shrub and plant care in the farthest corners of your property. There is no chance of cutting or fraying power cords, eliminating the danger of shock that is inherent in outdoor use of AC-powered trimmers. Grass shears come in two forms—scissor and rotary. The scissor type has two toothed blades, one of which slides rapidly sideways over the other. Rotary shears have either a disclike blade that cuts between two rows of stationary teeth or a knife-like blade that whirls in a round housing, like a miniature rotary lawn mower. Cordless grass trimmers are made in two styles—a hand-held version and a model with a 30-inch handle for stand-up trimming. They are light and small enough to keep on a mower or tractor and offer immediate power to trim around trees, flower beds, or shrubs. Cordless shrub and hedge trimmers are excellent for shaping shrubbery to maintain landscaping effects. They have double-edged blades with rows of teeth on each side. One blade is fixed, while the other vibrates rapidly, cutting stems and foliage that enter between the teeth. See chapter 30 for more details on trimmers.

Figure 26-6. DISSTON POWERPACK GRASS SHEAR MODEL 1020®. Cordless shears make grass trimming less of a chore in areas where other tools can't reach. The battery pack is built in and rechargeable overnight. Photograph courtesy of Disston, Inc.

Figure 26-7. A stand-up shears model allows you to walk along borders, trimming as you go. GRAF-WHALEN photograph.

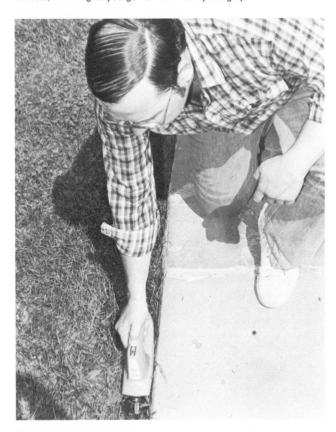

Figure 26-8. For neat finishing operations, the hand-held cordless shears are the final touch for the fastidious gardener. GRAF-WHALEN photograph.

Electric Screwdrivers

These make it possible to drive screws with power where there is none or where an extension cord is not practical. Under a full charge, the self-contained batteries of a typical cordless screwdriver store enough power to drive eighty 1-inch screws into pine without predrilling, and that's ample for most home and shop projects.

The tool operates with touch control and is very handy and time saving for jobs where many screws must be driven or removed. With the switch in either forward or reverse, the bit isn't actuated until slight pressure is applied to the driving end of the tool. Screwdrivers come with charger, drills, and driver bit. Full charge takes about 16 hours. See chapter 22 for details.

Soldering Irons

These are small convenience tools. They provide a tip temperature of over 700°F and typically can make about 125 electronic connections before having to be recharged. Several tip sizes and styles are available. See chapter 17 for more details.

Electric Drills

These drills make up in usefulness for the fact that they are not as powerful nor do they rotate as rapidly as their AC-operated counterparts. The typical cordless drill is designed for light- to moderate-duty applications. But, within their capabilities, they are handy and worthwhile additions to the tool box. Rechargers are built right into the handle or are available as separate units. See chapter 1 for more information.

Figure 26-9. Cordless trimmers free you from the restrictions of a trailing AC power cord, so you can reach and trim those shrubs and plantings at the far borders of your property. Photograph courtesy of Disston, Inc.

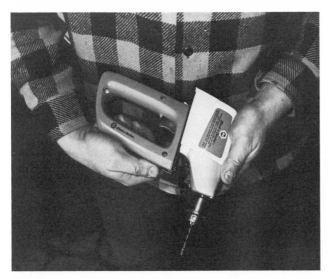

Figure 26-10. The slip-on battery pack of this manufacturer's line can power this electric drill as well as many other tool heads. GRAF-WHALEN photograph.

Modular Battery-Powered Tools

An innovative line of cordless tools collectively called MOD-4 is available from Black & Decker. These tools use a universal, modular Energy Pak® handle that houses four rechargeable nickel-cadmium cells, each with a life span of over 500 charge-discharge cycles. Buy one tool complete with an Energy Pak® and recharger. Additional tool heads can then be bought at significant savings, for there is no need to duplicate the power cells and recharger with each additional tool.

Safety switches are designed into the Energy Pak® handle with an automatic lock-off to prevent accidental shorting. The recharger plugs into a household 120-volt AC outlet and will do its job in 16 hours. There is no danger of overcharging if the Pack is left on the charger longer. A single Energy Pak® can power the following: hand-held grass shears that will easily cut the perimeter of an acre lot at 1,800 scissorlike cutting strokes per minute; upright grass shears with capability similar to the hand-held model; a shrub trimmer that will operate up to 30 minutes at 1,500 strokes on a single charge; a 1/4-inch drill rated at 10 inch-pounds of torque, operating at 750 rpm and capable of drilling 130 holes in 2-inch-thick wood; a sealed beam lantern that produces 6,300 candlepower (roughly equivalent to one-fourth the intensity of an automotive headlight) for about 3 hours from a fully charged Energy Pak®; or a 1-quart or 1-gallon sprayer that can handle small and large insecticide application jobs around the lawn and garden.

Figure 26-12. One battery pack can power many different tools. The pack handle (left) sits in its AC charger stand. Fitted to the drill head, cordless shear head, or lantern head, the battery pack gives you the flexibility of choosing the tool you need without the needless and costly duplication of power packs. GRAF-WHALEN photograph.

Figure 26-11. Cordless drills like this one give you the freedom to bore holes where AC power isn't available. GRAF-WHALEN photograph.

Figure 26-13. The charger stand for a battery-pack handle is a slide-in stand that occupies little space on your bench. It provides DC charging power from the AC line and can restore the battery's capacity overnight. GRAF-WHALEN photograph.

Figure 26-15. DISSTON POWERPACK MODEL 1000®. This unique battery pack plugs directly into the AC line. Its charger is built into the pack. And, once charged, the pack slips into any of several different tool heads to give you the power you need, when and where you want it. Photograph courtesy of Disston, Inc.

Figure 26-14. DISSTON POWERPACK LANTERN MODEL 1050®. Just the thing for power failures, this cordless lantern can be kept on charge until you need its powerful, comforting beam. Photograph courtesy of Disston, Inc.

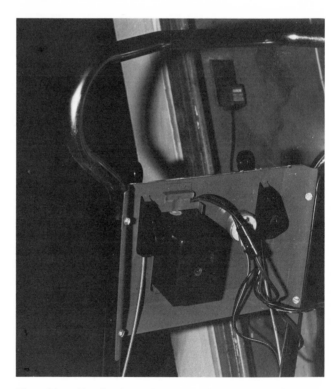

Figure 26-16. The electric-starting battery of this gas-powered mower is charged by a plug-in charger (background). Overnight, the battery stores enough charge to start your mower several times, saving your hand and back the needless effort of pull-rope starting. GRAF-WHALEN photograph.

27

Rotary Tillers

If you've ever wondered just how hardy your ancestors really were, remember that they lived in a time when the hoe and shovel were the tools used to till and cultivate the

Figure 27-1. Rotary tiller. GRAF-WHALEN photograph.

soil. Half an hour of back-breaking effort with these venerable tools can make you mighty glad that you live in the age of the gas-powered rotary tiller. If your chore is to break up the soil for a good-size vegetable garden, if you plan to put in an entire new lawn, or if you tire quickly of tedious cultivating in garden beds, a rotary tiller offers the earth-shattering power you need to get the smooth, frangible soil your seedlings will love.

WHY TILL THE SOIL?

Soil has four basic constituents—sand, clay, silt, and loam. The proportions vary, depending upon local geography. But, fundamentally, a good soil will contain enough of each ingredient to permit three things to happen: 1) Nutrients will enter the soil. Plants need at least 16 chemical elements for growth—carbon, hydrogen, oxygen, calcium, nitrogen, phosphorus, potassium, sulfur, magnesium, iron, manganese, copper, zinc, molybdenum, boron, and chlorine. These must be available in the soil or capable of entering from fertilizer materials spread on the soil surface. 2) Water will enter and remain entrapped within the spaces between soil particles. 3) Soil will yield under the slight but constant pressure of roots and rootlets so as to permit enlargement of the root system of the plant, supporting a greater growth above the soil surface.

Unfortunately, the soil surface can pack densely to a rocklike hardness that locks out water and nutrients, which makes it difficult for seedlings to penetrate and root in. This is especially true in soils having a high clay content. To get a green crop started, it's necessary to shatter and granulate the hardened mantle into the finest particles possible. Also, it's beneficial to turn under any organic content at the soil surface to provide later nourishment for new growth. These jobs are performed in a one-two sequence by the whirling tines of a rotary tiller.

HOW THEY WORK

Tillers use gear-drive, belt-drive, and chain-drive systems. In the gear-driven models, the engine is mounted so that its shaft is vertical, leading downward to an enclosed worm gear. The shaft turns the gear, which in turn rotates the worm. This converts the engine shaft's high rpm to a substantially slower, but higher, torque rotation of the shaft on which the tines are placed. Also, the action of the worm gear drive converts the direction of rotation from vertical to horizontal.

In chain-drive tillers the engine shaft turns a sprocket, which is fitted with a chain, very much like a bicycle chain. A larger sprocket at the other end turns only a fraction of a revolution for each turn of the engine sprocket. The slower-turning sprocket drives the shaft that turns the tines.

The belt-drive tillers are the simplest. A covered V-belt connects a pulley on the horizontally rotating engine shaft to a large-diameter pulley. This pulley turns a two-stage reduction gear drive, whose output turns the shaft that rotates the tines.

WHAT'S AVAILABLE

There are two basic types of rotary tillers. In one, the tines that pulverize the soil are up front and are gear- or chain-driven by the engine. The turning tines not only chop into the earth, but also pull the machine along. A pair of wheels at the rear help you move the machine from storage shed to garden bed. Generally, these are the favored choice of homeowners and account for most tillers sold. The second type of tiller has gear-driven tines at the rear, plus large, driven tires up front. These are usually husky machines, with brawny engines of up to 8 horsepower. They're really meant for the serious, professional, or nursery gardener, rather than the homeowner. Actually, these are junior tractors, and most are capable of towing attachments, such as furrowers, hillers, and drag-type cultivators.

The front-tine tiller is designed for the average home garden where clearances are small. With it you can till within a few inches of a shrub or a walk—a feat that isn't possible with the clumsier rear-tined machine.

Tillers are rated by the width of the basic tilling swath (without extension attachments), which ranges from 14 to 26 inches. The smaller-width machines have engines of 3 to 4 horsepower and are fairly lightweight (typically 75 to 100 pounds). Most feature a worm-gear drive and include transmissions that give one forward speed plus reverse. Medium-weight machines have engines in the 5-horsepower class and weigh in at about 140 pounds. They usually pack a worm-gear drive with one or two forward speeds plus reverse or a chain drive with a single

Figure 27-2. This 5-horsepower tiller has two speeds—high, for breaking up hard-packed earth and sod and low, for blending soil and cultivating. Photograph courtesy of The Toro Company, Consumer Products Div.

Figure 27-3. Tillers are rated by the width of the basic tilling swath (without extension attachments). Tines are readily removable for installation on extensions. GRAF-WHALEN photograph.

forward speed and no reverse. Last come the heavyweights with 7- to 8-horsepower engines, fancy transmissions that give up to four forward speeds plus reverse, cutting depths of up to 10 inches, and average weights of nearly 200 pounds.

Apart from size and power, the next most important characteristic is the type of tines found on the tiller. So-called "bolo" tines act like the sharp edge of a pick. They are good for cultivating and are designed to clean themselves. Other machines have "slasher" tines which are designed to chop and chew off about 1/4 inch of earth with each pass of a tine blade.

All machines feature "adjustment of tilling width," either by removing tines from the drive shaft, adding accessory tine extensions, or changing the ways the tines face. This gives quite a range of width and tilling patterns for jobs ranging from sod-busting to careful cultivating.

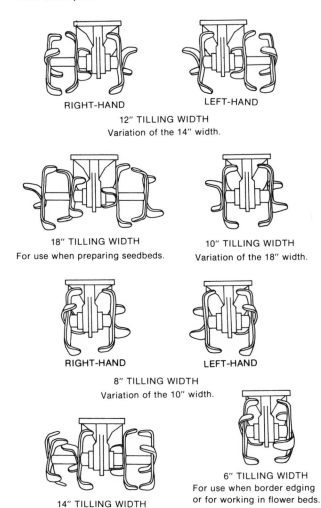

RIGHT-HAND   LEFT-HAND
12" TILLING WIDTH
Variation of the 14" width.

18" TILLING WIDTH
For use when preparing seedbeds.

10" TILLING WIDTH
Variation of the 18" width.

RIGHT-HAND   LEFT-HAND
8" TILLING WIDTH
Variation of the 10" width.

14" TILLING WIDTH
For use when cultivating row crops for border edging.

6" TILLING WIDTH
For use when border edging or for working in flower beds.

Figure 27-4. Tines can be arranged and extended to encompass a very wide variety of tilling jobs. You may need extension shafts and other accessories to match the tilling width to the task at hand. Check the manual for adjustment instructions and approved accessories.

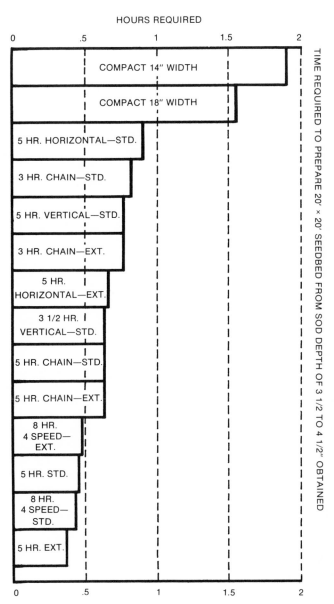

HOURS REQUIRED

TIME REQUIRED TO PREPARE 20' × 20' SEEDBED FROM SOD DEPTH OF 3 1/2 TO 4 1/2" OBTAINED

COMPACT 14" WIDTH
COMPACT 18" WIDTH
5 HR. HORIZONTAL—STD.
3 HR. CHAIN—STD.
5 HR. VERTICAL—STD.
3 HR. CHAIN—EXT.
5 HR. HORIZONTAL—EXT.
3 1/2 HR. VERTICAL—STD.
5 HR. CHAIN—STD.
5 HR. CHAIN—EXT.
8 HR. 4 SPEED— EXT.
5 HR. STD.
8 HR. 4 SPEED— STD.
5 HR. EXT.

Figure 27-5. This comparison chart shows the time required to prepare an average-size seedbed to a plantable depth using different tillers. Compact models take the longest time and greatest effort. Standard models differ only slightly in required time, with chain-driven models edging out other types. Large engines and extensions make tilling chores a matter of minutes.

IMPORTANT FEATURES TO LOOK FOR

The *safety* of a tiller is a difficult matter to quantify, because the very purpose of the machine is to slash and chew large areas of earth. As with all powered tools, operator knowledge and caution really determine how "safe" your tiller will be. However, a well-balanced machine with widely spaced guide bars and remote controls for engine speed and stop/go are definite "plus" factors. Also, look for a deflector shield above the whirling tines, to prevent debris and dust from being hurled back over the engine and you. Large wheels with open traction treads will help keep your tiller surefooted.

The *drag bar* behind the tiller is an important mechanism. It penetrates the soil and acts like an anchor, opposing the forward motion of the whirling tines as they chew into the ground and attempt to propel the machine forward. The drag bar thus makes the tiller easier for you to control and also sets the depth of tilling. Look for a drag bar that is sturdily forged. Also, it should have a pivot arrangement, so that the machine can be backed out of soft spots. This point is vital, especially in smaller machines that lack a reverse gear-drive. In these, pulling backward on the guide bar handles should cause the drag bar to pivot at an angle, so that the bar disengages naturally from the soil furrow it's been cutting.

Depth adjustment should be simple and positive without requiring the use of tools. The better small machines use a latching spring-loaded yoke that sets the drag bar "bite" relative to the machine's rear wheels. Setting for minimum drag-bar depth will slow the machine and increase the depth of the rotating tines' earth-chewing action.

TIPS FOR USING YOUR TILLER

Tillers look ominous and menacing, but they're really fairly easy to use once you've mastered the basics. First and foremost, be ready for some peculiar bucking and gyrations on the part of the machine, as it commences to chew into the soil. It is *normal* for the tiller to lurch from side to side and to bounce as its tines dig into and turn over the earth. The mark of an experienced hand in tiller operation is the operator who applies minimal force to the guide bars, keeping the tiller going where he wants it to without wearing himself out by fruitlessly attempting to check its wild gyrations.

Second, learn to evaluate soil condition before you begin tilling. Wet soil tends to ball up and stick to the tines and may result in poor conditioning. Wet, tilled soil may dry into rocklike lumps with a hard, crusty cover. This condition is not conducive to seed germination and plant growth. Wet soil may plaster onto the tine rotor, resulting in reduced penetration when tilling. In addition,

any abnormal buildup of soil on the belts and especially the gear box may eventually cause mechanical damage. Therefore, use the tiller only when the ground is dry, and wash it after use to remove any accumulated dirt and vegetation.

Third, set the tilling depth at a reasonable level, and adjust engine speed with the throttle, so that you have the right amount of control over the tiller. This is of greatest importance in cultivating (removing weeds), which should be done at the slowest possible speed to prevent plant damage.

Before starting the engine, engage the drag bar and adjust its depth so that the wheels are in the highest position, and run the engine at maximum speed. A penetrating drag bar tends to retard forward movement of the tiller, thus making it easier to control. Initially, untilled soil and grass are broken apart by pressing down on the handles to produce slow forward movement and maximum rotation of the tines. It may even be necessary to

Figure 27-6. Proper tilling stance is important. Don't get caught by the lurching gyrations of this earth-shattering tool. GRAF-WHALEN photograph.

hold back on the handles to further reduce forward movement. After the soil has been broken apart, slight upward pressure on the handles will produce faster forward movement of the tiller. During the actual tilling operation, do not try to maneuver (turn) while tilling deeply, because resistance against the side of the drag bar will be excessive and may eventually cause the bar to break.

Tilling

To condition the soil effectively a definite tilling pattern must be used. Till a single row; then skip a space equal to the width of the tines and make the return pass. Continue this pattern until the entire area is broken apart. Next, condition the entire area again by tilling at right angles to the previously tilled swaths. When the entire area is broken up, till deeply by raising wheels and adjusting handle force for a slow propelling rate. A 4-inch depth of conditioned soil is deep enough for most row crops and turf seedbed areas. Vine crops, however, usually require 6 or more inches of conditioned soil.

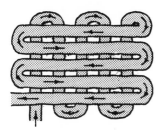

Figure 27-7. Tilling pattern.

Another application of the tiller is the conditioning of soil that has been tilled previously. Even though the soil has been conditioned before, the ground must be dry for effective reconditioning that may be required. Do not till when the soil is wet. Engine speed should be regulated to produce good pulverization of the soil, and this is affected by the type of soil being conditioned. Never condition the soil until it becomes sandy or powdery, because the surface will have a tendency to pack and resist plant growth. If the general texture of the soil is somewhat sandy, use only enough engine speed to loosen the soil for planting. Other than engine speed, the use of the tiller and tilling pattern is the same as when untilled soil is first conditioned. Keep the wheels adjusted so that an erect, nonstraining operating position can be maintained.

Cultivating

Effective weed removal, without damage to desirable plants, calls for delicate maneuvering of a tiller, and that means slow engine speed plus use of the drag bar to give you the greatest degree of control. You will, of course, need to follow your tiller manufacturer's advice on the proper number of tine blades to use and how they should be oriented.

RULES FOR SAFE USE

The wicked tines of a tiller don't know the difference between hard sod and soft flesh, so it's up to you to make sure your hands and feet steer clear of those whirling blades. Here are a few of the most important safety tips:
• Don't ever try to clean mud, roots, stones, or debris from the tines while the engine is running. Even if the gear shift is in neutral, you're taking a risk. Shut down the engine before you ever risk your hands.
• When backing the tiller under power, throttle down to idle speed and step off to one side. Remember that there's no braking from the drag bar in reverse, so too high a backing speed could jeopardize your foot. Practice will show you how to "feather" the clutch to ease the tiller backward without jeopardy to you.
• Keep your tiller in safe operating condition by tightening screws, nuts, and bolts before every use. Also, don't allow the engine to collect grease, vegetation, or other debris that might be a fire hazard.
• Till and cultivate the soil when it is dry. Wet soil can damage a tiller and cause frequent foul-ups.

ROTARY TILLER MAINTENANCE

• Check the engine oil level frequently; that is, every time you stop the machine. The engine powering the tiller operates at a relatively high constant speed under generally dusty conditions. Running the engine while the oil level is low and contaminated will lead to premature engine wear.
• Follow to the letter the manufacturer's instructions on oil change frequency and oil type.
• Clean the air cleaner frequently. This filter keeps dust out of the carburetor and cylinder, but ultimately restricts the air flow as the machine tills.
• Check all nuts, bolts, and screws for tightness each time you finish a tilling project.
• Keep the machine clean. Mud and vegetation tangled in the tines not only cut tilling efficiency, but also make the engine work harder than necessary. This same heavy layer holds moisture that will cause premature rusting of parts.
• Keep the tiller clean. While scrubbing and hosing the machine will do a good job of cleaning, you'll find that a high-pressure washer will keep your tiller looking like new. If you don't have access to one, take the machine to a coin-operated car wash and blast the dirt away.

Figure 27-8. The last step after a tilling operation is to check attaching hardware for tightness. Photograph courtesy of Simplicity Manufacturing Company, Inc.

Figure 27-9. Drive pulleys, belts, and control parts must be checked at regular intervals. Do not allow mud or vegetation to build up on these important parts. GRAF-WHALEN photograph.

Figure 27-10. Tines are attached to the drive shaft by a sturdy pin that is held fast by a cotter pin. These are easily removed to permit tine reversal or for ease of cleaning. GRAF-WHALEN photograph.

Figure 27-11. It is good practice to remove the spark-plug wire before caring for or storing your tiller. GRAF-WHALEN photograph.

Figure 27-12. The gearbox of most tillers must be filled with a good grade of SAE 90 EP gear oil. Change gearbox oil once a year, preferably at the end of the season. Remove the pipe plug to drain and fill with fresh oil. GRAF-WHALEN photograph.

Figure 27-13. Be sure to check operation of all controls before you begin tilling. Don't try to use a tiller you can't control. GRAF-WHALEN photograph.

28

Electric Tiller/Cultivators

Small seedbeds, especially those that are edged by stonework or walkways or that are adjacent to expensive shrubs and ornamentals, pose special problems in tilling. There's little room for managing a large tiller in these cramped quarters; and so, the electric tiller/cultivator may be an ideal choice if your tilling needs include a substantial amount of extra-care ground breaking.

HOW THEY WORK
Somewhat like a scaled-down version of its larger, gas-powered cousins, the electric tiller/cultivator is equipped with a pair of tines, which are rotated by a sturdy electric motor. This assembly is fitted to a tubular handle for easy, stand-up use. The control switch is placed for thumb actuation, and the device is easily controlled with one hand (for walk-behind operation) or with two hands (for delicate cultivating around existing plantings).

Figure 28-1. Electric tiller/cultivator. GRAF-WHALEN photograph.

The narrow width of the device allows it to be used between closely spaced shrubs or for weeding in tight rows. Also, the tines can be placed with great accuracy and can turn on a dime (unlike larger machines) to accommodate contours in bed layout. The tines can be stopped instantly and the machine lifted when it's necessary to stop what you're doing in a hurry.

IMPORTANT FEATURES TO LOOK FOR
Important features to look for are double insulation, sturdy construction, good balance, a spring-return power switch, and shields that are placed to prevent debris from being picked up and thrown by the tines. Easily removed tines are another important feature. This means an easier job of cleaning up debris that snarls behind the tines or of keening the edge of the tines after prolonged use.

As a replacement for laborious hand labor with spade, fork, or cultivating claw, an electric tiller/cultivator is a worthy addition to your gardening tools. Performance in clay soils is reasonable and tilling depths of 1 to 2 inches can be obtained in areas of limited size with only moderate effort. For working in fertilizer or compost in previously tilled soil, these compact machines are hard to beat. Also, they're very handy for spot weeding in vegetable garden beds, where a larger tiller would be too cumbersome or too much trouble to set up and use.

RULES FOR SAFE USE
Safety considerations noted for larger tillers apply to the smaller electric models, too. Also, use normal precautions for handling electric power tools outdoors. (You may want to consider a portable ground-fault interrupter for plug-in protection when using this and any other electrically powered outdoor tool. See chapter 40 for additional details.)

Figure 28-2. The compact electric tiller churns earth in small areas and is easy to control. GRAF-WHALEN photograph.

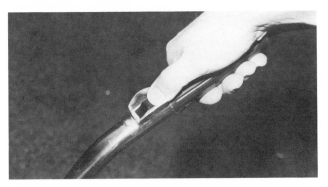

Figure 28-3. The convenient thumb switch of the electric tiller assures positive on-off control for safe operation. GRAF-WHALEN photograph.

Figure 28-4. For clearing debris that accumulates in tines, removal of parts should be easily accomplished with hand tools. GRAF-WHALEN photograph.

TILLER/CULTIVATOR MAINTENANCE

Maintenance of the electric tiller/cultivator largely consists of removing caked-on soil deposits after each use. Disconnect the machine from the power source and then wash under the forceful water stream from your garden hose. Accumulated vegetable matter is easily dislodged by removing the tines. Lubrication of the motor and transmission is rarely required since these are sealed in the factory. Tines should be sharpened occasionally as recommended by the manufacturer.

With only a small investment in care your electric tiller/cultivator can deliver season after season of labor-saving tilling, cultivating, and soil-turning action to help inspire a bountiful blessing of good green things from the soil of your garden.

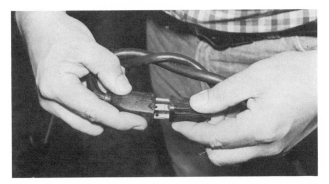

Figure 28-5. Tie a knot to join your extension cord to the tool's short cord. This will relieve strain on the socket and plug, preventing dangerous separation. GRAF-WHALEN photograph.

Figure 28-6. A washing with a garden hose makes electric tiller cleanup a simple matter. GRAF-WHALEN photograph.

29

Handy, Small Power Tools—Multi-Vator, Flexible-Line Trimmers, and Power Edgers

Here are three especially handy, small power tools to help you with a variety of outdoor chores. Each has the kind of versatility that puts it in a special class; and so, you'll find yourself reaching for these quite often in comparison to tools with a lesser number of possible applications.

MULTI-VATOR

You could classify this tool as a portable garden-cultivator. It's compact, AC powered, and does a very creditable job in cultivating small seedbeds where only a hand-type claw cultivator would seem the answer. However, it would be a shame to limit this clever little gadget's work possibilities to cultivating alone. And so, the manufacturer has made it possible for you to use the tool as the driving source for several different interchangeable attachments. These include a cultivating claw, a spade edger-blade, a sanding pad, a wire brush, and a scraper. Simply fastening the right attachment at the "business end" of the Multi-Vator® allows you to use the tool in many different outdoor jobs. You'll save gobs of elbow grease and liniment with its power-assist features.

Figure 29-1. Hand cultivating is just one of the jobs made easier by this compact AC-powered handful. GRAF-WHALEN photograph.

Figure 29-2. Quick-change attachments convert this handy power tool into a spader, sander, power brush, or scraper. GRAF-WHALEN photograph.

The basic drive unit of the Multi-Vator® consists of an AC motor within a double-insulated, high-impact, plastic housing, which drives a gear system and eccentric pin that rides in a slot in a pivoted plate. As the motor turns, the pin causes the plate to move from side to side, rapidly, and with considerable force. Part of the plate extends through the front of the case, and here the attachment is fitted by a single Allen-head screw. When power is applied, the drive plate moves the attachment back and forth through some 1,750 strokes per minute.

With the *claw-cultivator* attachment in place, the Multi-Vator® can rip into hard-packed soil around plantings—loosening, aerating, and breaking down the hard clumps into easily worked, fine particles. A long rear handle and an upright ring handle let you hold the Multi-Vator® comfortably in two hands and guide it with ease. The best method is to hold the tool at about a 15-degree angle and to pull the moving claw backward in a sweep of about 10 to 12 inches at a time.

If edging is your chore, a quick change to the *spade-edger* attachment puts a different tool in your hands. The moving spade, with its row of sharp teeth, easily slips between a walk and adjacent earth, cutting through grass and weeds that hug the edge. You'll find it easy to make a neat, well-defined edge anywhere with just a bit of prac-tice. Also, the spader can be used to lift sod patches quite neatly. First, slice through the patch; then get under it with the spade teeth and move the tool along, lifting out the patch as the teeth incise the deep roots.

If an outdoor painting job is in prospect, the three other attachments of the Multi-Vator® will come in mighty handy. First is a *scraper blade*, which can be used to re-move blistered paint, dirt, or other deposits from wood or metal surfaces. For finer work or to remove rust from outdoor metalwork, try the *wire-brush* attachment. To put a smooth finish on your preparation job, use the *sander* attachment. With this, you have the choice of using coarse- or fine-grit papers and you can get a smooth, professional-looking surface that will accept paint and look better, longer.

Note: When using the scraper, wire brush, or sander, you'd be wise to protect your eyes against fine particles and grit by wearing safety glasses or goggles. These are available at low cost wherever quality tools are sold.

FLEXIBLE-LINE TRIMMERS

Somehow grass keeps right on growing, up to the most irregularly shaped or hard-to-get-at areas of your lawn—around rock gardens, near trees, and in awkward corners. Lawn mowers and trimmers aren't much help in tight spots like these, because you run the risk of striking a tough obstacle (such as a rock) with blade-shattering

Figure 29-3. BLACK & DECKER STRING TRIMMER®. The string trimmer is a handy answer to trimming problems in tight spots along border edges and plantings. Photograph courtesy of Black & Decker Mfg. Co.

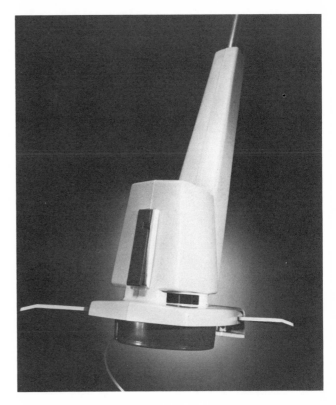

Figure 29-4. WEED EATER® SNIPPY™ MODEL 400. The high-speed motor of the string trimmer whirls flexible line with bull-whip cutting force. Photograph courtesy of Weed Eaters, Inc.

force. And so, the flexible-line trimmer is a boon to gardeners with tough cutting jobs. Instead of a blade, the trimmer whirls a tough, serrated nylon line in a circular 12-inch path at a vicious 8,500 rpm. With more cutting power than a bull whip, the line snaps off grass and weed stems as it rotates. But, because it's flexible, it can safely strike a rock or tree trunk, bounce off, and be cutting again in just a fraction of a second! Armed with such a trimmer, you can cut as close as you like to any obstacle in your garden without damaging it or the trimmer. If the line breaks or needs replacement, changing it is a simple matter.

Electric flexible-line trimmers employ high-torque universal (series-wound) motors of nearly 1-horsepower rating. The motor is encased in a protective high-impact housing, fitted to an extension handle with the hand grip and power switch for easy, stand-up use. An extension handle lets you hold the tool in a scythelike fashion, so you can easily direct the whirling line to areas to be cut and angle the motor and line to follow ground contours.

Figure 29-5. The power edger can cut vertically or horizontally. Here it is used to trim around delicate plantings. GRAF-WHALEN photograph.

A grounding-type power cord and plug are fitted to the tool for connection to an extension cord leading to an outlet that supplies operating power. The motor shaft is linked directly to a reel which carries the flexible line. The line protrudes through a hole in the circumference of the reel housing. And so, as the reel turns at high speed, the line stands out from the reel, responding to centrifugal force. As its serrated edge contacts grass blades at high speeds, the grass is sheared off. However, if the line strikes a solid object, it bounces off and is almost immediately tautened again by the rotational force, so that cutting continues where cutting is possible.

The trimmer is used in an easy, standing posture, balanced between the two hands on the upper and extension handles, respectively. The whirling line follows the plane of the rotating reel, and so, the motor should be kept in a position as nearly perpendicular to the contour of the cutting area as possible. You can angle the tool when needed to cut uneven areas, and (with power off) you can adjust the length of the line to set the diameter of the cutting swath. For general trimming tasks in hard-to-reach or uneven areas, you'll find the flexible-line trimmer hard to beat.

POWER EDGERS
The real secret in giving a lawn or garden a "manicured" appearance is to follow up the gross grass removal job with a careful edging treatment along curbs, walks, walls, around beds, near trees, and, generally, wherever the grass ends and something else begins. Edging separates a nongrass area from the lawn with a distinctive line that unmistakably sets off that which is natural from that which is man-made. And, since much of the beauty of a home lies in the counterpoint of clearly defined lines against a natural background, a conscientious edging job can make a world of difference in the "image" your home projects to the observer.

Unfortunately, manual edging is hard work. That is why a power edger is such a useful addition to the homeowner's arsenal of outdoor tools. A power edger uses a rotating blade to chop away grass growth in a precise path. It rolls along a walk edge or curb, carefully chomping out any grass or weed stems within the path of its rotating blade. Effortlessly, it draws a line between where the lawn ends and where stonework or plantings begin. The result is a sharply defined, well-manicured lawn that plays a pleasing visual harmony to the lines of your home.

A good power edger consists of a sturdy housing containing a fractional horsepower electric motor and a vertically rotating blade assembly, fitted with a wheel to allow the assembly to roll along a walk, curb, or bed edge.

Figure 29-6. The power edger gives the borders of your lawn a finished, well-groomed appearance. GRAF-WHALEN photograph.

Figure 29-7. The rotating blade assembly shears against a fixed blade for controlled cutting action. GRAF-WHALEN photograph.

An extension handle allows you to use the tool in a comfortable, stand-up posture, with a finger-actuated switch to allow easy power control. Some edgers also have the facility to rotate the power head to a horizontal position for trimming operations. This added feature is especially handy in trimming hard-to-reach areas, such as narrow spaces where a wide-mouthed lawn mower can't fit.

Figure 29-8. When rotating to a blade-horizontal position, the power edger is like a miniature rotary lawn mower—ideal for trimming areas where a big rotary can't fit. GRAF-WHALEN photograph.

30

Hedge Trimmers

If you've ever used a manual, scissors-type hedge clipper, you have probably suffered the sore shoulder muscles and palms that these primitive trimming devices seem designed to inflict. There is, however, no reason to put up with this kind of self-torture now that electrically powered hedge trimmers are available. Powered by an extension cord from an AC outlet up to 100 feet away from the hedge you're trimming or by a built-in battery in cordless models, an electric hedge trimmer lets you shear off stems neatly; with a turn of your hand, you can shape a hedge or bush in just a fraction of the time old-fashioned clipping would take.

Figure 30-1. Hedge trimmer. Photograph courtesy of Black & Decker Mfg. Co.

HOW THEY WORK

The source of the hedge trimmer's cutting power is usually a compact, high-speed, fractional-horsepower universal motor. This motor type starts easily under load and instantly whips up to rotational speeds of 18,000 rpm. The motor is usually enclosed in a nonconductive, tough plastic case, and its shaft is electrically isolated from the other metal parts by an insulated coupling. This double insulation makes the tool safe for outdoor use without grounding. In a single-stage trimmer, the motor's insulated shaft coupling fits to a helical pinion gear, which meshes with a larger-diameter helical drive gear. The down-facing side of the drive gear mounts an eccentric (off center) pin, enclosed by a cylindrical roller that is free to rotate. The outer surface of the roller slips into an ovalized slot in a plate, which is the rear extension of the movable cutter blade.

When power is applied, the motor rotation is converted by the 10:1 ratio of the gears, so that the drive gear turns at only 1,800 rpm. Force, however, is greatly magnified. The eccentric pin and roller move as the drive gear rotates, pushing against the driven plate slot and forcing the plate to slide forward. The roller turns and climbs upwards, since the slot now lies in the circular path of the eccentric pin. The movable blades slide forward, narrowing the gap to the stationary blades and shearing any intruding twigs or stems. Continued rotation of the eccentric pin commences aftward movement of the driven plate, opening the blades. Twigs that now intrude between the blades will be sheared on the aft-cutting stroke. When the eccentric pin again reaches the midpoint of the slot, the driven plate is fully aftward and the blades close again, assuring a complete cut on the aft-cutting stroke. Continued rotation of the eccentric pin brings it to the bottom of the ovalized slot, and another cutting cycle begins. Two linear cycles thus occur in each rotational cycle, increasing the cutting efficiency of the trimmer.

In two-stage trimmers, another set of gears is introduced into the power train to increase cutting force.

WHAT'S AVAILABLE

Electric hedge trimmers come in many models with clipping-blade lengths from 8 3/4 to 23 inches. Most better electric trimmers are of the reciprocating type. Two multi-toothed blades—one fixed, the other moving forward and back—catch hedge stems between them and shear on both the forward and backward strokes. There are also single-action types, which cut on only the forward stroke. Of the two, the fore-and-aft cutters definitely have the "edge," especially in getting into corners. Also, there are many different handle styles—wraparounds, straights, and those that need two hands to keep the trimmer chopping in a straight line. You'd do well to try several styles for balance, heft, and maneuverability before you buy.

Figure 30-3. A tall, well-established hedge is no match for a well-balanced, long-reach, AC-powered trimmer. GRAF-WHALEN photograph.

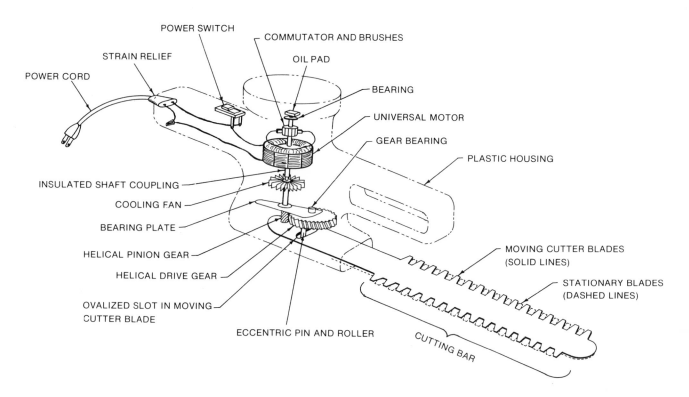

Figure 30-2. This simplified illustration shows how the motor's rotary action is converted to reciprocating shearing action at the cutter blades.

Try to keep in mind the jobs you'll be doing. For light trimming at ground level, where new shoots are your principal cutting chore, a light-duty AC or cordless model will be fine. But, if you've got to tackle a tall, well-established hedge while standing on a ladder and the stems are woody, consider a well-balanced, long-reach, AC-powered model with the largest motor size you can get and handle comfortably.

IMPORTANT FEATURES TO LOOK FOR
AC-Powered Trimmers
Safety comes first, and any electrically powered outdoor tool must provide protection against the hazards of electrical shock. Look first for the UL and CSA labels. These are the marks of Underwriters Laboratories and the Canadian Standards Association. They tell you that the trimmer has passed tough safety tests to merit listing by these two standard-setting groups. Look also for *double insulation*. This means that the case and handle you hold are made of nonconductive, high-impact plastic (of the same material that telephones are made of) and that the AC-powered motor is insulated from the metal parts of the trimmer by an insulating shaft coupling. If the trimmer isn't double insulated, there must be a three-prong plug on its power cord. For safety with this type trimmer, you'll have to use a three-wire extension cord, and make sure you plug it into a grounding-type, three-terminal AC outlet that will safely ground the case and motor.

Next, look for a convenient on/off switch that you can operate with the same hand that holds the trimmer handle. The switch should be easily accessible for quick action where you have to kill power, but recessed to prevent accidental actuation by clothing or twigs. Best of all is a "dead-man" power switch. It has a spring-return to the "off" position so that you must hold it "on" by gentle pressure while cutting. Releasing pressure instantly snaps the switch off and the trimmer stops. It's a very handy feature in case you should accidentally drop the trimmer or lose your balance while working on a ladder.

The current rating on an AC-powered trimmer's nameplate is a fair guide to its cutting capacity. Generally, trimmers rated at 2 amperes or less are single-stage types suitable only for trimming thin shoots and new growth. They do this at high blade-speed, and they are efficient for casual trimming. However, if you start cutting into woody stems with this class of trimmer, you may stall the blade and motor, causing the trimmer to whip violently in your hands.

On the other hand, heavy-duty, high-current trimmers of the two-stage variety have blade speeds much slower, but with greater shearing force. These will usually take woody branches in stride and are almost immuned to stalling. There is one drawback, though. The slow speed of the blades may tend to push light stems out of the way, rather than shearing them. This means a bit more effort in casual trimming, although it's compensated for by the superior cutting force you'll welcome when cutting back a well-established, overgrown hedge.

Importantly, most AC-powered trimmers have short (12 inches or less) cords, so you will need a good-quality, UL-listed extension cord. A strong consideration is the current-carrying capacity of the extension cord, which is determined by the size of the wire used in the cord. For a light-duty, AC-powered trimmer (2 amperes or less), you can use a cord of 18-gauge wire up to 100 feet in length. For heavy-duty trimmers, use a 16-gauge or 14-gauge cord. Try to pick a cord that's toughly jacketed, large in outside diameter, and preferably one that is bright yellow or orange in color. These are far less likely to get lost in the shadows while you're cutting, giving you a better chance that you won't accidentally cut through the power cord.

Cordless Trimmers
Completely self-contained and easy to handle, with no power cord to drag around and run the risk of cutting, cordless trimmers are also free of even the very slight shock hazard of today's well-designed AC-powered trimmers. But that doesn't rule out safety considerations. In fact, it raises another hazard point: The curious young child who finds a cordless trimmer with its battery pack in place needs only to operate the switch to inflict serious injury. Thus, look for a cordless trimmer that features quick, easy removal of the battery pack, so you can slide it out and store it under lock and key to be sure your "junior gardener" can't get hurt. You'll also want to check the cordless model for comfort and balance. They tend to be heavier than AC-powered types, because you're carrying the extra weight of the battery pack.

While we're on the subject of battery packs, check the specs on charging time. Most cordless types require overnight charging to give about 30 to 45 minutes cutting time. If your cutting requirements are greater than this, you may want to invest in a second battery pack, so you can continue cutting when the first battery poops out. Remember, too, that battery charging time requires that you preplan your trimming chores. Look for a unit with a fast recovery rate so that it will be ready to go when you are.

Apart from these considerations, rely on blade length and speed to tell you how effectively a cordless model will trim tender shoots and tough woody branches, applying the recommendations given for AC-powered models.

TIPS FOR USING YOUR HEDGE TRIMMER
AC-Powered Models

Because the cord of the trimmer is short, you will be using an extension cord. Don't rely on the tenuous friction grip of the tool's plug prongs in the extension cord socket; it is possible for the plug to slip part way out, exposing a bare metal prong carrying 120 volts with respect to the ground you're standing on! To be on the safe side, knot the extension cord to the tool's cord before joining the plug and socket. This way, as you pull the trimmer about, the stress will be applied to the knot, instead of to the mated plug and socket.

Be sure the trimmer's power switch is in the off position before you plug into the AC outlet. This will avoid surprises and injury! Lay out the cord so that it doesn't coil or tangle near your feet. Stepping on the cord can yank the tool out of your hands, turning those nasty blades on you! Keep the cord out of the path of the cutting blades by passing the extension cord over the shoulder opposite the hand that's holding the trimmer. In this way, only a short section of the cord is exposed between you and the trimmer, and you will always know where the cord is as you cut.

Finally, be sure that you use a brightly colored cord that's easy to see in the deep shadows of a hedge, and don't use your trimmer in the low visibility conditions of early morning or twilight hours. Be sure of what you're cutting by *seeing* exactly what you're cutting!

Cordless Models

Start with a fully charged battery pack no matter how simple the job may seem. You may run into unexpected tough cutting, and a full pack will eliminate the annoyance of stopping for a recharge cycle. Don't habitually use the trimmer for trivial chores that take just a few minutes of cutting; you will gradually reduce the service capacity of the battery pack. If you notice that you're getting far less than the stated cutting time, your trimmer's battery pack has probably lost capacity. To restore it, you'll have to discharge the battery completely, recharge, and then discharge and recharge it once more. In this way, the battery pack will regain its ability to deliver a longer period of use.

As mentioned earlier, a cordless trimmer should *never* be left where young children can get it—even for the minutes it takes to answer the phone or grab a quick lunch. Take it with you, keep it in sight, or lock it away.

For your own safety, never try to clear away debris from the blades of a cordless trimmer while your other hand is anywhere near the power switch. Turn off power, and, if you are on a ladder, come down to ground level and a stable surface on which to rest the trimmer, while you free

its blades of stems or pulp. Where something has jammed in the blades, pull the battery pack before you tussle with the blades. You may lose a little time, but you'll keep your fingers.

Finally, don't apply power to the trimmer unless you're cutting. It's senseless to waste battery capacity by running the trimmer as you walk or mount a ladder, *and* you'd be needlessly exposing yourself to injury.

Trimming Techniques

A wide, sweeping motion, feeding the blade teeth through the twigs is most effective. A slight downward tilt of the blade in the direction of motion gives the best cutting. One sweep will usually cut all twigs in the blade's path, but, if not, a return sweep, cutting with the other edge of the blade, should lop off the stragglers.

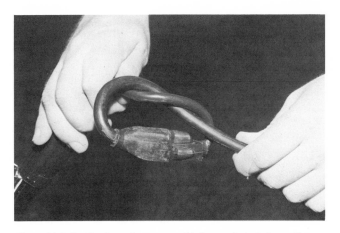

Figure 30-4. Don't rely on the pressure-friction contacts between the power plug and the socket of the extension cord. A knot tied as shown will relieve strain on these electrical parts and prevent separation. GRAF-WHALEN photograph.

Figure 30-5. An overnight recharge is all that is needed to get full cutting power for the next day's work. GRAF-WHALEN photograph.

Trimming Heavier Growth

To cut older growth with thicker twigs, use a "sawing" motion as you feed the blade through the growth. This clears the blade faster and helps to feed the thicker twigs into the blade teeth. Heavy branches should be fed slowly into the blade, using only a portion of the cutting edges. Should the trimmer stall on these heavy pieces, stop immediately and turn the switch off. Failure to do so could result in damage to the motor.

Side-Trimming Hedges

Hold the trimmer with blades vertical, and begin at the bottom and sweep up. To prevent the bottom of the hedge from being overshadowed, and thus becoming spindly through lack of sunshine, round the hedge or taper it inward, from bottom to top. These shapes will also be better able to withstand the weight of a heavy snowfall.

Level Hedges

To obtain exceptionally level hedges, a piece of string can be stretched along the length of the hedge at the desired height to serve as a guide line. The hedge may then be cut to just above the string.

Trimming Suggestions

Hedges: For maximum convenience in trimming and shaping, don't let your hedge grow more than about 5 feet tall and 30 inches wide. During the first year of growth, trim the top two or three times, each time several inches higher than it was after the previous trimming. When the growth at the base of the hedge fills out, start tapering the sides to keep the top of the hedge narrower than the bottom. After the first year, two trimmings during the growing season should be sufficient.

Figure 30-6. Use a sawing motion to obtain best cutting action in older, heavier growth. GRAF-WHALEN photograph.

Evergreens: Newly planted evergreens should not be trimmed the first year. After the first year, spring-growing varieties should be trimmed once a year, in spring, after the growth has emerged. Species that also grow through the summer should be trimmed in early summer, when new growth is 2 or 3 inches long, and again in midsummer. Trim only the new wood, as old branches without needles will not send out new shoots.

RULES FOR SAFE USE

• Keep children away. All visitors should be kept a safe distance away from the work area.
• Store idle trimmer indoors. When not in use, the tool should be stored indoors in dry, high or locked-up place, out of the reach of children.
• Don't force trimmer. The trimmer will do the job better and more safely when operated at the speed for which it was designed.
• Use the right tool. Do not use the trimmer for jobs it was not intended to perform.
• Dress properly. Do not wear loose clothing or jewelry. They could be caught in moving parts. The use of rubber gloves and footwear is recommended when working outdoors.
• Don't use trimmer in rain or on wet foliage.
• Don't overreach. Keep proper footing at all times.
• Keep both hands on the tool when using it.
• Do not lock switch on unless essential for a particular operation.
• Maintain trimmer. Keep cutting edges sharp and clean for best and safest performance. Follow manufacturer's instructions for lubricating.
• Avoid accidental starting. Do not carry the tool with your finger on the switch. Be sure trigger switch is off when plugging in cord or installing battery.
• Never grasp the exposed cutting blades or cutting edges when picking up or holding the trimmer.
• Keep hands and all parts of body away from blades. The edges of a trimmer are sharp and can cause injury even when the tool is off, so steer clear of blades.
• Use only for trimming normal shrubs and hedges found around houses and buildings.
• A cordless trimmer does not have to be plugged in. Remember this, because it is always in an operating condition.
• Wear gloves when trimming thorny or prickly growth.
• Don't feed twigs into the blade with your hands or reach over the moving blade to pick up clippings.
• Remove power pack from a cordless trimmer when the tool is not in use and before servicing.

• Before trimming, inspect area for wires, cords, glass, or other foreign objects that could come in contact with the blade.

• If twigs jam the blade, turn the tool off. Use a short stick to push the jammed material out of blade teeth.

• Do not operate portable electric trimmers in gaseous or explosive atmospheres. Motors in these tools normally spark, and the sparks might ignite fumes.

HEDGE TRIMMER MAINTENANCE
Blade Lubrication

In cutting certain types of dense, matted, or wet shrubs and hedges, sap or dirt may build up on the blades, reducing cutting efficiency. To test for this, turn off the motor. The blade will stop almost immediately, if too much dirt and sap are present. If blade coasts to a gradual halt, no cleaning or lubrication is needed.

To avoid the need for frequent cleanings the use of a dry silicone-spray lubricant is recommended. Spray the blades lightly, top and bottom, from a distance of 3 to 4 inches. One pass over each side of the blade is usually sufficient, but a second pass may be necessary if there is heavy dirt accumulation. Never make more than two passes. Turn on tool to work lubricant between blades. *Do not use an oily lubricant.* It will collect dirt and slow down the cutting action. The only time oil should be put on the blades is just before off-season storage. The oil should be wiped off after storage.

Blade Cleaning

Your trimmer will operate better and for longer periods with clean blades. After trimming, disconnect power cord or remove battery pack and clean the blades as follows: 1) Apply a liquid household cleaner, such as Fantastic® or Ajax Liquid®, full strength, to the blades. Allow the cleaner to soak in for about 10 minutes. 2) Scrub the blades with a stiff brush to loosen dirt and sap deposits. 3) Fill a bucket with hot water and immerse blade in water to a point just below the housing. Be careful not to get the motor housing in the water. 4) Rinse the blades under running water to wash away loosened deposits. 5) Wipe blade clean with a cloth. Be careful not to cut yourself. Allow blade to dry. 6) Spraying the top and bottom of the blade with silicone-spray lubricant after cleaning is recommended.

Winter Storage

Apply a light film of oil to the blades, after cleaning, to prevent rust during months of nonuse. Inspect the tool's cord and its companion extension cord for nicks and abrasions that might reduce safety. Repair or replace, as required. If your trimmer is supplied with a protective

plastic sheath, slip it on and store the trimmer in a high, dry place that children can't reach. If your trimmer is the cordless type, charge the battery pack before storage and be sure to store the pack separately to be sure that it can't be found and used to operate the trimmer by inquisitive children. Wrap the charged battery pack in a plastic bag and store it under lock and key.

Spring Activation

Wipe the oil film from the trimmer and check its operation (with AC power or battery pack). For optimum operation of cordless types, discharge the battery pack completely and then recharge. This will ensure full-charge capacity during the coming season.

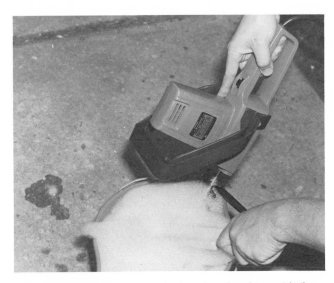

Figure 30-7. Clean off accumulated pulp and sap in a detergent bath after each use. GRAF-WHALEN photograph.

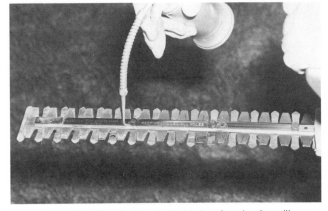

Figure 30-8. A light film of oil applied to blades after cleaning will prevent rust during off-season storage. GRAF-WHALEN photograph.

31

Rotary Lawn Mowers

The act of lawn mowing consumes more man-hours each year than any other lawn care chore. And yet, these hours could be made enjoyable with the use of a good rotary lawn mower that's in top condition. A well-kept, clean rotary mower with a sharp, well-balanced blade and (if gasoline powered) tuned engine can make grass cutting downright pleasurable! Rotary mowers cut through crabgrass and heavy weeds easily. They're the most maneuverable mowers, too, so they do the best job of trimming edges or mowing hard-to-reach areas around obstacles. What's more, the rotary is generally considered superior for mowing heights of 1 1/2 inches or more—the ideal height for most fine fescues, Bahias, and bluegrasses.

HOW THEY WORK

The rotary mower works on the vacuum-and-scythe principle. The engine or motor shaft rotates a carefully balanced blade, whirling it at speeds of up to 6,000 rpm. The blade turns within a housing (called the *deck*) and creates a partial vacuum at ground level, which lifts the grass to a vertical position; here the sharp edge of the horizontally rotating blade can shear it off, as would a scythe. Cut grass is sucked upward into the positive-pressure airstream near the deck undersurface and is expelled from a discharge chute. If the chute leads into a porous bag, the air blast will filter through the bag material, leaving the grass clippings collected within the bag. The height of cut is set by raising or lowering the deck on the mower's four wheels.

Self-propelled rotaries employ a power takeoff from the shaft that drives the cutting blade. In many, the shaft turns a pulley and drive belt leading to a larger pulley that turns much more slowly. This pulley then drives a cogged reduction stage which rotates a cross-shaft with grooved drive rollers. This turns against the rubber tires of the front and rear wheels, rotating the wheels and causing the mower to move forward. A simple, hand-operated mechanical clutch is used to engage or disengage the driver rollers from the mower wheels.

Figure 31-1. Rotary lawn mower. Photograph courtesy of The Toro Company, Consumer Products Div.

Figure 31-2. Under-deck view of the rotary mower reveals whirling blade and scooplike depression that sucks blade clippings up. The guard across the chute allows grass to be blown out, but protects hands and feet. GRAF-WHALEN photograph.

WHAT'S AVAILABLE

Rotaries are classified by the width of the swath cut through the grass by the rotating blade. Generally, the size range is from 18 to 22 inches. Narrow cutting widths mean less opposition to the rotating blade, so a gas engine or electric motor of about 2 1/2 horsepower will be found on small rotaries. Medium-size rotaries use 3 horsepower, and the largest sizes run 3 1/2 to 4 horsepower. Cutting width makes a slight difference in the time you'll take to mow your lawn, but remember that a larger rotaries are intended for use on hilly, terraced, or more effort to wheel around your lawn.

Rotaries are available in *hand-propelled* (push-type) and *self-propelled* models. Generally, mowers with narrow cutting widths and light-duty engines or motors are sold for use on small, level lawns and are hand-propelled. Larger rotaries are intended for use on hilly, terraced, or large lawns of 1/2 acre or more and are usually self-propelled to compensate for their greater weight and grass-bagging capacity.

Figure 31-3. A typical hand-propelled rotary mower with side bagging attachment. The single lever controls engine rpm and choke function. Photograph courtesy of The Toro Company, Consumer Products Div.

Figure 31-4. This rotary mower is an electric one, powered by its own built-in storage battery. Photograph courtesy of The Toro Company, Consumer Products Div.

Most rotaries sold today are gas-engine powered, and both four-cycle and two-cycle engines are in use. Two-cycle engines require a mixture of gasoline and special lubricating oil (one that burns without residue), which calls for some care in proportioning. Four-cycle engines need no such premixing, burn straight regular gas, and have a separate oil sump, which lubricates parts without getting involved with the combustion process. A myth persists that a two-cycle engine is "stronger" than a four-cycle engine of comparable size. Don't believe it! The real determinant is the *horsepower rating* of the engine, which is a measure of its capacity to do work. Engines of the same horsepower rating are identical in "strength," whether two or four cycle.

Electric-powered rotaries are available in AC-powered models that trail an extension cord back to an outlet or in cordless models that carry a built-in storage battery. If your lawn is large or far removed from a power outlet, or if it has a number of plantings or trees, the trailing cord of an electric rotary may be a nuisance or a hazard. The cordless types free you of this annoyance, but suffer from a distinct cutting-time limit imposed by the battery's capacity. Once it goes dead you're finished mowing for at least several hours, because the battery must be recharged at a comparatively slow rate. Also, with a cordless mower, you'll push about 25 pounds of storage battery around. You'll be working a bit harder as the price for convenience. Another drawback of the electrics is that the motor turns the blade more slowly than a comparable gas-powered model. This means tough going in tall weeds and you'll have to go back over the ground after mowing for proper cleanup of grass cuttings. Also, the longer the extension cord, the slower the motor will turn, due to voltage drop in the cord's electrical resistance. On the plus side, electrics are quieter than gas types, require no hazardous fuel handling or storage, produce no exhaust or smelly fumes, and are generally more acceptable to women (as well as neighbors in closely spaced developments).

IMPORTANT FEATURES TO LOOK FOR
Easy Starting
Electrics are inherently self-starting, so this concerns only gas-powered models. Most manually started types use a *pull-rope recoil starter*. The rope is coiled around a spring-loaded pulley inside the starter housing. A steady pull on the rope will spin the engine flywheel, forcing the piston to move down and up to draw in the fuel/air mix and then provide a spark from the ignition system. If all goes well on the first pull, the engine will start up on its own. If not, it's try, try, again.

Another manual starter is the *impulse* type. It has a crank handle you use to wind up a spring inside the starter. When you release it, the spring spins the engine flywheel several revolutions at a speed fast enough to start the engine.

Some mowers feature *electric start*. A small DC motor built into the engine housing is used to spin the flywheel through a gear-coupling arrangement. A battery supplies the juice to drive the starting motor and a key-operated switch closes the circuit. The motor spins until the engine catches or until the battery is exhausted. Just in case the latter happens, most electric start mowers come with a removable pull-rope that winds around a pulley on top of the engine for manual starting. The battery can be recharged overnight from a charger that fits into an AC power outlet.

In general, any method of starting will work fine, *if* the carburetor and ignition system of the engine are functioning properly, the blade is rotating free of obstructions, and proper technique is used for cold or hot starting (as outlined in the manufacturer's instructions). However, electric start, the most convenient method, can be the most troublesome if improperly used. If something isn't quite right on the first few starting tries, you'll fruitlessly use up the starting battery's capacity. If you catch the problem and correct it, you may discover that the overused battery lacks sufficient power to spin the flywheel. The same holds true for frequent stops and restarts. In fact, you may be tempted to leave the mower running at times you shouldn't (when refueling or when emptying the grass bag, for example), just because you're afraid there may not be enough battery reserve to restart. Keep the thoughtfully provided pull-rope handy, instead, and play safe by shutting down the mower at times like these as the manufacturer insists.

Reliability and Durability
Generally, the simpler any machine is, the more reliable it will be. And so, electrics get high marks for being ready when you need them. Next in order come the pull-start, hand-propelled gas models. Self-propelled mowers, with their more complex drive mechanisms, run third and electric start machines run a close fourth. However, careful engineering in the more complex, self-propelled and electric-start machines is a definite plus in terms of reliability.

Durability is another matter. If you consistently mistreat a light-duty mower, using it to cut wet grass or failing to give it reasonably good maintenance, expect to junk it after a couple of seasons. Even top-of-the-line models won't withstand being kicked around for long. In any case, here are some tips in picking a mower for the long pull: Look for a mower with a steel (at least 14-

gauge), aluminum, or magnesium deck. Steel has the greatest resistance to cracking should the blade bend and whack the deck at full power. Although steel *can* rust, this is rarely a problem. Aluminum and magnesium can't rust and they're lighter than steel, but they *can* break or crack under severe impact from the blade or a thrown object.

Next, check the depth of draw of the deck. A deep housing means a strong suction for good cutting in tall weeds and grass, and a deep housing offers better protection against objects being hit and thrown out, missilelike, by the blade. *But*, a deep-drawn deck means a long shaft between the engine (or motor) and the blade. This increases the risk of a bent shaft should the blade collide with a stone, tree root, or other unyielding object.

Look also for a single-piece blade of tempered steel, held to the shaft by two bolts, or by a bolt-and-stud arrangement that prevents loosening. Riveted blades can loosen up and be dangerous. Also, they tend to flex up and down when rotating at high speed, causing uneven cutting and "browning" of grass tips.

Safety Features

Like the automobile and chain saw, a rotary mower is a potentially lethal machine. Most reputable manufacturers have done a very creditable job in providing protection for the user, the bystander, and the child. But, no rotary is foolproof or child-proof! The safest machine is the one that's run by a user who has read and *follows* the safety instructions that come with the machine. Any other safety features built into the mower do not take the place of safe usage. Here are some safety features to look for:

Drag shield: A hinged plate attached to the rear of the mower deck, which drags along behind the mower. It prevents objects from being thrown backward toward the operator. It also keeps the operator from accidentally placing his foot under the mower.

Toe guard: A bar across the discharge chute opening, spanning the blade area. It is designed so that a foot placed accidentally into the chute will be forced either under or over the moving blade.

Safety discharge chute: An extension of the normal opening on the deck for the discharge of cut grass particles. It acts as a guide and deflector, causing particles to be thrown down and away from operator.

Enclosed deck: The shielding on the underside of blade openings for grass tips to make contact with blade. It prevents large objects from hitting the blade and restricts the path of foreign objects.

Grass bag construction: The bag should be made of strong fibers to prevent nails or other dangerous articles from piercing it and injuring bystanders.

Bag safety disconnect: There are two methods. One automatically shuts off the engine when the bag is removed; the second enables you to remove the bag with the mower in a standing position without placing hands on or near the discharge chute.

Refined drive systems: Some manufacturers have improved drive systems on self-propelled models to make operating and handling easier. This reduces the probability of injury from a mower out of control.

Enclosed blade: The mower deck should extend at least 1/8 inch below the blade so that foreign obstacles are kept under the deck when they hit the blade and are either discharged through the chute or deflected back toward the ground.

Operating controls: Controls should be placed so that the operator can reach them when standing behind the equipment. This eliminates the danger of blade contact or thrown obstacles when the operator bends over the engine to make adjustments on controls.

Protective guards: Shields should be present over all moving parts to prevent the snagging of the operator's hands or clothing.

Deck baffles: This is a feature that some manufacturers claim adds safety. It consists of baffles located in the airstream under the deck, which are designed to deflect foreign particles back toward the ground, rather than out the discharge chute.

Deep channel deck: According to some manufacturers, a channel in the deck creates air movement which directs particles into a specific area, thus reducing the possibility of objects being thrown out from under the mower.

Blade speed: Maximum blade speeds (typically 3,200 rpm) have been established to provide efficient cutting while minimizing the dangers of thrown particles.

Quality of Cut

The best guide here is the blade design. The blade should be shaped so that the cutting edge is narrower at the edge than in the middle, and the mid-portion must be higher than the tips to prevent the blade from rubbing the newly shorn grass and turning it brown. Look, also, for a lip behind the cutting edge that improves grass throwing and suction. This helps clear away debris, enabling the blade to cut evenly. You'll also want a simple method of raising or lowering the deck to change the cut level (typically, 1 1/2 inches in spring, 2 inches during hot summer weather, and 1 inch in fall). Steer clear of methods requiring tools or fussy adjustment.

Service and Ease of Maintenance

Pick a mower you can service yourself or one sold by a reputable manufacturer with a nearby dealer service or parts facility. Mowers are tough to transport by car, and you should have the comfort of knowing that you don't have to go far to get what you need in parts or service. Many manufacturers offer detailed service manuals for their products at a very low cost.

Bagging Attachments

Most rotaries are equipped to accept grass baggers. A porous polyester fiber or cloth bag is attached to a chute at the center of the right side or at the rear of the mower deck. Both types have advantages. The side chute helps protect users or bystanders against objects being hurled by the whirling blade, but is more prone to clogging when grass is wet. What's more, the side bag makes the mower unbalanced and unwieldy when it's full and where there's little space for maneuvering. The rear bag makes for a narrow, easier-to-handle mower with more evenly distributed weight. Also, the capacity of a rear bag is up to twice that of a side bag, meaning less frequent stops for emptying. However, the rear bag is very heavy when full and can be a nuisance to detach for dumping. What's more, its weight on the rear wheels may cause the driven front wheels of a self-propelled model to come up off the ground, giving you some handling problems.

TIPS FOR USING YOUR LAWN MOWER

- Clear the lawn of all debris before you begin to mow. It can cause injury to you, others in the area, and your mower.
- Don't walk on the grass immediately before you mow. To get an even cut, the grass should be upright. After you clear your lawn of debris, stay off it for a few minutes before you mow.
- Upright grasses should not be cut short. Most upright grasses grow best at about 2 inches—Bermuda grasses at 1 1/2 inches. Bent grasses are generally the only ones that should be mowed low—about 1 inch.
- Mow often. How often depends on the type of lawn, growing season, and height of cut. Mow often enough so that no more than one-third of the leaf surface is removed at one time.
- Tighten all mower parts periodically. If your mower develops an odd rattle, turn off the engine and check it for loose parts immediately.
- Cut in a different direction each time you mow. This adds to the appearance and helps prevent grass from growing and lying in one direction. Start by doing one or two mower widths around the lawn, then begin your cross-lawn cut.
- Mow with as few interruptions as possible. It saves time and it is better for your lawn and mower if you mow without constant stops and starts.

- Clean your mower. After mowing, clean the underside of your mower housing of clippings and dirt, and wipe off excess grease and oil from engine and housing.
- Check gas and oil before each mowing. While you're at it, make sure moving parts are properly lubricated. Regular fuel checking and lubrication also prevent the possibility of running out of gas in mid-job.
- With an electric mower, use only a brightly colored cord that stands out against the grass, so that you will not accidentally mow over it. It must be of a gauge suitable for the amount of current it will handle and of the three-wire type. Never use the mower unless the cord is properly grounded through a grounded outlet.
- Check the grass bag for rips. If the bag has holes or other signs of wear, change it before you mow. This way stones or other debris will be caught securely in the bag.
- Be sure your mower blade is sharp. Dull blades will tear and injure your lawn. A metal file can be used to sharpen rotary blades, though they should also be removed and sharpened professionally from time to time.
- Try to mow when your lawn is dry. Wet grass can clog your mower and stick to the mower housing. When this happens the grass blades are torn rather than cut, turning the tips brown. Also, grass tends to clump or stick together when wet.
- Cut grass in the late afternoon or early evening. This gives you good light and is also best for your lawn. The newly exposed tips and roots of grass adjust overnight; you avoid the shock newly cut grass may suffer by being exposed to the harsh sun.

RULES FOR SAFE USE

- Read the owner's manual. Your dealer should supply you with detailed starting and operating instructions, as well as a demonstration.
- Know your controls. Learn how to stop the engine quickly.
- Instruct all operators. Never allow anyone to operate your mower without complete instructions. Teach them all safety rules and operating instructions. Do not allow children to operate the mower.
- Make mower adjustments carefully. Do not overspeed engine or alter governor settings. Excess speed is dangerous and shortens mower life. Height adjustments should be made only after engine and blade have been stopped. Disconnect the spark-plug lead prior to performing service on engine or mower. Keep the lead away from the plug.
- Check guards and shields. Keep shields in place and secure at all times. Check grass or leaf bags for wear or deterioration and replace with new bag when needed.
- Clean the lawn. Free the lawn of sticks, stones, wire,

etc. They could be picked up and hurled great distances by the blade. Mow only in clean areas.

• Dress wisely. Don't wear loose-fitting clothing. Provide some external protection by wearing long, heavy denim trousers and heavy shoes. Never mow when barefoot or when wearing open sandals. Safety shoes are recommended.

• Take precautions before starting. Check all nuts, bolts, and fasteners for tightness, especially the blade nut. Disconnect the spark-plug lead during the check. Keep children and pets away from the mower just as you would keep them away from any cutting machinery. Keep hands or feet away from under the mower.

• Don't start the mower or engine until you are ready to mow. On self-propelled models place control handle in "out of drive" position before starting the engine. Be sure that the mower will not tip or roll during starting operation. Never stand in front of self-propelled mowers. Keep clear of discharge opening.

• Watch your mowing. Avoid striking trees, walls, curbs, or other solid objects with the mower. Never deliberately mow over any object. If an object is struck or if the mower starts to vibrate, stop mower immediately, remove spark-plug wire, and examine mower for damage. Replace damaged parts before restarting and operating the mower. Mow across faces of slopes and be extra careful of your footing. Control direction by hand pressure on the handle, not foot pressure on the mower housing. Do not lag behind or let the mower pull you; stay in command. Never run with mower. Mow only in daylight or good artificial light and never operate equipment in wet grass.

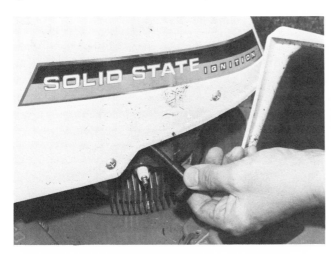

Figure 31-5. Removing the spark-plug lead before working on your mower is a safety precaution you should not overlook. GRAF-WHALEN photograph.

• Know when to stop the engine. The engine should be stopped before pushing mower across walks, drives, or roads; before resetting cutting height adjustments; and when leaving operating position, even for a moment. When stopping, remove the spark-plug lead and make certain that the blade has stopped before placing your hands or feet near blade area or cleaning the discharge chute. Never manually rotate the blade without first removing spark-plug wire.

• Take fuel precautions. Never add gasoline to a running or hot engine or while you are smoking. Fill the tank outdoors, wipe up spilled gasoline, and replace cap securely. Handle gasoline with care. It is highly flammable and a real hazard to your home. Use an approved safety container to handle and store gas. Keep engine free from accumulations of grass, leaves, or excessive grease; these combustible materials could result in a fire. To prevent possible explosion of fuel vapors, do not store mower near an open flame if mower has fuel in its tank. (Example: furnace or water-heater pilot light.)

• Never run a gas engine indoors. Starting or running a gas engine indoors is dangerous because exhaust fumes can collect. Carbon monoxide, which is present in the exhaust, is an odorless and very deadly gas.

• Remove the key when storing electric-start mowers.

• Keep electric mowers away from children. Never leave the mower where children can get at it. The smallest child can operate a mower switch and kill or dismember himself with its deadly, whirling blade. This particularly applies to cordless models.

• Service the mower. Have a competent serviceman make a thorough inspection of your mower at least once a year.

• Be competent. A rotary mower is no safer than its operator. It's up to you.

LAWN MOWER MAINTENANCE

With only seasonal maintenance in fall and spring, a mower can be kept in top condition and at its cutting best. Combine equipment care tips and the following tips for better and safer mowing, and you will improve your lawn while preserving your mower investment.

Fall Maintenance

Fall is the best time to put a mower in shape for winter. By winterizing a mower, years can be added to its life and a costly repair bill may be saved. Certainly, it will guarantee a quick start and full power the next spring.

Since you will be working with gasoline and oil, choose an outdoor area far from open flames and smokers—one where fumes can readily dissipate and an oil spill would not be disastrous. Running water from a garden hose will further ease the chore, especially if the mower is caked with grass debris below the deck. Since hardware has most likely become loosened by vibration and will need to be tightened, a tool kit, tablespoon, fresh can of oil (usually SAE 10W-40), and some absorbent rags should be kept handy.

Before cleanup chores can be done safely, the mower's tank must be rid of fuel. Fuel dumping is dangerous because a stray spark, struck as the mower is turned over, might ignite the fuel with catastrophic consequences. Play it safe and let the mower use up its fuel as it was intended—through the engine. Start the mower, throttle down to a low speed as soon as it is warmed up, and keep the mower in its normal position while running.

If the mower is equipped with a wash-out plug, you can hook a garden hose (without the nozzle) to a plastic cap in the mower housing. Turn the water on to moderate pressure for at least 2 minutes. The whirling blade of the running mower will forcibly distribute the water on the housing inner surface, loosening and safely flushing out the accumulated grass clippings. If the mower lacks a wash-out plug, a water stream from the garden hose can be directed into the discharge chute. Do so only from a safe distance and keep your face, hands, body, and the hose well out of line with the chute. Take care not to splash water up into the air cleaner or onto the hot exterior surfaces of the engine. After the flush-out is finished, all fuel must be used up before continuing. Do not leave a mower running for any reason and do discourage children and nosy pets from coming close, until the fuel runs out. When the engine quits, remove the spark-plug wire from the spark plug and coil it back for safety.

Gasoline contains sticky varnishes and waxy residues, so it is vital that the slight amount remaining in the tank after the engine has sputtered to a stop is removed. If this is not done, the gum formed by evaporation of the residual fuel will find its way into the fuel line during the winter, possibly clogging it next spring. To get the leftover fuel, wrap an absorbent cloth around a small-diameter dowel and insert it into the fuel tank, through the screw-top opening. Work the cloth-padded tip end around the tank bottom to sponge up the fuel that clings to corners. Discard the gas-soaked cloth, keeping it away from fire, smokers, and sparks.

If the mower is four-cycle engine powered, this is the time to drain the oil from the crankcase. Place a shallow pan on the floor and tilt the mower up, so that gravity will pull the warm, thinned oil and its contaminants right out of the engine. Be sure to drain the crankcase completely or the sludge that clings to the bottom of the crankcase will poison fresh oil by releasing carbon and tiny metal particles it holds captive. Replace the crankcase and fuel tank caps after the mower is completely empty

of oil and fuel. At this point, engine parts are much too hot to handle, so now is a good time to clean up the under-deck and check the mower's blade. By the time these steps have been completed the engine should have cooled to the touch.

Even though the under-deck area has been flushed with water as a preliminary, the pulpy accretions of the summer's mowing may have to be scraped off. Both a scraper (try a putty knife) and a wire brush may be needed to clear the dried grass pulp from the machine. It is smart to recheck the spark-plug wire and make sure it is safely tied up before proceeding. Next, turn the mower on its side. Do not balance the machine on its grass chute or plastic carburetor cover. This would fracture one or more mower parts. With the machine in a stable position, start cleaning the under-deck surface. Long, even strokes with the putty knife will soon pare away any stuck-on grass below the deck. In corners and tight spots clean away grass with the wire brush. Flush the undersurface periodically with water from the garden hose to wash away debris and soften any residual material.

Check the blade's condition. A bent blade may cause vibration and power loss. A dull blade will tear and injure the lawn. An out-of-balance blade is dangerous and can hurt both you and the mower. To check for a bent blade, place a straightedge, such as a yardstick, across the bottom of the housing. Align the blade below the stick and make sure that the blade tips are both about the same distance away from the yardstick. Next, check the blade by measuring the distance from the blade tip to the housing edge; then rotate the blade until the opposite tip is under the stick. If the two tips do not measure within approximately 1/8 inch of each other (relative to the housing edge), blade replacement is in order.

If blade condition warrants it, remove the blade and take it to the bench. Sharpen the blade at the original angle and be sure to dress out the nicks and dents that stones and roots have inflicted upon it. If the original blade of the mower is beyond repair, buy a new blade. The cost of a new mower could be saved with this inexpensive investment. While the blade is off, if the mower is a two-cycle type, take the time to clean away power-robbing carbon deposits from the mower exhaust ports. Insert a 3/8-inch-diameter dowel into the mower ports and turn to loosen carbon deposits. Remove the dowel, place the mower in an upright position, and pull the starter rope vigorously several times to blow the loosened carbon from the exhaust ports. Set the machine aright on its wheels before tackling the cleanup of the engine. First, check the carburetor's airway and be sure to clean the engine air cleaner. Generally, this will be an oiled polyethylene filter. Wash the filter element in a detergent-

Figure 31-6. A mower that lacks a wash-out plug should be flushed through the discharge chute after engine is stopped. GRAF-WHALEN photograph.

Figure 31-8. Drain dirty oil from the crankcase while engine is still warm to be sure of getting all contaminants out. GRAF-WHALEN photograph.

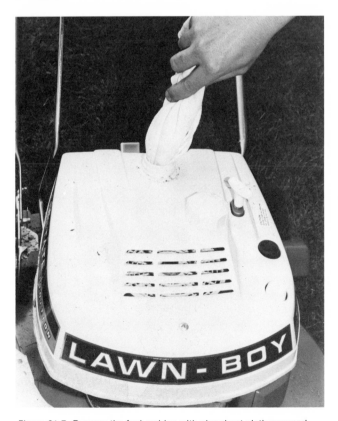

Figure 31-7. Remove the fuel residue with absorbent cloth wrapped around a dowel. Dispose of gas-soaked cloth in a safe manner. GRAF-WHALEN photograph.

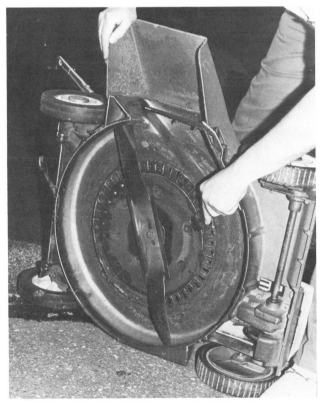

Figure 31-9. Remove pulpy residue from under-deck surfaces with a scraper. A wire brush may also prove helpful. GRAF-WHALEN photograph.

and-water solution and squeeze dry. Re-oil the filter by applying 5 teaspoonsful of engine oil to the sides and open ends of the filter element. Squeeze to distribute oil, as well as to remove excess oil, and reinstall the engine air cleaner. Next, use a soft brush and cloth to clean away debris from the engine exterior and upper deck. Pay particular attention to air-cooling fins of the engine. Any dirt, leaf, or grass residues act as insulators, retarding heat transfer from engine to air.

If the mower is a self-propelled type, take time to remove the cover-ups from the drive mechanism to get out clippings. Check parts and lubricate, if necessary. In a belt-driven model make sure that the belt is in good condition and free of any gummy or oily residue.

To get the grit off all surfaces before applying lubricants, apply a strong detergent car wash and hose down. Avoid flushing water into the carburetor air cleaner. Wipe the machine down using an old towel.

For easy operation, apply a drop or two of oil to the inner member of each control cable. Do so from the top and gravity will do the rest. Likewise, apply a drop or two to the pivots of control handles and wheel bearings, to smooth their operation. A light film of oil is the best corrosion proofing that can be given to a mower's engine interior. To apply, remove the spark plug and pour 2 tablespoons of 10W-40 oil into the cylinder. Crank the engine several times to allow oil to coat the cylinder walls and piston. Install fresh oil in the crankcase (if it is a four-cycle machine). Simply lift out the dipstick and pour in the required lubricant (typically, 10W-40) to the *full* mark on the dipstick. Do not skip this step. If the crankcase is left dry and oil is not added in the spring, the engine will ruin in only minutes of operation.

While the spark plug is out of the engine, clean away carbon deposits from the housing and plug tip. If the center electrode of the plug appears rounded, file it flat. A plug with square-edged electrodes fires more reliably than a worn plug with rounded electrodes. Check and reset the gap, as necessary. If the plug cannot be easily cleaned, replace it. Either way, install the plug in the engine, but do not connect the plug wire.

If it is a mower with conventional magneto ignition and hard-starting, a drop in power, or missing is noticeable, the ignition-breaker point-set may need replacing. Generally, points start pitting after about 50 operating hours. Since this entails dismantling of the magneto assembly, a professional might be able to do a better job. However, if you have the skill and specific details at hand, it is a job you can tackle yourself. If the mower bears the words "Solid-State Ignition," there are no breaker points, eliminating an annoying periodic maintenance task.

Figure 31-10. Sharpen the blade with a file at the original angle. Dress out nicks and dents. Be sure the blade is not bent. GRAF-WHALEN photograph.

Figure 31-11. Free exhaust ports of carbon deposits for best engine efficiency. GRAF-WHALEN photograph.

Figure 31-12. Remove porous, foam air cleaner, wash to remove trapped dirt particles, and squeeze thoroughly dry. Re-oil the air cleaner before reinstalling. GRAF-WHALEN photograph.

Figure 31-13. Vibration and use may loosen parts. Spring clips and other push-on fasteners are particularly susceptible. GRAF-WHALEN photograph.

Figure 31-16. Check the action of all control cables and be sure that their outer sheaths are securely attached to the mower housing. Only the inner control wire should move. GRAF-WHALEN photograph.

Figure 31-14. Be sure that drive belts are free of oil, dirt, and residue. Belts loosen as they wear, so check tension too. GRAF-WHALEN photograph.

Figure 31-15. A drop of oil on each bearing surface of parts that roll, slide, or rub will keep the action going smoothly. GRAF-WHALEN photograph.

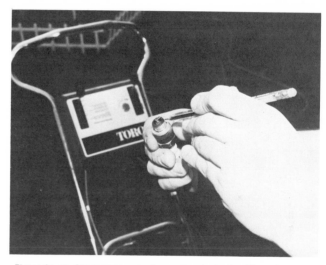

Figure 31-17. Check the spark-plug center electrode. File and regap, if necessary. GRAF-WHALEN photograph.

Figure 31-18. Be sure to charge the battery of an electric-start mower before putting it in off-season storage. A discharged battery can deteriorate or be completely ruined if left uncharged for long periods of time. GRAF-WHALEN photograph.

With electric-start mowers the power-pack starting battery should be charged for 48 hours before off-season storage. This can be done with the battery in place on the mower, using the plug-in charger supplied by the manufacturer. Do not leave the battery on charge beyond the recommended period. Leave the battery disconnected from the mower wiring after taking the battery off charge.

Figure 31-19. For long-term storage, use blocks to keep mower wheels off the floor, so that flat spots don't form on the wheels. GRAF-WHALEN photograph.

As a final inspection, go over the mower carefully. Tighten any loose hardware and be sure to replace any lost pieces. Bagging chutes and grass deflectors are now commonly made of plastic. If any such part is cracked or broken, do not take chances—replace it. Also, be sure to carefully inspect the bag to determine its future serviceability. Sun, moisture, sagging loads, and flying shards take their toll on catcher bags. Especially, check the zipper and that part of the bag which joins the chute. Mend torn or abraded areas, if possible, or replace the bag.

Storage
Be sure to choose a dry area for storage to reduce chances of rusting. To keep the rubber-tired wheels of a mower from flattening, block under the housing to raise the wheels off the floor with four bricks or scraps of wood. A plastic drop cloth may be used to cover the mower and keep it clean.

Spring Maintenance
Remove the mower from its place of storage and thoroughly inspect it. If no parts are damaged or lost, check the crankcase oil level (if it is a four-cycle engine) and top up, if necessary. Fill with regular gas. (Premium contains benzene, which can swell and ruin carburetor parts in small engines.)

Connect the spark-plug wire to the spark plug, set the choke control, and pull the starter. The mower should come to life in just a few tries, ready to face another summer of lawn-care duty.

32

Power Rake/Thatchers

Thatch is a matted layer of dead grass, imbedded in the turf, lying just above the soil of your lawn. It is the non-living debris that is the by-product of a lawn's ceaseless renewal of lush, living grass. The problem with thatch is that it builds up, season after season, below the living grass that makes your lawn such an object of pride. And, with this buildup, it gradually seals off the soil surface, so that fertilizer, air, and moisture do not reach the living grass roots. Deprived of nourishment, the grass weakens and becomes more susceptible to disease and insect infiltration. The result? *More* thatch; and a vicious circle is perpetuated that can rob you of your lawn's beauty if left unchecked.

Spring is the time for removing thatch, and it's possible to do a fair job with a hand rake, if your physical stamina is great enough. However, there is a better,

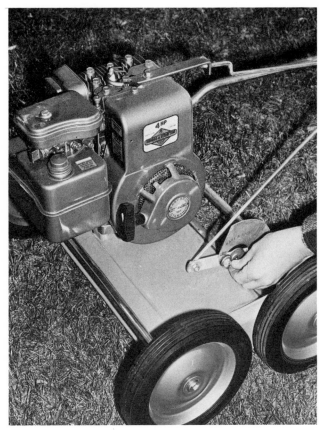

Figure 32-2. The maximum depth of thatching is set before the engine is started. Locking adjustment in place beforehand reduces the possibility of too deep a cut. GRAF-WHALEN photograph.

Figure 32-1. The thatcher is used and operated much like a lawn mower. The handle raises and lowers the cutter assembly, setting depth of thatching. GRAF-WHALEN photograph.

easier way, with the use of a power rake or thatcher. A power rake is a gasoline-engine powered garden tool that is designed to lift and cut away the thatch layer from your lawn, while not harming the healthy, living grass. The object is to bring the thatch to the surface, where it can be easily gathered by a lawn vacuum, sweeper, or conventional raking.

HOW THEY WORK

Power rakes are equipped with husky gas engines in the 4- to 5-horsepower range. The engine provides rotary output to a pulley and belt drive that spins a rotating horizontal shaft, which carries a series of specially shaped cutter blades. The shaft is placed below a housing for safety and to prevent thatch from being expelled toward the operator. The rotating cutters slice past vertical living grass to incise the matted thatch on the turf surface. As thatch is cut, the blades also lift it to the grass surface, so that it can be easily collected later. To accommodate different grass heights and thatching depths, the cutting height of the wheeled housing is easily adjusted from the operator's position behind the machine.

WHAT'S AVAILABLE

There are two basic types of power rakes available—the *tine-reel* type and the *knife-and-flail* type. Of the two, the tine-reel type provides more gentle action in thatch removal, because it does not disturb the soil or living grass. However, the knife-and-flail type provides greater versatility. It can be used not only to thatch, but to slice into the soil to depopulate weed overgrowth, to prepare for new seeding, or to aerate the soil at periodic intervals. Depending upon your needs, you may find it more advantageous to rent a machine of either type before settling on a final type for your lawn care chores.

IMPORTANT FEATURES TO LOOK FOR
Easy Starting

Like most lawn mowers or tillers, the power rake usually comes with a pull-rope starter. Look for a model that features easy start-up with only moderate effort.

Adjustable Cutter Clearance

It should be easy to change the height of the cutting knives without tools and in a minimum of time. Look also for a positive-locking feature on the height adjustment. This will ensure that the knives stay at the level you've selected to avoid accidental destruction of part of your lawn.

Comfort and Safety

The power rake should move easily on large rubber-tired wheels, and its lift control should be immediately accessible to your hands, while standing at the operating position behind the handle. Presence of a woodruff key in the engine drive-pulley will protect the engine (and you) from

Figure 32-3. The sharp rotary cutters of the thatcher are on a common shaft, but are staggered to ensure good cutting, lifting, and throwing action. GRAF-WHALEN photograph.

Figure 32-4. Easy starting is a key concern in outdoor power tools like the thatcher. The pull-cord should be conveniently placed, and you should be able to brace the machine from a comfortable position. Heavy boots are a good safety tip for outdoor work. GRAF-WHALEN photograph.

Figure 32-5. The woodruff key between the engine shaft and drive pulley is designed to shear if cutter blades are suddenly bound up. Like a mechanical "fuse," the key prevents twisting and damage to engine parts under overload conditions. GRAF-WHALEN photograph.

injury should the cutters strike an immovable object. The key is designed to shear when excess force is applied. Replacements cost only pennies.

Look also for a "kill" switch that will instantly stop the engine by grounding the spark-plug tower. A sturdy metal or alloy housing should protect you from debris brought up by the rotating knives, and a protective shield should be located behind the knives to guard against debris being thrown back at your legs at ground level.

POWER RAKE/THATCHER MAINTENANCE

Apart from standard engine care, your power rake should require minimal care. Hardened cutters rarely require more than seasonal dressing with an 8-inch mill file, although more frequent sharpening may be needed where slicing is performed in hard soil. Because all drive belts stretch with use and "seat" into the drive pulleys, expect to adjust belt tension at some time after the first hour or two of operation and seasonally, thereafter. Belt adjustment should be a simple matter. Ask for a demonstration before you buy.

The similarity in seasonal maintenance requirements between a power rake and a rotary lawn mower suggests that you read and follow the care tips suggested for the lawn mower (see chapter 31) and apply them to the care of your power rake during off-season storage.

Figure 32-7. Don't forget to drain oil and refill the crankcase with fresh lubricant at recommended intervals. The oil-drain plug on thatcher engine is placed to simplify the emptying of oil into a shallow pan. GRAF-WHALEN photograph.

Figure 32-6. Belts stretch in time, so make seasonal belt inspection part of your thatcher's maintenance plan. GRAF-WHALEN photograph.

33

Shredder/Baggers

Not so long ago, you could tell that it was autumn by the crisp chill of the air and the scent of burning leaves. Today, the air still turns cold as fall deepens, but it's a lot *cleaner* thanks to bans on open burning and growing awareness. It makes good sense to either shred and bag leafy debris or to recycle Nature's bountiful, cast-off foliage into rich *humus* that will renew and invigorate the soil, from which new growth will spring.

Humus, as any organic gardener will tell you, is decayed vegetable matter. It is usually made in a *compost heap*, where bacteria and fungi go to work on leaves, twigs, hedge trimmings, vines, and plant stalks, to reduce this organic matter to a soil additive that can make your

Figure 33-1. Shredder/bagger. Photograph courtesy of The Toro Company, Consumer Products Div.

garden soil more fertile and friable. To help things along, most knowledgeable gardeners shred organic matter into tiny pieces before composting. This hastens the conversion process into humus, because more surface area, on which natural bacteria can work their organic chemical magic, is exposed. What's more, the finely pulverized material makes a superior humus that's easily worked into soil, helps it to hold water like a sponge, and makes tilling a much easier job.

The power tool that makes this possible is a shredder/bagger—a gasoline motor-driven gardening aid that can chew up dry leaves, twigs, branches, hedge trimmings, plant stalks and stems, vines, and all the other cast-off organic materials of your garden into finely pulverized bits. As a bulk reducer, it's unsurpassed. The chewed-up material often has less than 10 percent of the bulk of the original material. And so, whether you choose to compost or bag your outdoor leftovers, a shredder/bagger is a powered helper worthy of your consideration.

HOW THEY WORK

A gasoline engine is fitted atop a housing roughly resembling that of a rotary lawn mower. Inside the housing, the engine's shaft turns two or three rotary cutting blades, which pass between shear plates attached to the housing. A discharge chute exits from the housing and usually has a fitting that accommodates the mouth of a vented plastic bag. In operation, the whirling blades create a suction force that draws material that you drop into a hopper atop the housing into the blades. Caught between the blades and shear plates, the material is ripped, hammered, and finely pulverized by innumerable hard blows of the blades. Finally, the shredded material is blown out the discharge chute into the waiting bag. Vents or pores allow the air to escape, leaving the powdered debris trapped within.

When operated without a bag, the shredder/bagger can blow chewed-up debris directly out onto a lawn, into beds, or into a compost heap. (This requires utmost care for safety.) The material is chopped so finely that it will hardly show when spread as a light mulch over a large area.

WHAT'S AVAILABLE

Shredder/baggers are a distinct group in a larger family of outdoor waste-processing machines that range from heavy-duty *chippers* (used by professionals to dispose of whole trees) to *compost grinders* (devices that process waste, but simply chew it up without providing bagging service). Most shredder/baggers have the versatility to handle the range of tasks needed by homeowners. For processing bulky materials, the machines are provided with a vertical hopper. You simply feed in twigs, stalks, clippings, or even soft wood branches, and gravity draws the material into the whirling blades of the shredder, where it is instantly pulverized. For higher-volume leaf processing, most shredder/baggers are capable of accepting a *leaf ramp* in place of the hopper. The ramp acts as a ground-level "mouth," into which you rake leaves. Suction, created by the internal whirling blades of the machine, draws in the leaves, while an exhaust blast of air blows the pulverized material out into an attached bag. To appreciate the bulk-reducing ability of one of these machines, consider that the chewed-up contents of twenty-six bushels of leaves is reduced to just *one* easy-to-handle bag of mulch, measuring only 45 inches in length by 24 inches in diameter. If you hate to tussle with voluminous trash, the shredder/bagger is a labor-saving answer to your problems.

A shredder/bagger is rated by its engine horsepower because the rotating shredding blades can deliver only as much cutting, shredding force as the engine is able to supply. For light-duty work, where leaves, clippings, and garden trimmings are the principal disposal problem, a 3 1/2-horsepower unit may be all you need. Moving up to a 5-horsepower unit means that you have the added capacity to chomp soft wood limbs and branches of trees, as well as the lighter diet of the smaller machine. At the top of most lines is the 8-horsepower machine. It gives you the greatest range of chewing and bagging capabilities, increasing the size limits of material that can be pulverized, while also speeding up the processing of lighter materials.

Figure 33-4. Leaves raked onto the leaf ramp are air-drawn into the shredder/bagger, which then quickly pulverizes them and blows this bulk-reduced matter into an attached bag. Photograph courtesy of Gilson Brothers Company.

Figure 33-2. A gasoline engine provides the rotational muscle to drive a shaft, which turns the powerful cutting blades that pass between shear plates attached to the housing. GRAF-WHALEN photograph.

Figure 33-3. The vertical hopper eagerly accepts twigs, stalks, and clippings dropped into it. Gravity then draws the material into the rapidly whirling blades of the shredder. GRAF-WHALEN photograph.

IMPORTANT FEATURES TO LOOK FOR
Easy-Starting Gas Engine
Look for a model that has compression release to ease the yank required on the starter cord. In larger models, electric start is a convenience.

Adaptability to Hopper Feed or Leaf Ramp
Some debris-processing chores are best done standing, and a hopper that feeds from the top puts gravity to work for you when feeding heavier materials into the shredder. However, leaves and clippings are more quickly processed by raking them up a ramp into the machine. You should be able to make a changeover quickly, so that your shredder/bagger can be doubly effective for you.

Safety Features
Your shredder/bagger should be so designed that it can't be operated without a hopper or leaf ramp in place. This is vital to safety, because either of these covers the inlet to the housing, in which the deadly blades are located. The usual approach is a safety switch that disconnects the engine ignition if the hopper or leaf ramp is removed. Your unit should also have some kind of baffles to prevent chips and debris from being thrown back at you through the hopper entrance.

Mobility
A shredder/bagger weighs in at a 100-plus pounds. This is a good enough reason for not wanting to move it very often. But you will have to wheel it from storage to use point, at least, and the easier this is made for you, the better. Two rear wheels and a U-foot up front are fairly standard in most models. A handle (attached to hopper or housing) that extends back beyond the wheels will let you move the shredder/bagger as easily as a lawn mower. The larger the wheels, the more easily it will roll.

Cleaning Out and Blade Replacement
You should have easy access to the shredding chamber, so that if a jam-up stalls the engine, you can clear the offending debris. Sometimes just removing the hopper or leaf ramp will give you all that you need. If the problem is wet leaves, though, you may have a messier dismantling job before you can ungum the works. Ask questions before you buy and have someone show you how easily (or otherwise) you can clean the shredder/bagger's interior. Also, remember that it may be necessary to replace a dull or broken blade at some point in the shredder/bagger's life. Check that you can easily do this yourself and you'll save a costly headache later.

Easy Storage
If (as in most homes) storage space is at a premium, choose the most compact dimensions you can get with the engine horsepower rating and other features you want. Although most hoppers are removable, the space you save may not be worth the nuisance. As a better idea, remove the bag and bagging attachment and store *inside* the hopper to save space. A handle that folds obligingly is another blessing. (Don't forget the space you'll need to store a leaf ramp accessory and supply of bags.)

TIPS FOR USING YOUR SHREDDER/BAGGER
• Take safety precautions. A shredder/bagger's inner workings can be extremely dangerous. Keep your hands and face out of the hopper when the engine is running. Also, be sure to keep away from the discharge chute and never allow pebbles or stones to fall into a running machine—they can become projectiles if struck by the high-speed blades, and they pack enough speed to not only tear through a plastic bag, but to inflict injury on a bystander. Also, if your unit's manufacturer recommends wearing safety glasses or other suitable eye protection, heed the advice.
• Shred dry material. Wet leaves and twigs make a pulpy mess that's hard to shred and well near impossible to bag. Jam-ups and stall-outs are inevitable when processing saturated materials. You'd do better to wait for dry conditions, when materials will shred better and remain airborne within the air blast exiting into the collection bag.
• Don't force feed the shredder. It is possible to feed in

Figure 33-5. Large rear wheels and smaller, free-turning front wheels make it possible to move the shredder/bagger from place to place with relative ease. GRAF-WHALEN photograph.

material at a rate faster than most shredders can handle. This is especially true if you are feeding the hopper leaves from a bushel basket. Experiment a bit, gradually increasing the quantity you're processing at each gulp, until you detect the proper rate. Also, before you try processing heavy branches or sticks, be sure that your model will stand the diameter and hardness of the material you're feeding in. Soft woods up to a 1/2 inch in diameter are okay for most models. Check specs before feeding in larger diameters. Otherwise, you risk destroying the shredding mechanism.

• Know what to do if a stop-up occurs at the inlet. Use a stick or branch (within the shredding diameter limit, so that if it falls in, it won't damage your machine) to poke materials into the machine. *Never use your hands to clear a clogged inlet while engine is running.*

RULES FOR SAFE USE
• Read the instruction manual carefully. Be thoroughly familiar with the controls and proper use of equipment.
• Never allow children to operate a shredder/bagger.
• Keep the area of operation clear of all persons, particularly small children and pets.

Figure 33-6. Hand protection is a *must* when using a shredder/bagger. The use of safety glasses is also recommended. GRAF-WHALEN photograph.

• Check fuel before starting the engine. Don't smoke while fueling! Do not fill gasoline tank indoors, when engine is running, or while engine is still hot. Wipe off any spilled gasoline before starting engine.
• Do not change engine governor settings or overspeed engine.
• Do not put hands near rotating parts. Keep clear of discharge opening at all times.
• If the equipment should start to vibrate abnormally, stop the engine and check immediately for the cause. Vibration is generally a warning of trouble.
• When cleaning, repairing, or inspecting, make certain that the blade and all moving parts have stopped. Disconnect spark-plug wire and keep wire away from plug to prevent accidental starting.
• Shut engine off and wait until blade comes to a complete stop before unclogging chute.
• Check blade and engine mounting bolts at frequent intervals for proper tightness.
• Keep all nuts, bolts, and screws tight to be sure equipment is in safe working condition.
• Never store equipment with gasoline in the tank inside a building where fumes may reach an open flame or spark. Allow engine to cool before storing in any enclosure.
• To reduce fire hazard keep the shredder/bagger free of grass, leaves, or excessive grease.

SHREDDER/BAGGER MAINTENANCE
The design similarities between the shredder/bagger and the rotary lawn mower extend into the servicing each deserves when being put into "mothballs" for the winter season. Engine care is essentially the same, as are tune-up, lubrication, and requirements for checking the blades and housing for damage. See the section on rotary lawn mowers for general details. But, by all means, be sure to check your shredder/bagger's instruction manual for specific points that need your seasonal attention.

STARTING A COMPOST HEAP
To convert shredded materials into useful humus, you'll need a compost heap. Here is an easy, inexpensive way to set one up. First, select a shaded, out-of-the-way, well-drained spot on your property that is hidden from your own and your neighbors' view. To keep things tidy, you'll need a simple restraining structure, such as a 5-foot cylinder of heavy wire-mesh fencing. To make such a cylinder, you will require a piece of mesh about 16 feet long by 5 feet wide. Simply roll it into a cylinder, clip the wire ends with cutting pliers, bend and interlock the wires, and stand the cylinder on end in the place you've chosen.

Fill the cylinder as follows: Place a 6-inch-deep layer of shredded leaves, clippings, or other garden matter in the bottom. Then pack it down tightly and add a layer of fertilizer (5-10-5 or a lesser amount of 10-6-4 will supply enough nitrogen to get things going). Water the mix liberally, but not soaking. This "base" will give nitrogen-loving bacteria a good start. You may also wish to sprinkle in one of the commercially available compost "activators."

After a week or so, aerate your starter mix by forking it over to distribute bacteria and fungus and speed the decomposition rate. You'll find that the pile has some internally generated heat (up to 140°F at the center), which is a sure sign of an active decomposition process. This heat is an essential by-product that works to kill most weed seeds and animal disease organisms too.

At this point, you can now add in and pack down another 6-inch layer of shredded material and another sprinkling of fertilizer. Keep the pile moist (not soggy) to assure good bacterial growth. Keep building your pile in this way, forking it over before each new addition. Within 3 to 4 months, with luck, you should have a rich, crumbly humus for your seedbeds, garden beds, or for potting plants.

A few extra pointers: You *can* add kitchen garbage to the pile, such as fruit peels and cores, vegetable trimmings, coffee grounds, and eggshells. However, steer clear of grease, fats, bones, or other substances that will attract insect pests and rodents. Also, if most of the material you're composting comes from acid-loving plants (evergreens, azaleas, rhododendrons, etc.) your humus will be acidic. If you want to neutralize the acid, add a thin layer of limestone each time you fork over the pile.

34

Snow Throwers

What could be more charming than a snug, cozy evening by the fire, as wintry winds whip the falling snow outside into dancing whorls of whiteness and drifts change the shapes of familiar objects into fantasy curios. No wonder poets and songwriters have such strong praise for a snowfall! But there *is* a morning after, and the snow that was last night's delight becomes the enemy in the cold light of morning.

Figure 34-1. Snow thrower. Photograph courtesy of The Toro Company, Consumer Products Div.

Traditionally, the snow shovel has been the back-breaking answer to snow removal, but the wrenching, time-consuming task of shoveling heavy snow from *here* to *there* is the forerunner of sore muscles, aching backs, exhaustion, and blisters. To all but the most athletic members of our culture it's also a taxing burden on an unprepared heart. That's why snow throwers have become such a popular power tool in snowbound suburbia. In just a fraction of the time you'd spend shoveling, these chugging marvels scoop up and hurl great quantities of snow away from your driveway, walk, or parking area. Powered by a gasoline engine and often self-propelled, the snow thrower can take the stinging effort out of snow removal, so that winter's wonderland needn't be a wasteland of drudgery for you.

HOW THEY WORK

The motive power of a snow thrower begins with the engine, which is almost universally a four-cycle type (though smaller models use a two-cycle engine). Small throwers, meant for push-around work, use a chain or V-belt drive to the rotating drum and paddle. The chain (or belt) connects unequally sized sprockets (or pulleys) so that the high speed of the engine shaft is swapped for more push power at the paddles. In straight, single-stage auger types, the engine often drives the auger through a combination of V-belt-and-pulleys and chain drive, so that the auger rotates at high speed. This is essential, because the throwing action comes from a paddle at the auger's center—to get good throwing distance, high paddle speed is essential. In one type of two-stage thrower,

Figure 34-2. The biting power of the auger is evident. GRAF-WHALEN photograph.

the engine's shaft output turns the impeller blade at high speed through a belt-driven pulley, and a shaft from the impeller's center turns a gearbox that makes for a slower-turning auger with greater biting power than a single-stage machine. For self-propelled models, a clutch and drive transmission are added to the power train. A cross-shaft is belt- or chain-driven by the engine, rotating a drive wheel that can be engaged to a right-angle mounted disk geared to the thrower's wheels. The drive wheel can be engaged to the center or edge of the disk, and where it engages determines how fast the disk turns and, therefore, how fast the wheels move the thrower. For reverse, another wheel is interposed between drive wheel and disk to reverse direction of rotation.

WHAT'S AVAILABLE

The basic parts of a snow thrower are engine, blades or scoop to break up the snow, auger or paddles to pull the snow in, impellers to eject the snow, and a chute or vanes to direct the snow stream away from the area you're clearing. These parts are fitted together in roughly three distinct ways to form three distinct types of snow throwers—the paddle-type, single-stage thrower; the auger-type, single-stage thrower; and the two-stage, auger/fan-type thrower. These types are described here in ascending order of snow-handling capacity, which is determined by the width of the machine and its single-stage or two-stage classification.

Paddle-Type, Single-Stage Throwers

These employ a scooplike housing with a rotating drum, fitted with two paddles. Usually push-type machines, these rely on you to force the scoop into the snow. There the rotating paddles bite off a snow chunk (the width of the scoop), whisk it around the scoop, and hurl it up and away through a series of deflector vanes that can be angled to left, right, or straight. These vanes determine where the accelerated snow stream will be thrown as you move ahead. The action is continuous and comes about because of the paddle design. These machines are efficient for clearing small drives and walks, are usually light enough to be lifted onto stoops or raised porches that need clearing, and are a fine choice for city dwellers and owners of small suburban homes in areas where snow rarely exceeds a fallen depth of 4 inches. Paddle-type, single-stage throwers can clean an average-width 50-foot driveway of a 3-inch powdery snowfall in about 10 minutes. Aluminum and rugged plastic are the chief materials, which contribute to low cost and low weight. Scoop widths range from 14 to 22 inches, and gas engine displacements rarely exceed 2 horsepower.

Figure 34-3. This easy-to-handle, single-stage, paddle-type snow thrower can hurl dry snow up to 20 feet. GRAF-WHALEN photograph.

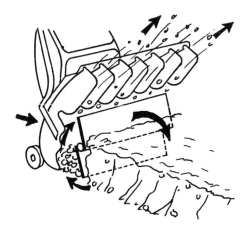

Figure 34-5. The rotating paddles whisk snow chunks around the scoop and then hurl them away through a series of adjustable deflector vanes.

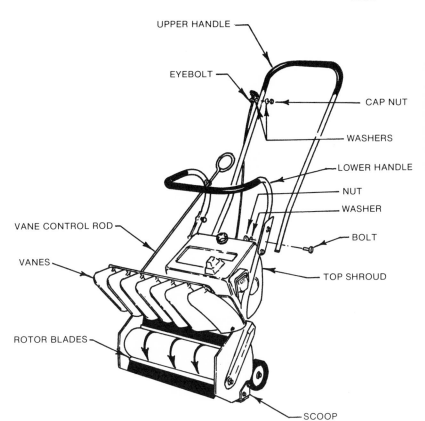

UPPER HANDLE

EYEBOLT

CAP NUT

WASHERS

LOWER HANDLE

NUT

WASHER

VANE CONTROL ROD

BOLT

VANES

TOP SHROUD

ROTOR BLADES

SCOOP

Figure 34-4. The basic parts of a paddle-type, single-stage thrower.

Figure 34-6. The drive chain and sprocket arrangement transfers rotational energy from the engine to the rotating paddles. GRAF-WHALEN photograph.

Auger-Type, Single-Stage Throwers

Clearing widths of these machines average 20 inches and engines are huskier (usually 3 horsepower). The "front end" is a large metal scoop with a rotating auger formed of two reverse-pitch metal spirals, which rotate toward common paddles at the center. The idea here is to break up the snow with the augers and force it toward the center from both sides, where the rotating paddles will lift and hurl it upwards, through a discharge chute at the top of the scoop. The chute can be positioned to throw the snow to left, right, or ahead of the clearing path. Materials are steel throughout, and the weight of this machine precludes lifting for most purposes other than transporting it in a car's trunk. Both push-type and self-propelled models are offered. This class will handle snowfalls of the order of 6 to 14 inches and can take on wet or hard-packed snow, as well as powder.

Auger/Fan-type, Two-Stage Throwers

About the last word in snow throwers, these heavyweights feature clearing widths of up to 36 inches and have the huskiest engines (5 to 10 horsepower). They are capable of tackling any snow condition up to depths of 3 feet and more. Their truly wondrous clearing capacity comes from the combination of the slow-speed auger; plus a rotating, power-driven, high-speed auger; plus a rotating, power-driven, and high-speed impeller fan. The auger breaks and feeds snow to the impeller, which throws it

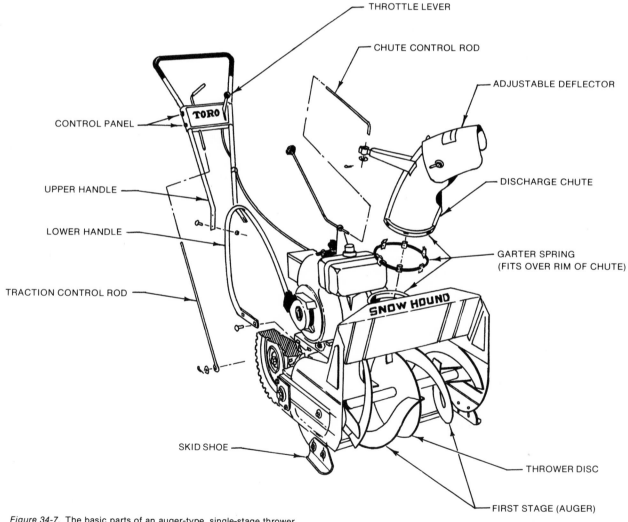

Figure 34-7. The basic parts of an auger-type, single-stage thrower.

194

up and out a chute to a distance of 40 feet or more. To offset their substantial weight, virtually all are self-propelled models and feature transmissions that give you a choice of up to five forward speeds plus a powered reverse. Big, deep-tread, rubber-tired wheels are standard on these machines, and most accommodate tire chains for an even better bite in slippery snow. To simplify starting, many include a plug-in, AC-powered or batteried electric-start system.

Figure 34-8. This electric-start, two-stage, walk-behind thrower can remove as much as 1 ton of snow per minute. Photograph courtesy of The Toro Company, Consumer Products Div.

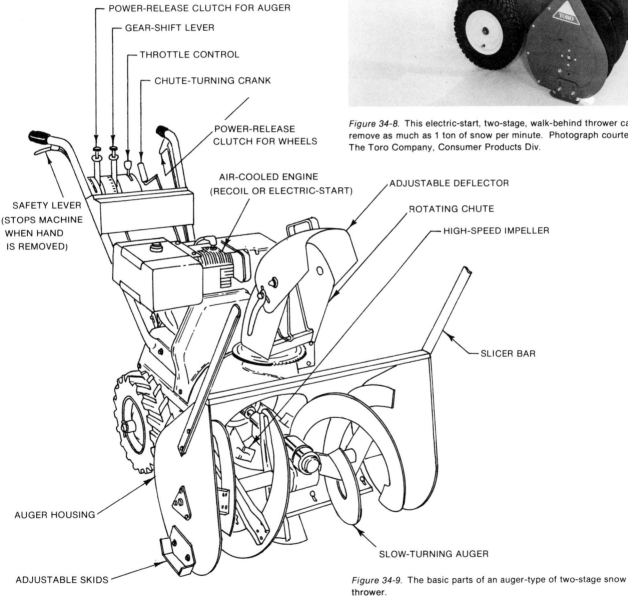

POWER-RELEASE CLUTCH FOR AUGER

GEAR-SHIFT LEVER

THROTTLE CONTROL

CHUTE-TURNING CRANK

POWER-RELEASE CLUTCH FOR WHEELS

AIR-COOLED ENGINE (RECOIL OR ELECTRIC-START)

SAFETY LEVER (STOPS MACHINE WHEN HAND IS REMOVED)

ADJUSTABLE DEFLECTOR

ROTATING CHUTE

HIGH-SPEED IMPELLER

SLICER BAR

AUGER HOUSING

ADJUSTABLE SKIDS

SLOW-TURNING AUGER

Figure 34-9. The basic parts of an auger-type of two-stage snow thrower.

IMPORTANT FEATURES TO LOOK FOR
Choosing the Size You Really Need

Like any tool, a snow thrower should be well suited to the task you have in mind. If you live in a snow-belt area and have a lot of surface to clear, an investment in a heavy-weight two-stager makes sense. Its huge snow-clearing capacity will offset the higher cost, greater storage bulk, more costly operation, and inconvenient transportation for servicing—all of which are a natural part of owning a big machine. But where snow accumulation is lighter or surface clearing need is smaller, a trade-off to a more compact, less costly, easier-to-handle, single-stage machine may give you a better return; and in this family you'll find a competitive choice of models, each directed toward satisfying needs of homeowner groups, one of which may include you. To help you narrow your choice, the accompanying table lists performance of several different snow thrower sizes.

Ease of Handling

Ranging in weight from a featherlike 23 pounds to a brutish 400-plus pounds, snow throwers offer a very broad range of handling features that must be studied in light of your real needs. If you have decided on a manual, light-weight model to clear a walk, drive, steps, or porch, does the machine offer well-placed handles that will help you lift it into place? Does the snow-clearing action help to pull the machine forward, so that you don't have to push and strain? Can you tilt the machine back, so that its wheels can roll up and down steps or curbs to prevent damage to the scoop? Is the machine well balanced, so that it can be stored by hanging on a garage or basement wall?

If an intermediate model is your clearing choice, does it have a self-propelling feature with a separate control to disengage the auger? This will help you to safely get the machine from its storage location to the snow removal site without risking injury from thrown objects.

If your choice is a heavyweight, does it have independent wheel clutches, so that the self-propelling mechanism can be used to turn the machine and maneuver it naturally? Does the bladelike bottom of the scoop have a pivoting feature, so that the machine can clear uneven surfaces without uncomfortable bumping, lurching, or sudden stops? Are the tires heavily cleated or lugged, so that you can count on a deep bite with superior traction in hard-packed snow? Your answers to these questions will help you choose a thrower that's right for you.

Safe Placement of Controls

Everything you need to guide and control your snow thrower should be accessible at your normal position *behind* the machine, away from the "business end" that bites the snow. Throttle, clutches, auger/impeller drive lever, and discharge chute or vane control should be within easy reach of your hands, posing no risk in use. Remember that numbing cold decreases your response time and blowing, powdery snow can drastically cut your visibility. A properly designed snow thrower will have controls placed with forethought to these real-world conditions to give you the best, safest control of your snow thrower.

Snow-Clearing Performance of Common Snow Throwers

Class	Single-Stage Machines					Two-Stage Machines			
	Paddle			Auger		All have at least 12″ Impeller			
Size	14″	18″	22″	24″	26″	24″	26″	32″	36″
Dry snow depth for good performance*	6″	6″	8″	10″	10″	14″	16″	16″	20″
Driveway clearance in 30 minutes (16-foot-wide drive)	50′	60′	75′	100′	150′	150′	150′	200′	300′
Drift clearing capability in single pass	Requires several passes			14″	20″	24″	28″	28″	30″

*Wet snow reduces the effective clearing performance of all types. Saturated snow will halve machine's capacity and can be thrown only half as far.

Figure 34-10. The control knob that adjusts the discharge chute can be easily and safely manipulated, even while the machine is in operation. GRAF-WHALEN photograph.

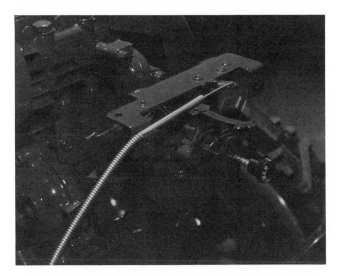

Figure 34-11. The primer button is used to make starting easier. It is readily accessible on most smaller models. GRAF-WHALEN photograph.

Figure 34-12. For sure-fire operation, the spark plug must be well protected with a rubber boot that keeps out ever-present moisture. GRAF-WHALEN photograph.

Ease of Starting

While a cranky engine in a summertime tool is just a nuisance, a hard-starting snow thrower engine is a tenfold headache. When you're out in the hostile cold, your body burns up its energy reserves mighty quickly. So, if you wear yourself out getting the machine going, you're tired before the real work begins, and that can mean trouble, because tired people make mistakes. Look for a snow thrower equipped for easy starting. Most smaller models have primer buttons and manually operated chokes, which require a bit of know-how to use properly. Be sure that the dealer goes over the starting procedure with you. Look also for good protection of the engine and ignition parts against snow infiltration. Snow is only snow when it's cold. On a warm engine it becomes water that can drain away spark energy. Similarly, look for a well-protected carburetor, preferably one that's surrounded by a heater box that prewarms the air drawn into the carburetor throat. These condense snow *outside* the carburetor and help ensure good engine performance by raising air temperature to a level that helps volatize the fuel for easy burning.

Electric start in a husky snow thrower is an option that increases in attractiveness as you go up the scale of engine sizes. This is especially true in the colder climates, where a snow thrower stored in an outdoor shed or unheated garage chills down to the point where the oil in its crankcase becomes thick and opposes cranking. If a power line is readily available, choose a model with an AC motor-starter. Alternatively, you may wish a battery-start type that carries a 12-volt automotive battery and starts like your car. These latter models are fitted with an alternator to recharge the battery and usually feature a flood lamp to light your way in clearing tasks after dark or in the early morning hours before sunup.

Convenience

A gas tank that's easy to fill and is sized to hold enough fuel for at least a half hour's operation is a definite "plus." So, too, are easily adjusted skid shoes on either side of the scoop in auger-type throwers. Also, the scraper blade at the bottom of the scoop should be adjustable, or, better yet, spring-loaded, so that the machine won't lurch or jolt on rough spots. A discharge chute (or vanes), controllable from the usual operating position, will save you annoyance each time you turn around for another pass. *Don't overlook ease of maintenance:* A machine you can care for yourself will save you costly professional repairs, *and* you'll probably be spared the aggravation of transporting its heavy bulk to a service shop.

TIPS FOR USING YOUR SNOW THROWER

• You may want to wax the inside of the discharge chute before the season starts. This makes it easier for wet or sticky snow to pass up the chute. (Units having slick plastic vanes don't require this treatment.) Another tip: A few drops of antifreeze put into the control cables will help to prevent control freeze-up in low temperatures.

• To assure positive starting in winter keep the gas tank on the engine filled to the top at all times with clean, fresh, regular gasoline or antipollution, unleaded, regular gasoline. This will help prevent water condensation caused by sudden temperature changes, resulting in unsatisfactory engine performance.

• Once you're ready to get going, move your snow thrower outside, and, if it has been stored in a heated area, allow the entire unit to equalize its temperature to that of the outdoors before operating in the snow. If the machine is put into the snow when it is warm, the snow will melt on the machine and turn into ice. This can foul up controls and even cause damage to the machine in extreme cases.

• Before you start up, think about what lies beneath the white stuff ahead of you. Gravel, stones, toys, and other debris can become deadly missiles if scooped up and thrown by the machine. If you expect these, hold the clearing height at somewhat above-ground surface. (On small machines, you control this by handling; on larger models, you'll have to adjust the skid shoes.)

Figure 34-13. A warning that should never, never be ignored. GRAF-WHALEN photograph.

• Start in the manner prescribed by your machine's manufacturer. On small models, a primer button will be used to squeeze extra fuel into the cold carburetor to help get the machine going. Beware of excessive priming—it can lead to nasty backfiring. Larger models have more sophisticated start-up controls, but can also be ticklish in cold-weather starting. Start only outdoors and don't breathe in exhaust fumes. Once the engine is running, allow a brief warm-up until the choke is no longer needed; then rev up and head for the snow!

• Start removing snow from the center of the area to be cleared, working outward. Change the throwing direction of the discharge chute so that snow is thrown into areas that don't have to be cleared (lawn or grass strips adjacent to drive or walkway, etc.). If snow is especially dry and powdery and there is a wind blowing, try to favor the wind's direction with the discharge. If snow is wet and you're concerned about it plugging the discharge chute, maintain enough scoop pressure to keep the machine as full as possible with snow. This will force snow up the chute and keep it from plugging. If, however, the chute *should* plug, *stop the machine completely before attempting to clear it!* Trying to clear a plugged chute on a running snow thrower with your hands or poking at it with a stick are deadly dangerous!

• For more satisfactory snow removal and to avoid side spills, slightly overlap each path you make. Should the street plow leave a hard-packed, 3- to 4-foot drift at the end of your driveway, let your machine travel into this drift. When the engine starts to labor, stop moving forward and allow the machine to discharge all the snow it can. When the engine stops laboring and is back up to speed, move further into the drift, repeating the above procedure. Slowly, the drifts will be cleaned away without stalling the engine.

• If a heavy, prolonged snowstorm is predicted, you will have less work to do if you will start the job of snow removal when snow is only 4 or 5 inches deep, rather than allowing it to accumulate.

• For safety's sake, keep people away from the snow being discharged from the chute. If the machine should pick up and throw a stone or other foreign object, it could cause serious injury.

• When you've finished clearing, your snow thrower will probably be soaking wet from melted snow. Don't shut the engine off, but let it run at idle for a while. This will keep the engine warm, and its radiated heat will dry critical parts of the ignition system and starting mechanism. This is especially important in very cold temperatures, because wet parts will become icebound if the engine is shut off prematurely.

RULES FOR SAFE USE

• Never allow children to operate a snow thrower and never allow adults to operate it without proper instruction.
• Know the controls and how to stop quickly. *Read the owner's manual.*
• Dress properly for cold weather, avoiding bulky garments that slow your movement or hinder your footwork.
• Handle gasoline with care—it is highly flammable.
• Use an approved gasoline container.
• Fill gas tank outdoors—never while engine is running. Wipe up spilled gasoline.
• Replace gasoline cap securely.
• Keep children and pets a safe distance away at all times.
• Stay in your safety zone behind handles when operating machine. Never leave this position without shutting engine down.
• Give your complete and undivided attention to the job at hand. Take a break when you become tired.
• Never direct discharge toward bystanders or windows or allow anyone in front of, or near, the machine while operating. Personal injury or property damage can result from debris thrown by this machine.
• Adjust skid height to clear a gravel or crushed rock surface.
• Maintain solid and secure footing at all times.
• Never look into discharge chute while engine is running. Do not put hands or other objects in discharge chute or scoop.
• Disengage power and stop engine before cleaning discharge, removing obstacles, making adjustments, or when leaving operating position.
• Never place hands or feet under or into rotating parts or concealed areas. Keep hands and feet clearly away from auger, belts, pulleys, gears, etc., while engine is running.
• If snow thrower should vibrate or strike a foreign object, stop engine immediately, disconnect spark-plug lead wire, and check for damage or loose parts. Repair damage at once.
• Do not use machine when temperature is below –30°F.
• Follow specific maintenance instructions provided by the manufacturer, supplementing data in this chapter.
• Disconnect spark-plug wire before making any adjustment or repair.
• Store gasoline in an approved red metal container in a cool, dry place.
• Keep machine in good operating condition and keep safety devices in place.

SNOW THROWER MAINTENANCE

A snow thrower isn't much more difficult to care for than a lawn mower. However, it does require attention to lubrication and some regular maintenance. Because it's always wet and possibly exposed to chemical ice-thawing salts, there is a greater possibility of corrosion in components such as drive chains. An occasional flush with fresh water will help wash away salts; and periodic oiling of the chains, bearings, and any metal surfaces that rub, slide, or turn against each other will pay handsome dividends in trouble-free operation. Pay particular attention to control cables, rods, and linkages. An oil film on these is also a sure preventive against ice formation that could jam things up.

Crankcase oil should be chosen with special care, according to the machine manufacturer's instructions. Below 40°F, SAE 5W-20 or 10W is generally recommended. Above that temperature, SAE 30W is the usual choice. However, recommendations vary, and your machine's manufacturer knows best. Follow those instructions to the letter.

Figure 34-14. Regular careful attention to the chains, belts, and bearings, which must work in harmony to keep the machine in good operating condition, is most important. GRAF-WHALEN photograph.

199

Apart from lubrication, your in-season maintenance will mostly consist of an occasional check for missing parts, or, perhaps, tightening parts loosened by vibration. In time you may also have to adjust belt or chain tensions in the auger drive or wheel drive to compensate for stretching that occurs as parts wear in.

To protect your machine's metal surfaces, you may want to apply a coat of wax. This will also prevent snow from sticking.

Spring Maintenance

When the last gasp of winter dies down, it's time to put your snow thrower in mothballs for the summer. Wheel it outside to a safe area away from kids, pets, and nosy neighbors; start it up and use up any remaining fuel in the tank. (If there's too much fuel and you'd rather not have the racket for long, siphon out the tank first and then start up and use up the residual fuel.) Once the engine sputters and dies, disconnect the spark plug and clean out the fuel tank with a cloth, so that no gas remains to form a waxy residue in the months of storage 'til next snow season.

Figure 34-15. As part of the regular maintenance procedure, check the condition of the pull-cord by pulling slowly on the starter handle, so that the full length of the cord can be examined. GRAF-WHALEN photograph.

While the engine is warm (and, presuming that your snow thrower engine is a four-cycle type) open the crankcase drain plug and drain the oil into a pan. (Don't install fresh oil just yet.) Next, go over the machine carefully and tighten loosened parts. If anything is missing or broken, now's the time to replace it. Check for binding in control cables and rods, and check belts and drive components carefully for wear and loss of tension. Replace or adjust, as necessary. Don't forget the pull-cord in manual-start machines. If it's worn, replace it, too.

By this time, the engine should have cooled down and you should be able to remove the spark plug. Check its electrodes for wear (rounded center electrode or tapered edge electrode). If it's even slightly worn, install a new one, properly gapped. Before you do, however, pour a tablespoon of fresh SAE 30W oil into the plug hole and crank the engine to form an oil film over its internal parts. Now, wash down the machine with a garden hose to remove any salt accumulations or other material that may corrode parts. Wipe dry and allow any residual water to air dry. When the machine is perfectly dry, lubricate all of its parts (as recommended by the manufacturer). Apply a coat of wax to the scoop and discharge chute, or spray on a coating of silicone. You may also want to wax and polish all other large metal surfaces to keep your machine looking new and to ward off corrosion.

As a final step, fill the crankcase with fresh oil (four-cycle engines only), replace the oil filter and gas tank caps, and move the thrower to its storage location. Block it up on scrap lumber or bricks to take the weight off the wheels and keep the tires from going flat. To keep it dust-free until you need it, cover it with a drop cloth (plastic types are available at very low cost). Covered and cozy, your snow thrower will slumber through the heat of summer, but will be ready to go when snow time rolls around again.

35

Power Sprayers

Between the aerosol can, the finger-worked or hand-pumped bottle sprayer, and the husky, compressor-driven air sprayers, a new range of power sprayers for home, garden, and shop use has come into existence. All electrically powered, these sprayers give you the convenience of applying liquids in controlled mist form, effortlessly and precisely. A principal application is spray painting. Here the sprayers offer the prospect of truly professional results that brush painting can't match in terms of evenness of film and freedom from annoying ripples and sags. More than this, though, sprayers can apply fungicides and pesticides to outdoor plants and foliage with greater accuracy than hit-or-miss hand or pump sprayers; and they're useful for indoor jobs, like applying wax to floors, woodwork, and paneling, disinfecting rooms, or mothproofing closets.

WHAT'S AVAILABLE
Airless Sprayers
As the name implies, there is no compressed air source associated with operation of these sprayers. Instead, the airless sprayer breaks up the paint (or other liquid) into a fine mist in either of two ways—a pump-and-nozzle arrangement or a motor-driven, rotary, misting arrangement.

Figure 35-1. Power sprayer. GRAF-WHALEN photograph.

Figure 35-2. This ELECTRO AIRLESS PAINT GUN® gives you good coating action with minimum overspray and maximum control. It holds a quart of paint or other liquid and is all metal in construction for durability. GRAF-WHALEN photograph.

Either method produces a gentle spray stream consisting of finely atomized paint, instead of a mixture of paint and air. The result is an easy-to-control spray that settles evenly on a surface, with minimum overspray and wasted paint. Methods of controlling the spray differ somewhat. In the pump-type sprayer, an AC-powered vibrator pump pulses paint against the nozzle opening to create the spray; the adjustable "throw" of the vibrator determines the pattern *and* quantity of paint delivered with each pump stroke. More refined is the motor-driven rotary type. Here, a rotating disc whirls paint mist against an adjustable "gate" opening. You can vary the width of the gate opening to set the spray-pattern width from 1/2 to 18 inches, *and* a variable electronic speed control for the motor lets you preselect and deliver as much or as little paint as you wish *within* the selected pattern width. This extra degree of control simplifies matching of paint viscosity to a given job and gives good coverage with little risk of unsightly sags and overspray.

Compact Air-Compressor Sprayers

A scaled-down version of professional spraying gear, this unusual design features an air-delivery system consisting of a free-moving piston that is operated by a simple AC-powered electromagnet and spring. Pressurized air is delivered by the compressor piston and travels through tubing to a spray-head attachment, which consists of a paint canister with an attached spray nozzle. The force of the air atomizes paint against the nozzle and ejects the spray toward the surface to be covered. Professional results are obtainable with reasonable practice, and the system can easily handle latex or oil paints, shellac, varnish, and lacquer. The gun is a bleeder type, which means that air moves through it all the time, as long as the compressor is on. When you press the trigger, paint is sprayed. A knurled button adjusts paint flow to the required thickness. The spray pattern is determined by changing nozzle caps on the spray head—one for nor-

Figure 35-3. Compressed air is the force behind this BLACK & DECKER POWER SPRAYER. As in professional models, the compressor is separate from the spray gun and joined by an air hose. GRAF-WHALEN photograph.

Figure 35-4. Filled with pesticide or other garden chemicals, a sprayer can apply material where it's needed, in just a fraction of the time a hand-operated sprayer would take. GRAF-WHALEN photograph.

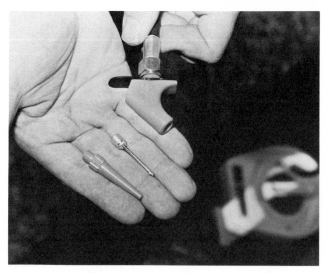

Figure 35-5. Accessories for the compressor section of the BLACK & DECKER POWER SPRAYER include an inflator head, needle, and slip-on balloon inflator. GRAF-WHALEN photograph.

mal, one for narrow.

One of the pleasures of this system is its extra use as an inflator, either of bicycle or car tires, footballs, basketballs, or pool toys. Simply replacing the spray head with the correct inflator attachment automatically sets the air pressure output to the optimum range for each job.

Cordless Garden Sprayers
Application of herbicides and pesticides to plants around your garden is a simple task with a handy cordless sprayer. Powered by a built-in nickel-cadmium battery supply that can be recharged overnight from your household AC power outlet, the cordless sprayer gives you the freedom to roam about your property and effortlessly apply controlled amounts of spray to cherished plantings, free of the limitations and nuisance of dragging an extension cord behind you. Press a button and the batteries energize a motor-driven pump that forces premixed liquid through a nozzle which then converts it into a spray. The nozzle is adjustable, permitting fine or coarse sprays for different applications. The nozzle is mounted on an extension tube that pivots up or down, saving you the discomfort of bending and stooping to spray hard-to-reach areas. The sprayer's tank removes for easy cleanup and has graduated markings to aid you in proportioning concentrates and water.

Figure 35-6. When fitted with the right accessories, the compressor can be used to inflate balls for various sports. GRAF-WHALEN photograph.

Figure 35-8. Cordless carry-around sprayers like this Hudson model have the capacity and reach for most ground-level and shrub-garden spraying jobs. GRAF-WHALEN photograph.

Figure 35-7. The drudgery of manually pumping up a flat tire is completely unnecessary. The compressor of the BLACK & DECKER POWER SPRAYER can do it for you. GRAF-WHALEN photograph.

Figure 35-9. The adjustable nozzle of the HUDSON CORDLESS GARDEN SPRAYER® gives fine or coarse spray and changes the distance and width of the sprayer's throw. GRAF-WHALEN photograph.

TIPS FOR USING YOUR POWER SPRAYER
Spraying Paint

• Select the right paint. Choosing a paint that's suitable for spraying isn't difficult. Just about all available paints can be used in a sprayer, *providing that you thin to the correct viscosity!* A sprayer will choke on thick paint that has to be troweled from the can. To help you make this adjustment, manufacturers supply detailed instructions with the sprayer. Some even provide handy thinning aids, such as a cup that drips out paint in a specified time when viscosity is correct or a pronged device that drains free of paint in a period of time, telling you how much thinning is required. Thinning is important to gain proper "leveling" of the sprayed-on paint film, so that a smooth surface results. Paint that is too thick when it hits the surface will create a rough, uneven texture, and you will actually need *more* paint to gain an even-textured appearance. Thin only if you are using the paint manufacturer's recommended thinner. Also, if there seems to be a "skin" or any particles in the paint, strain before use by pouring it through a piece of cheesecloth or an old nylon stocking.

• Prepare the surface properly. The surface to be painted should be smoothed and free of wax, oil, or other contaminants. If you're painting over a previously varnished or shellacked surface, don't expect a permanent bond from water-base paints. Oil-based enamel will give better results. Best, however, is the removal of the old finish with one of the superefficient strippers now available. *All* paints adhere well to a wood surface that hasn't been "plugged" by a coat of old paint or varnish. Fill any blemishes with a compatible filler (wood putty, spackle, jointing compound and tape, etc.) well in advance of painting and smooth before spraying.

• Test before spraying. Try out your sprayer after thinning and loading paint, using a spare piece of board or other material as your target. This will ensure that your preparation is correct and will also give you some practice in "feeling" the right spraying technique for the paint you're applying. It will also help you to "fine-tune" the settings of your sprayer so that there is no mishap when you start painting your real "target" surface.

• Protect areas not to be sprayed. Some overspray is unavoidable in all sprayers. Prepare your area well, so that the spray is confined to the area or object you wish to cover. Masking tape, newspaper, and drop cloths are helpful. Use them liberally and you'll be spared a messy cleanup job afterward. If the object you are spraying is small, you can fashion a "spray booth" from cardboard, newspaper taped into shape, or an old carton. This will confine the spray as effectively as an industrial spray booth.

• Protect yourself before spraying. No paint or finishing material is meant to be inhaled or absorbed through the skin. Some of the fine mist created by a sprayer stays airborne for a while and is easily inhaled. Absorption is also possible through the pores of the skin. Protect yourself with a low-cost inhalator mask, if spraying indoors where good ventilation isn't possible. Plastic glasses are a good investment, too. Work gloves and an old long-sleeve shirt will cover your skin and minimize the chances of absorption. Outdoors, where good ventilation is possible, the need for these precautions is not as great. Also, remember that most finishing materials are flammable when sprayed.

• Don't spray in a room where there is an open flame (a gas-range pilot, furnace, etc.) *and do not smoke* while spraying. It's also a good practice to shoo away children, pets, and kibitzers, not only for their safety, but so that you can concentrate more completely on the job at hand. And, of course, don't forget good electrical safety practice in handling a sprayer powered from the household AC outlet.

• Learn the right spraying technique. After establishing the basic settings and "feel" with a test run on a scrap surface, you are ready to approach the real painting job. With most small sprayers (airless or air type) it's best to begin with the nozzle about 12 inches from the surface. Keep your wrist flexible and move the sprayer in a line or sweep that keeps this distance constant as you spray. Moving the sprayer in an arc that changes distance between the nozzle and the surface will result in an uneven film with color variations and sagging. Likewise, moving too far away from the surface will create a "fog," because paint droplets arrive dry at the surface and bounce off. Several light passes at the right distance from the work, as opposed to one heavy coating, will produce a smooth, professional surface, free of sags and blemishes. Avoid interrupted movement or on-off switching as you make each pass or else irregular texturing will result. On vertical surfaces, apply a light "fog" coat first. Give this a moment to set and then move in and spray the surface in the normal fashion. The "fog" coat will help ensure good adhesion and prevent sagging of subsequent coats, as a smooth film is formed. For horizontal surfaces, such as a tabletop or ceiling, spraying at a 45-degree angle is best, unless the nozzle can be tilted with respect to the supply tank. In any case, don't tilt the sprayer too sharply or you may interrupt paint feed.

• Clean up after spraying. To keep your sprayer operating at peak efficiency and to prevent problems, clean it immediately after use. Empty remaining paint from the tank and wipe away any excess paint from the pickup mechanism and tank inner surface. Then partially fill the tank with the paint manufacturer's recommended solvent or thinner and reassemble the sprayer. Spray this (in a safe area, preferably outdoors), shaking the sprayer as you do, until the solvent no longer shows any trace of paint. Remove the tank, and, using a cloth moistened with solvent, wipe away any last traces of paint from the mechanism and tank. If water-base materials have been used, a wash in warm running water is the way to clean up.

Spraying Other Materials

Wax, mothproofing materials, herbicides and pesticides —just about any liquid—can be spray applied with a bit of care and practice. In general, adhere to the safety precautions outlined for spray painting plus those of the manufacturer, and pay particular attention to cleanup.

Special Notes for Use of Cordless Garden Sprayers

Spraying to control insect pests, weeds, and plant diseases can make your yard and garden more beautiful and more enjoyable. For best results—and to help protect the environment—it's important that you apply spray materials correctly. Here are a few suggestions to help guide you.

• Apply spray material where the trouble is. Because insects are more commonly under plant leaves, it is especially important that you spray there. Diseases, in particular, start and spread on either side of the leaf. Cover the entire stem system, too. Be sure to stop all trouble or the infestation will continue to spread.

• Apply spray materials properly. Cover the plant as uniformly as possible. Spray to just the point of run off. Avoid wasteful drenching.

• Mix spray materials exactly as recommended. Measure accurately, just as recommended on the manufacturer's label. Weak mixtures won't do the job; strong mixtures can do harm. With a cordless sprayer in which you can accurately premix the spray material, you know that you're applying the amount of spray material that will do the job best.

• Plan a spray program. Stop insects and diseases before damage is done. Many experts suggest spraying an all-purpose material every week or 10 days. This is especially important in preventing disease infestations such as fungus.

• Start early in the season. In spring, before leaves appear, apply early or dormant spray on woody plants—rose bushes, small trees, shrubs, vines—to kill overwintering pests. This helps plants to a healthy, vigorous start for the new season. Wet bark thoroughly and be sure to get spray into all crevices.

• Know how to spray lawn weeds. Adjust nozzle for a coarse spray to avoid drift. This is important when spraying near flowers and shrubs that can be harmed by weed killer. It's best to have a special sprayer set aside for weed spraying only because if sprayer isn't cleaned thoroughly, traces of weed killer can harm desirable plants.

• Spray a "mosquito barrier" in your yard. First, be sure to drain breeding areas—stopped-up roof gutters, stagnant bird baths, etc. Then spray a recommended material on mosquitoes' daytime resting places—nearby plants, shrubs, walls, ceilings. Treat cool, shady places. Be sure to get under leaves. Result: Days of mosquito- and bug-free comfort.

• Know the best time of the day to spray. Generally, before the heat of the day is best. Avoid hot, windy days.

RULES FOR SAFE USE

• Read and follow all directions on spray material container.
• Read directions before opening container.
• Store spray materials in original container.
• Keep away from children and pets.

36

Lawn Vacuums

Cleanup chores are a big part of the job of keeping your lawn looking its very best. In spring, there's winter's legacy of twigs and debris. In summer, grass clippings and remnants of trimming jobs in the garden must be removed from the lawn. Autumn brings the abundant burden of leaf fallout, as everything once green in your garden sheds its foliage for the coming winter.

Figure 36-1. Lawn vacuum. GRAF-WHALEN photograph.

If you've stoically faced this hard work armed only with a rake and trash bag, you have a pleasant surprise in store once you try a lawn vacuum. These powerhouse outdoor cleanup aids chop hours off the time you spend grooming your lawn. Like a huge "vacuum-cleaner-on-wheels," this device has the suction to pull leaves, grass clippings, and twigs off your lawn, chew them into fine mulch, and deposit them in a large-capacity bag for easy emptying later. It is to raking what the household vacuum cleaner was to the broom—a modern way to save your time, your hands, and your back, so that you can spend your hours outdoors a bit more pleasantly.

SHOULD YOU OWN A LAWN VACUUM?

Is your property at least a quarter of an acre? Is it primarily grass, without obstacles like peculiarly shaped beds or rock gardens that tend to break it up into a series of irregularly shaped grass "islands"? Do you have many trees either on your property or nearby? Do you regularly spend at least half an hour cleaning up your lawn after a weekly grass-trimming session? If you don't compost your clippings, do you regularly have at least two 30-gallon trash cans (or bags) filled with clippings to deal with on trash-collection day? If your answers are "yes," you have a cleanup need that one of these machines can satisfy nicely.

As these items suggest, the need for a machine of this kind is one that is very specific to the lawn cleanup chore your property presents. Thus, before you invest, determine whether you need the machine. Next, think about what you need it to do. Will you use it to pick up clippings after mowing? Do you need a self-propelled model or will a push-type handle your needs? Finally, where will you store this helpful, but large, addition to your lawn machine arsenal?

A lawn machine that is a companion to other machines (such as a lawn mower, trimmer, or chain saw) has several of the earmarks of a *luxury*, because its principal help to you is in the cleaning up of the debris these other machines have created! And so, you should weigh the purchase of a lawn vacuum against your *real* needs.

HOW THEY WORK

A lawn vacuum handles cleanup chores by creating a moving airstream of sufficient magnitude to lift and carry along lawn debris. The airstream is usually created by a 5-horsepower engine-driven impeller, rotating within a housing that has an intake port and an exhaust port. In most designs, the intake port is covered by a large, bolt-on snout, which is at the front of the machine. The snout directs the suction created by the impeller downward, so that air and debris are sucked into the impeller chamber, where the whirling blades break it into a fine mulch. This is then forced out the exhaust port into a cloth or fiber bag, which has screenlike openings that permit the air blast to exit, while keeping the mulch trapped in the bag.

Combination Vacuum/Blowers

With a few quick changes, some machines can be converted from a *vacuum* to a *blower* that is very handy for pushing autumn leaves into easily handled piles. All that's necessary is to remove the snout and replace it with a protective, bolt-on cover. Then change the hookup of the impeller chamber, so that air is drawn in at about knee height in front of the machine and then exhausted at ground level toward the side of the machine. With this arrangement, you merely circle around the debris you wish to pile up, blowing it toward the center.

Self-Propelled Models

To ease cleanup chores, some models feature a power takeoff from the engine that drives the rubber-tired wheels of the machine. A belt-and-pulley arrangement is used to provide speed reduction and increased turning force to the wheels. A simple squeeze-clutch on the handle lets you engage the power drive to the wheels when you need its assist (for example, when pushing the machine on an upgrade, with a heavy, nearly full bag of lawn debris). In many cases, however, you will not require the power assist (for example, when using a combination unit as a blower).

Figure 36-2. A lawn vacuum that has been converted to a blower operation, showing parts removed. Note the safety shield over the air-intake opening. GRAF-WHALEN photograph.

Figure 36-3. A safety screen is necessary to protect hands from vicious, whirling impeller blades. GRAF-WHALEN photograph.

Figure 36-4. This typical propulsion mechanism uses a splined drive shaft turning against rim of rubber tire. GRAF-WHALEN photograph.

WHAT'S AVAILABLE
Combination Vacuum/Shredders
These machines provide suction pickup and debris-mulching functions. A metal snout can be removed and replaced by a bolt-on vertical hopper to make the machine into a shredder. Those jobs they do, they do well, and they're available principally as self-propelled models. But these should not be confused with machines that are convertible to blower operation.

Combination Vacuum/Blowers
These machines can function equally well as vacuums or blowers and usually have tough, molded snouts that are held in place by hand-tightened hardware with large, knurled knob heads. Parts required for changeover should be stored right on the machine where they're hard to lose.

IMPORTANT FEATURES TO LOOK FOR
Versatility
A machine that can vacuum and mulch or blow has features you can put to work in many seasonal cleanup chores. And so, you should weigh the features of the machines for which you're shopping and their prices against your *real* needs. If you have no trees, a blower feature is an added cost without much purpose; ditto for the mulcher feature, if you dump your debris in the trash can. Also, self-propulsion is a nice luxury, but, if your property isn't too large and is mostly level, you may find a push-type machine perfectly adequate. Try to locate the blend of features that best suits your real needs. You'll find this the way to get the best buy for the dollars you're spending.

Storage Space
These machines tend to be fairly large because of the volume of the vacuum bag. So, if in-season storage space is limited, you'll want to consider the machine's space requirements. All have removable bags, but handle designs are awkward, usually one-piece, right-angle shapes. Designs with folding or easily removed and replaced handles should be considered if space is *really* limited, especially for winter storage.

Controls and Positions
A combination throttle/choke control, placed on the handle where you can easily reach it, is a definite feature. So is a "dead-man" squeeze-clutch handle that engages wheel drive only when you want it and disengages when you let go. Other controls, such as the height control, which sets the snout's position above ground for debris pickup, should also be positioned where their settings

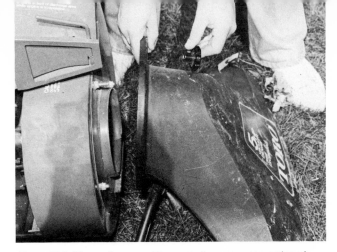

Figure 36-5. The easily removable snout allows easy conversion of the lawn vacuum to a lawn blower. GRAF-WHALEN photograph.

Figure 36-6. Height control sets the position of the snout above ground. A high setting is used in rough and uneven terrain. Normal and low positions are meant for flat, level ground. GRAF-WHALEN photograph.

Figure 36-7. The squeeze-handle control of the propulsion mechanism provides safety. GRAF-WHALEN photograph.

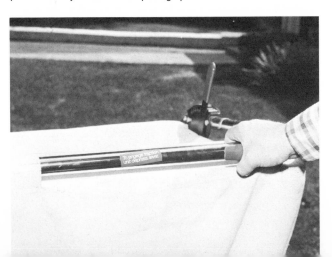

Figure 36-8. Deflector door control is near blower exhaust on some models. Don't adjust while the machine is running. GRAF-WHALEN photograph.

Figure 36-9. Blow-stream velocity can reach speeds of 100 mph. Its force is evident by the flattening of the grass in the foreground of the photograph. GRAF-WHALEN photograph.

Figure 36-10. The bag attachment should be simple and engineered for easy emptying. GRAF-WHALEN photograph.

can be easily changed from a normal-usage position safely behind the machine. On machines that convert from vacuum to blower operation, no remote control is provided for the deflector door that changes blow-stream direction from front-out to side-out. That being the case, you must be sure to turn the machine's engine off *before* using that control. The blow stream of one of these machines reaches speeds of 100 mph and more, which can pose flying debris hazards, especially to the eyes.

Simplicity of Bag Attachment/Detachment

Well-designed machines feature bags with zippered sides, so that the bag can be opened (machine off) to dump its contents into a mulch pile or compost heap without detaching the bag from the machine. However, dumping the bag's contents into a trash can *will* require bag removal. Generally, the neck of the bag has an inner elastic, which stretches snugly over the discharge chute of the impeller chamber. The handle provides rear support for the bag and may use a combination of a slip-over web belt plus grommets and pins. Choose the design that combines largest volume and greatest ease in slipping the bag on and off. Do remember that a nearly full bag will weigh 40 pounds or more, depending upon moisture content. If the bag is tricky to remove and install when empty, things surely won't be any better when it's full of debris!

Figure 36-11. The elasticized mouth of the bag fits securely to the metal exit of this lawn vacuum. GRAF-WHALEN photograph.

Tool-less Changeover from Vacuum to Blower

A sure sign of ingenuity in the manufacturer's design-engineering department is a combination machine that doesn't need a tool kit or skilled mechanic to change over from vacuum to blower (or shredder) operation. Look for large screw knobs that can be hand turned and self-storage on the machine for parts that must come off to make the change.

TIPS FOR USING YOUR LAWN VACUUM
Engine

Prepare and care for the engine of your lawn vacuum as described in the manufacturer's manual. If it has a four-cycle engine, oil in the crankcase should be at proper level and free of blackening contaminants, such as soot or carbon. If you have doubts, change oil before using the machine. (For summer use, most manufacturers specify SAE 30 or SAE 10W-40 oil, with service classifications SC, SD, or SE.) Additives should never be used.

For fuel, choose fresh regular-grade gasoline. Low-lead or no-lead fuels burn without contaminating deposits that can foul plugs and valves. Don't use gas that's been lying around since last season. Waxy residues form in stale gas, and these can gum up the carburetor of your machine's engine. Also, don't *ever* use premium gas (its benzene content swells seals in the carburetor and can foul up your engine); ditto, as far as white stove gas or gasoline additives are concerned. Neither has any place in your machine's engine.

Machine Preparation

Assuming that you are going to use the machine for vacuuming, install the bag (engine off) and check everything for snugness (hardware, controls, gas tank cap, etc.). Adjust the height of the snout with the machine's height control, so that you can push the machine forward without encountering opposition. Most machines will encompass an adjustment range from a smooth driveway to thick, lush turf covered with clippings.

Vacuuming

Start the engine, allow a minute for warm-up, and then adjust the throttle for maximum speed (greatest suction). Push forward, toward the area to be cleaned. If grass trimmings are the debris to be picked up, use your machine as a "push" type, ignoring the self-propulsion feature if it has one. You will find it useful to pass over and back above the surface to be cleaned, until all debris is sucked up. Ideally, you should vacuum a newly mowed lawn when cuttings are dry, such as in the late afternoon. Wet grass fouls the impeller and will soak the bag, reducing pickup efficiency. Also, heavy, wet grass will necessitate more frequent bag emptying than will dry grass.

If twigs and trimmings are your cleanup chore, move slowly and steadily, picking up as you go. Don't be alarmed by the loud "ding-and-ping" as twigs are chewed up by the impeller. Keep pressing on until the bag becomes laden with chopped material. Don't hesitate to use self-propulsion to help move the machine when necessary. Likewise, if a slower pickup pace is needed to get all the debris off the lawn, skip the self-propulsion and use the machine as a push-type, moving back and forth over the ground until you've got it all.

Figure 36-12. Use only an approved gasoline container for storage of fuel. Be sure your container is equipped to work with your lawn vacuum to prevent spillage of fuel. GRAF-WHALEN photograph.

Figure 36-13. A bag that opens wide for emptying into trash cans is an important feature if you do not choose to compost or mulch. GRAF-WHALEN photograph.

Emptying the Bag

If you've set aside a mulch pile or compost heap, you may want to dump the bag there. If so, just push or self-propel it there, stop the engine, and open the bag to drop the finely mulched particles. Alternatively, remove the bag and dump into a trash can, or you can surround the bag with a plastic trash bag and shake out the remains into one or more bags.

Recognize Your Machine's Limitations

If a twig is too big for your machine to suck up, it is too much for it to digest. *Never* hand feed material into the snout or impeller! You run the risk of serious bodily injury, or you could badly damage the impeller. Be philosophical and think about how much work your machine has saved you, even though you may have to go back to pick up a few large branches by hand.

After Vacuuming

Remove the bag from the machine and be sure it's empty. Never allow wet debris to remain in the bag where it can cause mildew and rot, which weaken the fabric. For longest bag life, open the zipper surfaces and turn the bag inside-out, so that it can dry thoroughly before the next use. If splinters or shards have torn holes in the bag, mend them with needle and thread before a larger section rips open.

Figure 36-14. It is good practice to stop the engine and disconnect the spark-plug lead wire before removing the bag for emptying or when maintenance is required. GRAF-WHALEN photograph.

RULES FOR SAFE USE

• Never allow children to operate the machine and never allow adults to operate it without proper instructions.

• Know the controls and how to stop the machine quickly.

• Handle gasoline with care—it is highly flammable. Use only an approved gasoline container and fill gas tank outdoors—never while engine is hot or running. Wipe up any spilled gas before starting engine. Do not smoke while refueling and be sure to replace gasoline cap securely. Open doors if engine is run in a garage or other enclosed area; exhaust gases are extremely dangerous.

• Instruct bystanders to stay a safe distance away at all times. Be sure to clear work area of objects that might be picked up and thrown or that might wrap around the impeller.

• Never leave the vacuum unattended without shutting engine down.

• Give your complete and undivided attention to the job at hand and never operate a lawn vacuum without the bag in place (unless, of course, it is a combination unit that has been changed over to blower operation).

• Do not place any part of your body in the rotor area until you are sure the rotor has stopped turning; the impeller rotor continues to turn for a few seconds after the engine is shut off. Do not put hands or face into, or near, the bag when the rotor is turning.

• Check before each use for loose fasteners or parts.

• Stop engine and disconnect the spark-plug lead wire before removing the bag, cleaning the discharge chute, removing obstacles, when leaving the machine, or during maintenance. Check the bag frequently for wear or deterioration. Replace with a new bag if you have the slightest doubt about its safety.

• When machine is converted to a blower, do not stand in front of discharge area.

LAWN VACUUM MAINTENANCE

Gas engines used in lawn vacuums are usually husky four-cycle types, rated at 5 horsepower. These require draining and refilling of the crankcase at the interval prescribed by the manufacturer (usually after the first 5 hours of operation when the machine is new and at 25-hour intervals, thereafter). Oil is best drained after the engine has been warmed up and after any residual fuel in the gas tank has been used up. Don't attempt to drain oil while there is gas in the tank, as some will spill on the hot engine parts, enveloping the work area in dangerously explosive fumes that only need a chance spark to ignite. If there is too much fuel in the tank to use up within a few minutes of running time, use a siphon to drain gas back into a safe container. Use up the rest by running the machine at idle. When it sputters to a stop, close the throttle and remove the spark-plug lead. Hot oil should be drained into a shallow pan, after opening the drain plug and tilting the machine over the pan. Then wipe away dirt around the filler plug opening and pour in the recommended quantity of fresh oil. (Generally, SAE 30 or SAE 10W-40 grade, with service classification SC, SD, or SE.) Check oil level carefully; then reinstall the filler plug. Wipe any spilled oil off the engine and other parts of the machine.

To ensure an uninterrupted flow of clean air to the carburetor, remove and clean the air filter every time you change oil. The filters used in most lawn vacuum engines are porous foam types which use an oil film to trap fine dust and grit in the foam pores. Remove the element and wash it in kerosene or liquid detergent and water. Squeeze like a sponge to wash out the oil and its trapped dirt particles. Wipe out the air-cleaner housing with a cloth that has been wetted with a few drops of fresh oil; this will pick up residue and help prevent dirt particles from falling into the carburetor throat. Saturate the clean filter with fresh oil and then squeeze to remove excess oil. The clean, oiled filter element is then placed back in the air-cleaner housing and the cover replaced.

You should also lubricate the wheel bushings and sliding inner shafts of control cables each time you change oil. Take care not to get oil on pulleys or belts, where it can cause slippage.

General maintenance should include cleanup of dust and debris, especially from the fins of the engine. These are the engine's "air-cooling system," and a blanket of dust can cause poor cooling and overheating, which

shortens engine life. A brush and cloth are all you need to keep the machine clean.

Check hardware for snugness and replace any parts that are missing. Cables should move without binding, and all control functions should be smooth and easy in their operation.

Don't feel that you have to "adjust" the carburetor. Chances are its factory setting is more precise than you think. If the engine sounds just a trifle "rough" at idle, it has been set slightly rich. At full speed, though, the air-fuel mixture will probably be "on-the-money," for best performance. If you try to smooth out the idle, you'll be running the engine lean at high speed, penalizing performance.

Hard starting or missing point to ignition problems. Most often, a worn or fouled plug will be the cause and simple replacement, the cure. Be sure that the new spark plug's gap is set precisely before installing.

After prolonged operation (200 hours or more), engines which use breaker points in their magneto ignition systems may become cranky and "sputtery" due to wear out of the point surfaces. You can replace the points yourself by fairly simple removal of the magneto housing and flywheel, below which the points are located. (The horizontal-shaft design of lawn vacuum engines makes ignition work simpler than in vertical-shaft mower engines.) Breaker point-gap is critical, and can't be guessed at. If you are not equipped to measure point gap precisely, have your machine serviced at a local dealer's shop.

Self-propelled lawn vacuums use V-belt drive systems. In some, the flexible belts will gradually stretch, until the drive system slips. Recognizing this, the manufacturer provides tension adjustments, to take up the slack. These should be adjusted at every oil change, to keep the drive system at peak efficiency. Eventually (after hundreds of hours) the adjustment range will be used up and it will be necessary to change the belt.

Off-Season Storage
Ready your lawn vacuum for winter (or for more than a month's storage) by running it until the fuel tank is completely dry; then remove the spark plug and pour 1 ounce (2 to 3 tablespoons) of SAE 30 oil directly into the spark plug opening. Crank slowly to distribute the oil within the engine; then replace the spark plug.

Be sure that the bag is empty, clean, and dry to prevent rot and the stench of decaying vegetation.

Figure 36-15. The oil-drain plug is located on the side of the engine, allowing easy drainage when the machine is tipped to the side. GRAF-WHALEN photograph.

37

Riding Mower/Tractors

An increasingly familiar sight in suburbia is the *riding mower* (or, as it is sometimes called, the *lawn tractor*)—a homeowner's version of the mighty machines that were once seen only in farm country. A fairly recent innovation, riders and tractors have found a solid niche in the homeowner's power equipment arsenal. They multiply the do-it-yourselfer's ability not only to mow large lawns, but to handle outdoor snow-removal jobs; plow and till the soil; mulch and bag leaves; 'doze earth; aerate, roll, and cultivate sizable plots; spread fertilizer, seed, and pesticides; and carry loads that would otherwise strain human muscles and patience well beyond endurance.

Riding mowers are four-wheeled, self-propelled machines with a 24- to 36-inch rotary mower assembly per-manently fitted to the undercarriage. A body fitted to the chassis provides seating for the operator (rider seats are usually adjustable to two or three positions), a steering wheel and controls, and protective covering for the engine and mechanical parts. Engines of riding mowers usually are rated from a minimum of 3.5 horsepower to a nominal maximum of 8 horsepower. The rating is most important, because the engine must supply enough power for good cutting action, as well as movement of the mower (and the weight of its rider) over rough or sloping terrain. For most large lawns, this leaves comparatively little reserve power for hauling and pushing jobs, and so, only manufacturers of larger models offer accessories to increase the versatility of the riding mower. This

Figure 37-1. Riding mower/tractor. Photograph courtesy of Allis Chalmers Corp.

Figure 37-2. JACOBSEN MARK III RIDING ROTARY. A typical riding mower features an engine behind the driver, plus a cozy seat and comfortably placed controls. Photograph courtesy of Jacobsen Manufacturing Company.

essentially restricts the riding mower's function to grass cutting and bagging chores, with occasional use possibilities in lawn cleanup and mulching jobs.

IMPORTANT FEATURES TO LOOK FOR

Some models have a front axle that pivots up and down, so that when a wheel goes down in a hole or depression or goes over a hump, the cutting unit remains level. Gravity is used in others to keep the cutting unit level at all times, even when the lower deck edge is not in contact with the ground.

A number of riders have a guard rail that extends the full length of the deck, from front to rear along the bottom edge of the deck sides. These keep the deck from coming in contact with the ground and prevent the blade from scalping ridges and mounds.

If the rider has a blade clutch which enables the user to stop the blade and keep the engine running, the blade should be capable of reaching a full stop in 3 seconds or less. If the blade merely coasts to a stop, you will have to exercise more caution in use. In general, a fast-braking blade is to be preferred from a safety standpoint. Also determine whether the clutch can be eased into the "on" position or if it "grabs" and tends to kill the engine.

Some riders start moving when the engine is running and the gear-shift lever is put in forward or reverse position. But many will not move until the safety-clutch pedal is pushed down and held down by the operator's foot. Requiring this second operation is another useful safety factor.

Figure 37-3. This riding mower is equipped with a front-axle design that floats the mower over the contour of the ground, providing even, nonscalp mowing. Photoraph courtesy of Allis Chalmers Corp.

Cutting heights usually range from 1 1/4 to 3 1/2 inches. Those that require removal of wheels or bolts or that require loosening of nuts and retightening to change height should be down rated, if you have the need to frequently change cutting height. All better rider-models have construction that raises or lowers the deck with a level or by turning a crank.

Moderate foot pressure on the brake pedal should stop the rider quickly, and an easy-to-reach and easy-to-set brake lock should hold the rider even on a fairly steep slope.

Rider blades, since they are longer and are subjected to much more engine power than hand rotaries, should be sturdier. When a blade is turning at a high speed, the tips tend to flex, and this tendency is increased if the blade is not as carefully tempered at the center as it is at the cutting edges. A reinforcement bar at the center of the blade helps prevent this. However, if the edges of a channel bar extend so far down that they rub the grass tops, they will tend to brown the grass.

In general, the cutting properties of a rider can be judged by the same criteria used to judge standard rotary lawn mowers (see chapter 31).

Front wheels range in diameter from 8 to 12 inches, with rear wheels of 10 to 16 inches and some as large as 20 inches. Tires are usually pneumatic, but some semipneumatic are used on low-priced models, and some have semipneumatic in front and pneumatic on the rear. Pneumatic tires are tubeless on a number of models. Large tires have eye appeal, but are more costly, require extra power, and tend to raise the center of gravity.

Easy steering and rugged steering gear are very important. A lightweight woman should be able to steer the rider over any terrain. A turning radius of 32 inches is about the smallest you can expect to find. Most are somewhat broader in their turning characteristics. A small turning-radius increases maneuverability and is a plus. Check this on models you look at.

Easy accessibility of all controls is also important. This includes gas throttle, transmission positions, brakes, brake lock, blade clutch, and height adjustment and safety clutch, if any. Transmissions vary from one speed forward, neutral, and reverse to five speeds forward, neutral, and reverse, with most models having three speeds forward. Driving speeds range from 1 to 7 mph, depending upon the load.

The center of gravity in a rider should be as low and as far forward as possible, preferably in front of the operator. Locating the driver's seat as far forward as possible is a safety feature, particularly on slopes and inclines. This is particularly true on models having the engine mounted behind the operator. Rear-mounted engines

Figure 37-4. Compact riders have a small turning radius for easy trimming around beds. The grass-collector bag has given way to the rear-mounted collector in some designs. Photograph courtesy of The Toro Company, Consumer Products Div.

Figure 37-5. Where maneuverability is important, this optional, easy-empty, rear-mounted grass catcher can be fitted to certain Toro mowers. Photograph courtesy of The Toro Company, Consumer Products Div.

sit solidly on the frame of the rider. Front-mounted engines may sit solidly on the frame or they may be mounted on the deck. This positions the rider's center of gravity safely forward.

Because the engine on a rider drives two things—the blade and the rear wheels—some low-priced riders may have the blade attached to the engine shaft, like an ordinary rotary. But practically all more costly models have a belt-driven blade, and usually such mowers have a blade clutch.

On most models, another belt runs from the engine to the transmission, and a chain runs from there to the differential. Many of the more deluxe models combine the differential and transmission in one sealed housing. This is called a *transaxle.* Such riders usually have two belts and no chain. Easy accessibility of belts and chains is best, and easy accessibility of all parts that may require replacement is equally important.

Easy removal of cutting units is desirable, so that where these accessories are available from the manufacturer, the machine can be used as a snowplow or to pull attachments. Some of the more common attachments for riders are plows, cultivators, trash carts, can carts, snowplows, and lawn sweepers.

Electric starters are available on some models. They add to the cost, but are desirable on engines of higher horsepower.

Some riders can be upended on rear or front end without the dangers of oil or gas drainage. This permits storage in a comparatively small space and also makes all parts beneath the mower easily accessible for maintenance.

Larger lawn tractors have attachment facilities for rotary mower assemblies on their undercarriages, often featuring tandem mowers that cut huge 6-foot swaths of grass in a single pass. What's more, their styling more closely resembles the traditional appearance of their larger farm cousins. And why not? Some pack the power punch of engines rated up to 20 horsepower. This extra mechanical muscle plus more complex transmissions, power takeoff features, and large range of accessories multiply their usefulness to homeowners, whose seasonal chores span the gamut from lawn care to more formidable tasks, combining the jobs faced by the owner of a small farm with those of a guy who still must catch the 6:18 A.M. commuter train on snowy winter mornings.

Ordinarily somewhat heavier than a riding mower, the typical lawn tractor has a front-engine design with a built-in battery-start feature. This affords a convenient design arrangement for hookup of accessory devices, while it also places the gravity center of the machine ahead of the driver for greater operating stability.

Pneumatic tires of large diameter and heavy-tread design are standard on a lawn tractor, assuring you of even, surefooted handling and maneuvering ease. Rack-and-pinion steering is another feature that simplifies handling. Controls are carlike and easily mastered, with smooth-shifting transmissions giving up to eight forward speeds, plus reverse.

Figure 37-6. A lawn tractor has enough "muscle" to tackle even tough earth-moving jobs like this one. Photograph courtesy of Allis Chalmers Corp.

Figure 37-7. An accessory cart lets you haul heavy or bulky materials with your lawn tractor. Photograph courtesy of Simplicity Manufacturing Company, Inc.

38

Cordless Electric Shears

It's funny how far the edge of your lawn seems to extend along a curb or walk when you're viewing it on hands and knees, armed only with manual, scissorlike shears. You snip-snip-snip, inching along at a torturously slow pace, clearing a few grass blades here, a clump there. The hot

Figure 38-1. Cordless electric shears—the BLACK & DECKER MOD 4 CORDLESS GRASS SHEAR®. Photograph courtesy of Black & Decker Mfg. Co.

sun sends rivulets of perspiration trickling down your hands and face to fall and mark the ground you've so painfully manicured. And soon your sore hand can attest to the strength and resilience of the tenacious grass that seems to grow only along the *edges* of your lawn!

Experiences like this one have helped convert countless home gardeners to the joys of *cordless electric shears*. Available in both hand-held and stand-up models, these neat little power tools provide the perfect power complement to the gas- or electric-powered lawn mower. That's because they go where the big blades *can't* or *shouldn't* be used, and they give you effortless trimming power that doesn't tax your hand, back, or patience.

HOW THEY WORK

All cordless shears use a built-in battery as the power source. They may use nickel-cadmium batteries (in the most expensive models) or rechargeable alkaline batteries in popular-priced models. In either case, the battery supply must be recharged from the AC power outlet. A charger supplied by the manufacturer is the typical method. These are always special-purpose designs, usable *only* with the device with which they're sold. To be sure that you don't mix up chargers and risk harming batteries, manufacturers frequently use special connectors on their chargers that won't mate with other devices.

In general, all cordless shears use a series-wound universal DC motor as the drive source. It turns at high speed within a second after power is applied. Gearing is used to convert the motor's high-speed/low-torque output to a lower-speed/higher-torque value. The output gear is fitted with an eccentrically mounted pin. This engages an oval slot on the movable cutters, so that the pin presses against one or another part of the slot, in sequence, throughout one revolution of the drive gear. The movable cutters are pivoted on the fixed cutters. And so, for one revolution of the drive gear, the eccentric pin causes the movable blade to swing left and right, and then back to left. The force at the cutter blades is a direct result of the gear-reduction ratio. Thus, although the blades appear to move slowly in relation to the motor's speed, the gearing magnifies the closing force at the cutters for greater shearing power.

WHAT'S AVAILABLE
Hand-Held Models
Designed for easy, one-hand holding, these compact, lightweight electric shears feature a pair of multi-blade cutters (one fixed, one movable) that gobble up grass in a 3-inch-wide path. The movable cutters swing from side to side, opening to admit grass stems, and then closing over the fixed cutters, so that their sharpened edges shear off the grass blades at the height at which you're holding the unit. The case is smooth and flat on the bottom, so that you can slide the unit along the ground surface as you trim. Cutter operation gives a shear stroke as the blade moves left, and then another as the blade moves right.

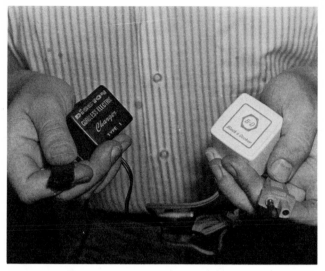

Figure 38-3. To prevent a mix-up between chargers and tools the plugs are shaped in a unique way. GRAF-WHALEN photograph.

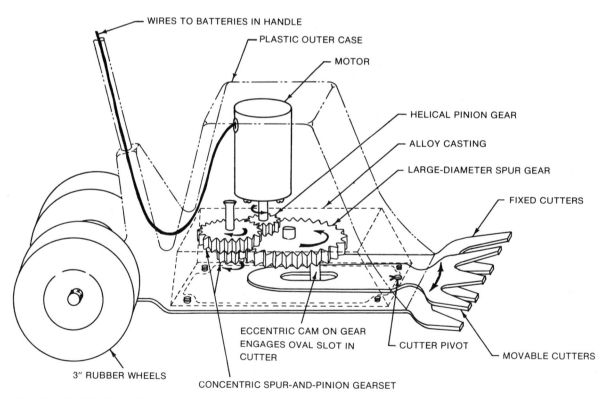

Figure 38-2. This simplified illustration shows how rotary motion of the motor shaft is converted to side-to-side shearing force at the cutter blades.

218

Hand-held models also have the advantage of being useful in trimming pulpy, light, new growth (not woody stems) of bushes and ornamentals. They're also useful in clearing out weeds before cultivating and in shaping or cutting back light, flowering growth. In short, you'll find them handy wherever you might use scissors or hand-operated shears, and their cutting limitations are about the same. The difference lies in the hand-saving power source that drives the cutters.

Stand-Up Models

These are really dedicated grass trimmers, useful for finishing up the lawn-grooming tasks around plantings; near walls, walks, and lawn ornaments; and next to curb paving; where it might be dangerous to risk running the hefty power mower. Most such models feature a pair of 2-inch-diameter wheels, placed toward the rear of the unit's case, with a 3- or 4-foot tubular shaft extending upward to an angled hand-grip. This allows you to stand upright while trimming and to wheel the shears along at a comfortable pace, darting from left to right to catch errant grass blades with effortless ease. The power switch is conveniently placed on the handle, is usually thumb- or finger-actuated, and is spring-loaded, so that power shuts off if you release pressure. The wheels act as a fulcrum, so that you can tip the shearing cutters down by raising the handle, or vice-versa.

While not as versatile as the hand-held models, the stand-up variety is so comfortably useful in lawn trimming that it's worth having, even if you already have a hand-held type. Also, it *is* possible to use the stand-up type for long-reach trimming, if you are shaping a tall bush with light, new growth. Simply use two hands (one on the handle and one on the tubular shaft) to direct the cutters where you want to snip. Remember that the same limitations that apply to scissors or hand shears apply to electric shears. Don't try to cut anything you wouldn't try cutting with scissors.

Combination Hand/Stand-Up Models

These combine the freedom of a hand-held cordless model with the best features of a stand-up design. The objective is to give you a mix of features to suit the widest possible range of tasks where use of cordless shears is indicated.

To achieve these ends the manufacturer has made his device *modular*; that is, the *shear head* (which contains the electric motor, drive train, and cutters) forms one unit, the *energy pack* (containing the batteries and power switch) forms a second unit, and the *extension handle* (containing connecting wires and slide-on fittings to accommodate the other two) forms a third unit. In es-

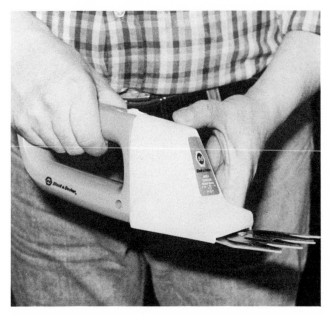

Figure 38-4. Hand-held trimmers feature easy-to-grasp handles with a convenient thumb-actuated power switch. GRAF-WHALEN photograph.

Figure 38-5. BLACK & DECKER MOD 4 CORDLESS UPRIGHT GRASS SHEAR® Stand-up models extend your reach and are comfortable to use when edging. Photograph courtesy of Black & Decker Mfg. Co.

Figure 38-6. This cordless model is made up of modular parts, which fit together to form a stand-up or hand-held trimmer. GRAF-WHALEN photograph.

Figure 38-7. This easy, snap-together assembly converts the trimmer from hand-held to stand-up operation. Photograph courtesy of Disston, Inc.

sence, *you* assemble the tool you need for the job at hand, using these modular units. Want a hand-held model? Then slide the energy pack onto the shear head. When mated, the two form a tough assembly that gives you the equal of a dedicated, hand-held model. Want a stand-up model? Just slide the energy pack off the shear head to the extension handle (which has wheels) and slide the energy pack onto the opposite end of the extension handle. The result? A stand-up shears unit equal to the dedicated stand-up models. It really is simpler than it sounds to piece together the shears you need for a particular task. Even though no tools are required to do so, however, people who shy away from mechanical tasks may not feel comfortable with this unique approach. Nevertheless, if you have a need for quick-change shears and a tiny bit of mechanical savvy, you'll find a combination unit a *best buy* in terms of versatility and usage for the dollars you spend.

IMPORTANT FEATURES TO LOOK FOR
Positive Off-Locking Feature
Cordless tools spell t-r-o-u-b-l-e, if a young child can get to one when you're not around to head off disaster. Look for a tool that features a button you have to press or turn to unlock the thumb- or finger-actuated switch. This will make it doubly difficult for junior "helpers" to hurt themselves should the tool fall into their hands in an unguarded moment.

Figure 38-8. A positive off-locking feature will prevent serious injury if your trimmer should fall into junior's hands in an unguarded moment. GRAF-WHALEN photograph.

Easily Replaced Cutters

Cordless shears take a tough beating in normal use. Their blades are usually made of hardened steel, which is brittle. This means that the cutters may break in an accidental fall or if you apply too great an up- or down-force with your hand when shearing into a woody root. Cutters should be readily obtainable and easily replaced with a minimum of tool work. Of course, cutters *do* become dull, and they can be resharpened using an accessory sharpening-stone, usually available from the manufacturer. After several sharpenings, the cutters may lose their ability to shear grass. Replacement will then be in order.

Longest Cutting Time Per Charge

The cutting time you get from cordless shears is determined by the battery capacity (ability to deliver energy) and the size of its motor. Generally, choose the one that gives the longest operation per charge. Also, look for the shortest recharge time. The majority are rated at 16 hours to recharge a completely discharged battery to full capacity.

TIPS FOR USING YOUR CORDLESS SHEARS

Safety first! Read the safety tips and make them a habit. They're small, but they are *not* toys, and those cutter blades can inflict nasty cuts if treated with less than the utmost respect!

Grass Trimming

For the best results you should trim only on a dry day, regardless of the fact that water or moisture in the grass or on the ground does not create an electric shock hazard with this tool. Just be sure not to cut through any electric cords that may be in the area.

Keep your hands and feet well away from the blade and maintain a stable working position so that you don't slip. Don't overreach, and avoid banging cutters against curb, wall, or other hard surfaces. Feed the cutter into the grass at a rate that allows it to keep up its cutting speed; feed slower if the blade slows down. Watch out for foreign objects in the grass.

Pruning Soft, New Growth

You can trim light growth on plants, bushes, or ornamentals, so long as the stems are soft and pliable. Work slowly inward, using several strokes to trim off a bit at a time. Don't plunge right in and try to cut stems in bunches. You'll foul the blades and use up excess power that will quickly drain the battery.

Overhead Trimming

Don't stand directly below the shears while trimming; small bits and pieces may fall into your eyes. Use a ladder if need be, and try to stay on a horizontal level with the growth you're cutting.

RULES FOR SAFE USE

• Keep children away. All visitors should be kept a safe distance from the work area.

• Store idle shears indoors. When not in use, the shears should be stored indoors in a dry, high or locked-up place, out of the reach of children.

• Don't force shears. Shears will do the job better and more safely when operated at the speed for which they were designed.

• Consider the job. Do not use the shears for jobs they were not intended to perform.

• Dress properly. Do not wear loose clothing or jewelry. They could be caught in moving parts.

• Don't overreach. Keep proper footing at all times.

• Maintain shears with care. Keep cutting edges sharp and clean for best and safest performance. Follow instructions for lubricating.

• Avoid accidental starting. Do not carry the shears with your fingers on the switch or locking button.

• Never grasp the exposed cutting blades or cutting edges when picking up or holding the tool.

• Keep hands and all parts of body away from blades. The edges are sharp and can cause injury even when the tool is off.

• Cordless shears don't have to be plugged in. Remember this, because they are always in an operating condition.

• Wear gloves when trimming thorny or prickly growth.

• Don't feed grass into the cutters with your hands or reach over the moving blade to pick up clippings.

• Before trimming, inspect area for wires, cords, glass, or other foreign objects that could come in contact with the blade.

• Know what to do if grass or twigs jam the cutters. Turn the tool off. Then use a short stick to push the jammed material out of blade teeth.

• Be careful not to cut any electric cords that may be in the trimming area. There is no electric shock hazard from the shears themselves.

• Do not operate shears in gaseous or explosive atmospheres. Motors in these tools normally spark, and the sparks might ignite fumes.

CORDLESS SHEARS MAINTENANCE
Cleaning Up the Cutters

After you have finished trimming, you will usually find that sap and dirt have accumulated on the blades. If these deposits are allowed to dry, extra power from the battery will be required the next time you use the shears and cutting capacity between charges will be reduced.

It is easy to remove sap and dirt deposits when they are fresh and moist, but difficult after they become dry. Therefore, it is recommended that you wash the blades in water after each use. Hold the blades under a running faucet or in a pan of water and turn the tool on to help dislodge the deposits. If the buildup of sap is difficult to remove, it may be necessary (with the motor off) to scrub the blades with soap and a stiff bristle brush. If the sap has been allowed to dry, a full-strength household detergent can be used to soften and remove the sap. Let the cleaner soak in for a few minutes; then remove the deposits with a stiff brush and rinse in water.

After cleaning, wipe the blades with a cloth and allow them to dry. Then apply a few drops of light machine oil to the top of the blades. Turn the shears on for a few seconds to work lubricant between the blades.

Charging for Best Battery Life

If you've used your shears for about one half hour or more, you should help to keep the batteries fresh by overnight charging. It's important that they be well discharged *before* you charge, because the chemistry of the batteries

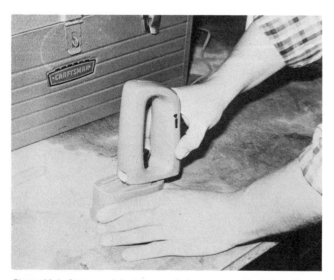

Figure 38-9. Some modular trimmers feature power units that can be used with several different tool heads. Here such a power unit is being slipped into a charging stand for overnight recharge. GRAF-WHALEN photograph.

has a "memory" quality. This means that if you use the tool only slightly, then run to charge it immediately afterward, the batteries will "remember" that you only needed a small capacity. Pretty soon you'll find your shears delivering shorter and shorter periods of operation. The cure for this memory problem is to run the tool to completely discharge the batteries, then charge and discharge again. After a few such cycles, you'll be surprised to find your shears working for longer and longer periods until maximum capacity is regained. Deep discharge followed by overnight charging is the way to keep your cordless shears' batteries lean and muscular.

Cutter Sharpening

After every two or three big cutting jobs, you'd be wise to lightly keen the edge of the cutters with a sharpening stone. Some manufacturers offer an accessory stone that slips over the cutters and sharpens them while you apply power. Alternatively, you can use a hand stone to whet the cutting edges. Beware of excessive sharpening, however. Each pass of the stone removes blade surface that can reduce shearing force on thin grass stems. If you sharpen too much, you might destroy cutter performance, necessitating blade replacement.

Dressing Out Nicks

The cutters may be nicked by biting a nail, wire fence, or stone. These nicks can usually be ignored, unless a burr that impedes the blade's action forms. In this case, use a fine, flat file or sharpening stone to dress the burr flat. Don't worry about the nick. It affects only a tiny part of the blades and has little impact on cutting performance.

General Cleanup

Don't use strong solvents on the molded plastic cases of today's cordless shears. Some of these are solvents for plastic, including dry-cleaning fluid, gasoline, lacquer, or paint thinner and are, therefore, too strong.

Lubrication

After cleaning or before winter storage, flow a few drops of light machine oil over the cutters. This forms a film that locks out corrosion and keeps the cutters moving freely.

Cleaning Electrical Contacts

Surfaces meant to transfer electricity can't do so properly if they're coated with grass juices, dirt, or other nonconductive foreign matter. Keep the charging contacts clean by occasionally and lightly wiping them with finest-grit sandpaper. Bright surfaces offer the least resistance to current flow, and that means strong performance from your shears' motor.

39

Power Winches

Pulling and hauling heavy loads is a problem as old as mankind. Ancient Egyptian architects faced it in building the pyramids; so did the mysteriously vanishing sculptors who raised the enigmatic stone faces on Easter Island; and, in a variety of less awesome projects, the task of moving burdensome objects is a problem we may all face from time to time.

It might be a matter of hauling a car or camper out of a ditch or deep snow or beaching a boat for winter storage or clearing large rocks or a felled tree. In any case, it's a job for "super-muscle," and that means calling on the mechanical strength of a power winch.

Surprisingly light in weight (about 25 pounds), a power winch combines a small gasoline engine, a reduction gearbox with three or more stages, and a windlass. For all its small size, it has brute power to move objects up to 12,000 pounds in weight. All that's needed is a sturdy cable, a solidly anchored object to serve as an immobile base (such as a tree), a strong line between the winch and the object to be hauled, and the power winch to wind up a line. The secret lies in the geared-down twisting power (torque) of the winch. The gas engine runs at fairly high shaft-speed and its shaft has only a moderate torque. But by placing a series of small-to-large gears between its shaft and the windlass, speed is exchanged at a 100:1 ratio for greater torque. That's what makes it possible for this small marvel to slowly pull great masses with seemingly Herculean strength.

Figure 39-1. Power winch. GRAF-WHALEN photograph.

WHAT'S AVAILABLE
Power winches are offered in lightweight, portable, self-contained units and as accessory items that operate in conjunction with the gas-engine driving section of your chain saw.

Self-Contained Power Winch
These feature an all-in-one combination of two-cycle gas engine, 100:1 ratio-reduction gearbox, and windlass in a rugged housing of heat-treated cast aluminum. Engines operate with the 16:1 mix of gas and oil which is common in two-cycle power plants. Compact and light in weight,

these units are equally adaptable to storage in car trunk, boat, or trailer and can be backpacked to the area where needed. A bolt anchorage is provided on the housing to secure an anchoring cable to a tree (or other immovable object). The windlass accepts a 7/16-inch polyester braided line, which is controlled by a few pounds of tension on the line's free end. Lifting- or pulling-speeds on the end connected to the object to be hauled range from a crawling speed to 40 feet per minute. A reverse-lock mechanism is provided to lock the windlass in case the engine stalls or is stopped.

Chain-Saw-Powered Winch

Lacking a built-in engine, these feature adapters of heat-treated steel, which engage to the power shaft of most chain saws. Thus, the winch provides only the adapter, reduction gearbox, and windlass. Although much smaller than the all-in-one units, these add-on types pose the extra work of setting up the chain saw and attaching it to the winch. Lifting and pulling power is limited by the chain-saw engine and the strength of the connection between the engine shaft and gearbox. Typically, these units provide about 65 percent of the pulling power of all-in-one winches. A reverse-locking feature is also obtainable.

TIPS FOR USING YOUR POWER WINCH

The anchor cable supplied with most winches is a galvanized-steel aircraft-type cable of 3/16-inch diameter, eyeletted to accept an anchor bolt and nut at the winch end. A similar eyelet at the opposite end of the cable can be attached to a hook or tie-down point on a tree, footing, or pier. The winch is placed on level ground, and the polyester line is fed out to a hook or other tie point on the object to be hauled. Four or more turns of line are wrapped around the windlass, and the engine driving the winch is started. After the engine has started, it is adjusted to suitable speed with the throttle. Control of the winch is obtained by pulling on the free end of the line so that it tightens around the windlass drum, increasing tension. The tighter the pull, the faster the windlass will take up slack in the line and commence pulling. Pulling tension is exerted between the line and anchorage, with little effort fed back to the control line in the operator's hands. It is possible to vary pulling speed very effectively by the degree of tension exerted on the control line.

While operating the winch, the user should observe strict safety precautions and should be careful not to stand directly behind the windlass. Should the line break, tension will snap it backward with bulletlike velocity. Standing to one side reduces risk of injury from accidental line breakage to a very slight possibility.

Figure 39-2. The self-contained TRIWAY MANUFACTURING MINI WINCH® features built-in gas engine and sturdy, transportable assembly. GRAF-WHALEN photograph.

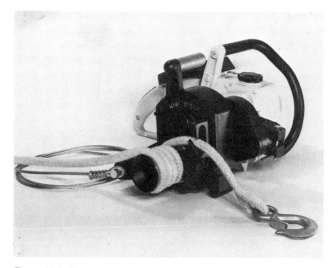

Figure 39-3. The chain-saw-powered mini winch is an add-on unit that gets its pulling force from your chain saw's engine. Photograph courtesy of Triway Manufacturing, Inc., Winch Division.

Figure 39-4. Aircraft-type cable leads from bolt on foot of winch to solid anchor (tree, etc.). GRAF-WHALEN photograph.

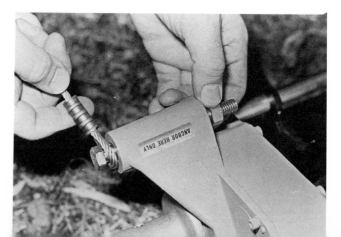

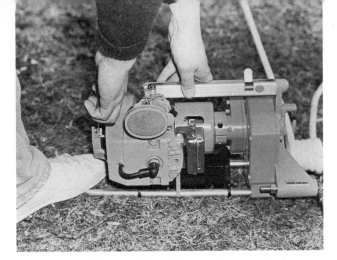

Figure 39-5. The engine is started after the anchor cable has been placed and the line loosely wrapped on the windlass. GRAF-WHALEN photograph.

Figure 39-6. Winch engine speed is set by adjusting the throttle lever. GRAF-WHALEN photograph.

Figure 39-7. The hook and closure at the end of the polyester line have many possible uses. Here the line has been secured around a tree limb and will be drawn tightly, lasso style. GRAF-WHALEN photograph.

For added pulling power, some winch manufacturers recommend use of a snatch block at the load end of the cable. This is a block-and-tackle arrangement involving a second line and anchorage point, which doubles the pulling power through a pulley arrangement.

RULES FOR SAFE USE

• Observe all normal precautions in handling fuel; don't smoke or fuel the winch in the presence of an open flame. Never run the gas engine in a closed area, as it emits lethal carbon monoxide.

• Don't allow fuel, oil, or greasy substances to collect on any surface of the winch or nearby ground. Fire hazard or dangerous slippage can result.

• Be sure that the anchorage points you select are sufficiently sturdy to bear the load you are pulling. Know the weight of the object you're hauling, and stay within the limits set by the winch manufacturer.

• Don't use tension lines other than those recommended by the manufacturer; polyester line is standard. Due to their enormously greater spring rate and sharp edges, steel cables can cut into soft winch materials and represent a great hazard should the line break.

• Don't expose yourself to injury from an accidental line break. Stand to one side of the winch. Wear gloves, if necessary, to protect against burns in controlling pull of the windlass.

POWER WINCH MAINTENANCE

Most winches require little maintenance to keep them in top operating condition. Keep all hardware tight, grease the primary shaft of the winch at recommended intervals (typically, every 5 hours of operation), and be sure to use the recommended gas-oil mixture. To maintain friction, occasional adjustment of the throttle control lever may be required. Keep cables and lines coiled when not in use. Inspect frequently and replace any that show signs of weakening or fraying. In all-in-one units, seasonal cleaning of the air filter is recommended together with periodic check of spark plug, wire, and (after prolonged operation) ignition breaker-points. Adjust carburetor only if there exists a significant tendency to stall under rated load.

40

Ground-Fault Interrupters

The earth you stand on is an electrical conductor. In electrical parlance, it is called *ground*. And so, when we refer to something as being *grounded*, we mean that it is electrically connected to, or in contact with, the earth. By itself, that doesn't mean a lot. But here's the kicker:

Figure 40-1. Ground-fault interrupter. GRAF-WHALEN photograph.

For safety purposes in our complex electrical-power distribution network, *one of the two wires that supply 60-cycle alternating current power to your home is grounded!* Electricians call it the *neutral* wire. The other wire is called *hot*. To make something electrical work in your home, it is connected between the hot and neutral contacts of an outlet (hot is the smaller opening, while neutral is the larger opening). Thus, a voltage of 120 volts AC can be measured between the hot contact of an outlet *and anything conductive that contacts the earth!* Because many electrical devices have metal cases or parts and an accidental contact between these parts and the hot wire of the line might place *you* in a lethal pathway, most electrical standards have required that such parts be grounded by a third wire. The thinking here is that an accidental short will merely cause a momentary overload that blows a fuse or pops a circuit breaker, without exposing you to the deadly risk of electrocution should insulation fail in a device you're using or a tool you're holding. That's why modern outlets have the third ground contact and many tools have three-prong plugs.

Unfortunately, this approach isn't 100 percent effective, because there are so many ways that a device that *should* be grounded can wind up not being grounded at all! Consider, for example, how many millions of outlets there are that can't accept a grounding-type plug. Installed years ago, before modern standards went into effect, these two-contact outlets beg users to find a way around the problem of mating a device with a three-contact plug to a two-contact outlet. In many cases, users simply clip off the plug's third contact (the ground pin) and use the device ungrounded; or they may use a so-called "cheater adapter." This has a three-contact input side and a two-contact plug side, with a wire and lug ground connection that's supposed to connect under the grounded screw that secures the outlet's cover plate to the outlet. Or they may plug an extension cord which has been designed to take two-contact and three-contact plugs into an outlet. Such poorly designed extensions simply extend the hot and neutral wires; the ground pin of a device's three-contact plug often winds up in contact with nothing but *air*—and that can mean trouble!

Because grounding methods do not completely assure safety, two new approaches to the problem have sprung up. First is *double insulation*—a method of building new tools and electrically powered devices, in which electrical parts are completely insulated from any metal parts liable to be contacted by the user. Also, the device is housed in a completely nonconductive housing. Second is a new type of safety unit that works with *any* electrical device, old or new, double insulated or not; it's called a *ground-fault interrupter* (or gfi for short).

The gfi has three forms—it may be part of the electrical power box that supplies current to various outlets in your home, it may be a replacement outlet that fits in where the old outlet used to be, or it may be a plug-in accessory that you use between a present outlet and the device with which you're working.

Regardless of how it's physically made, all gfi's work the same. They monitor the current flowing through the hot wire to a device and the current flowing through the "neutral" wire of the device. These currents are compared and should always be the same. If the current through the hot wire *exceeds* the current through the

Figure 40-2. Ground-fault protection circuitry can be built into individual duplex receptacles or into circuit breakers that can protect several receptacles. Photograph courtesy of Leviton Manufacturing Company, Inc.

neutral wire by as little as *five thousandths of an ampere* (that's .005 ampere, or 5 milliamperes, which is about 1/30th of the current it takes to light a flashlight bulb), the gfi immediately switches off power to the device it's serving. Why? Because the gfi "knows" that any excess current is passing to ground via a pathway *other than the neutral wire!* That could mean a short or fault in the device you're using, and the path *could* be through your body to ground. Thus, the gfi will not allow current to reach deadly levels where electrocution is possible. It disengages power before a malfunction can allow current of deadly proportions to flow; and it does so in 1/40th of a second—faster than you can blink your eyes!

HOW THEY WORK

The ability of the gfi to detect imbalance in the current flow through the hot and neutral wires of a 120-volt AC outlet stems from use of a *differential current transformer*. This sounds imposing, but it's actually just a device that has a few turns of wire, wound on a core of magnetic material. There are three such windings—one for the hot wire, a second one for the neutral wire, and a third one that leads to some special solid-state circuitry. Here's what happens: The transformer is arranged so that if equal currents flow through the two supply wires, voltages are induced in the third winding that *cancel*. But, if the current through the hot winding is greater than that through the neutral winding, there *will* be a voltage output to the solid-state circuitry through the third winding. Instantly, the circuitry will react, activating a *ground-trip solenoid* (a mechanical device that is like a switch, but can be electronically activated). The solenoid opens contacts, so that power in the hot wire cannot reach the outlet and, thus, can't reach the tool or device you're holding.

For periodic checking (as required by the National Electrical Code) all gfi's have a built-in test button. You push this every month or so and an internal circuit in the gfi momentarily takes from the hot wire a little more current than that which flows through the neutral wire. This should cause the gfi to trip. If it doesn't, the gfi is not working correctly (a rare, but possible, condition) and needs replacement. In most cases, you'll simply push in a reset button and continue to use your gfi for electrical protection.

Of course, if you are using your gfi and it *should* trip, don't assume that it's not working properly. Chances are, the tool or device you're using has a fault that could be dangerous. Don't disbelieve the gfi's warning—have the tool checked, no matter how inconvenient it may be to stop what you're doing. The gfi may have saved your life.

WHAT'S AVAILABLE

There are three basic types of gfi's—*circuit breaker, wall receptacle*, and *portable*. This family of types has come about because of different needs and requirements. Here is a rundown on each type.

Circuit-Breaker GFI's

If your home has a circuit-breaker box at the main power panel (rather than an old-fashioned fuse box), you can replace it with this type of gfi. It will serve the dual purpose of breaking on large-scale overload currents, *as well as* ground-fault currents. The interesting feature of this type is its ability to extend ground-fault protection to *any outlet receptacle served by the branch circuit that feeds through this device.* Thus, by replacing one standard breaker, you can provide "instant" ground-fault protection at several locations in your home, providing that power reaches those locations through a common branch. That's the "good" news. The "bad" news is that there are numerous incidental (or leakage) current paths that naturally occur in the best of wiring systems. Wires, like all electrical conductors, have the property of *capacitance*, which simply means that a perfectly well-insulated, hot conductor, carrying alternating current, can transfer a minute current to another conductor (such as a grounded conduit or another wire), just because it's in close proximity. The degree of transfer is slight, but it accumulates with the length of the branch wiring and the number of electrical devices on the entire branch being served. And so, a circuit-breaker-type gfi "sees" the accumulated leakage of *all* the circuits it serves. This means that the tolerance of the gfi is reduced. If normal "leakage" of the branch is 3 milliamperes and the gfi is set to trip out at 5, plugging in a device that has a slight leakage of 2 milliamperes will cause the gfi to trip. This means a long walk to the circuit breaker box to reset the tripped gfi. It can also lead to disenchantment with the very real benefits of ground-fault protection. There is no such thing as a free lunch, and a circuit-breaker type of gfi should be used only to protect *dedicated* circuits (to swimming pool pumps, patio lights, etc.) where the natural "leakage" of the branch is not so great that it will eat up the gfi's tolerance.

Wall-Receptacle GFI's

This protective device is designed to replace a standard duplex receptacle in shop, kitchen, bathroom, or outdoor application. It fits within a standard NEMA outlet box and protects *only* against ground faults in a device plugged into it. The advantage here is that any natural "leakage" in the branch circuit leading to it is ignored. In terms of convenience, this type of gfi can be reset at the same

location at which it trips; and, since it protects *one* outlet, rather than an entire branch circuit, its tripping won't plunge other sections of the house into darkness. This gfi type is a good choice for swimming pool owners, as well as for bathroom or shop, or wherever you desire maximum protection of a limited area of electrical device use.

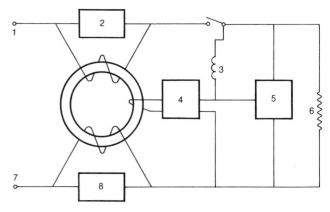

1 HOT	5 RESET CIRCUIT
2 TRANSIENT SUPPRESSOR	6 LOAD
3 CIRCUIT BREAKER	7 NEUTRAL
4 SENSE CIRCUIT	8 TRANSIENT SUPPRESSOR

Figure 40-3. A ground fault is a current leak from the hot side of the line through a path that bypasses the load. The gfi senses the imbalance and activates a trip to open the line.

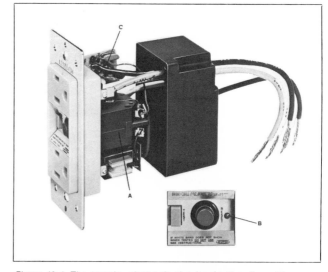

Figure 40-4. The complex electronic circuitry for the gfi must be so designed that it requires no more behind-the-panel space than the standard nonprotected receptacle. Photograph courtesy of Leviton Manufacturing Company, Inc.

228

To provide extended-area coverage, feed-through, receptacle-type gfis are also available. The use of these will be described later.

Portable GFI's

Whether or not you have "dedicated" gfi's protecting branches or selected outlets in your home, a portable gfi is a sensible investment for anyone who uses electrically powered tools outdoors or in the basement or garage. In practical terms, there is no way that you can prevent your body from coming in contact with the earth or conductive surfaces that are electrically the same as the earth when working in any of these environments. A damp concrete floor is an electrical *ground;* so is the soil you may be walking on while pushing an electric mower or using an electric saw or drill; and even if the tool you're using has been quality-engineered, the possibility always exists that a fault may occur, making *you* a part of a lethal electrical circuit. Portable gfi's are designed to give you that extra bit of protection against just such a fault. Plugged into an outlet, a portable gfi will trip if any device plugged into *it* shows a ground fault. In effect, a portable gfi just about nullifies any shock hazard in the use of electrical devices. It goes where you go, and you use it where you need it.

TIPS FOR USING YOUR GFI

When you consider the number of electrical devices in use today, the possibility of failure isn't so remote as it may seem. That's why the National Electrical Code now *requires* use of gfi's for protection of outdoor electrical circuits near swimming pools, as well as in bathrooms, kitchens, hospitals, and at construction sites. The simple truth is that the gfi has proven its ability to prevent needless loss of human life in much the same way that fuses (and later, circuit breakers) have protected buildings from the ravages of fire caused by gross electrical failures.

To anyone who has ever overloaded an electrical device (running an electrical drill to "stall" while drilling, using an outdoor power tool to the limits of its ability, etc.) the possibility of failure has certainly flashed through your mind. If so, the use of a gfi to protect you and your loved ones from the real hazard of an electrical fault should prompt you to buy and use one of the approved types now offered today.

Circuit-Breaker GFI's

If you've recently added an electrical circuit to serve a swimming pool, bathroom, or kitchen, you should use a circuit-breaker gfi to protect your family in these sensitive areas. Doing so means replacing an ordinary circuit breaker with a gfi type that combines the fire-protection features of a circuit breaker with the life-protection features of a gfi. What you'll be adding to the circuit-breaker box is the ability to protect your loved ones from deadly electrical shock caused by faulty electrical devices.

Replacing a breaker with a gfi may require the services of a licensed electrician, depending upon the requirements of your local electrical code. However, the task involved is fairly simple. First, find the breaker that serves the electrical branch you want to protect. Note the physical dimensions and the current rating of the breaker. Stop by at your local electrical-supply house and obtain a gfi-type breaker with the same current rating and installation dimensions. Install during daylight hours by turning off the main power switch, removing the standard breaker, and installing the gfi breaker in its place. Be sure to test after installation, following the gfi breaker manufacturer's recommendations.

Receptacle-Type GFI's

You may wish to replace one or more standard duplex outlet receptacles with receptacle-type gfi's to protect against faults in any device plugged into these receptacles. (It's important to note that *only* those devices that are plugged into a receptacle-type gfi are protected unless it is a feed-through type.) What you gain in a gfi of this type is convenience of installation (because the gfi takes the place of a standard outlet receptacle with no built-in protection) plus ease of testing and resetting (because the gfi is close at hand, not hidden away in a power box in the basement or garage).

Alternatively, you can get a *feed-through* receptacle-type gfi. With this type, you can not only gain protection at the receptacle you're replacing, but you can also *extend* this protection to other outlets down-line of the gfi receptacle. To permit this, a feed-through gfi receptacle has two extra wires (or terminals) in addition to the normal three (hot, neutral, and ground). These two extra wires extend *protected* hot and neutral to the next outlets and fixtures in the branch. Thus, by installing a receptacle-type, feed-through gfi on a branch that serves a bathroom, you can extend its protection to lighting fixtures and other outlets that receive their power *through* that gfi. This means that every electrical item in your bathroom can be ground-fault protected with just *one* gfi.

To install a receptacle-type gfi, turn off power to the affected branch circuit (by flipping the branch circuit breaker at the power box or by removing and pocketing the fuse). Next, remove the cover plate screw on the wall receptacle and lay the plate aside. Remove the two long screws that secure the duplex receptacle and pull the receptacle outward for access to its terminal screws.

If the gfi you're installing is a three-wire type, simply

connect hot (black), neutral (white), and ground (green or bare wire) to the appropriate terminals, following the manufacturer's diagram. This type will protect *only* devices that plug into this outlet. Install into the box, taking care to dress wires carefully, and replace the cover plate. Test, as recommended by the manufacturer.

If the gfi you're installing is a feed-through type and you have determined that everything down-line of this box is fed *through* this box, connect the feed-line hot, neutral, and ground to the gfi; then connect its protected hot and neutral feed-through wires to the respective wires that feed the down-line branch circuit. Because of the extra wiring, feed-through types tend to be somewhat bulkier than straight three-wire types. You may find it a tight squeeze to get the wiring, connectors, and other components back into a snug outlet box. Some manufacturers solve this problem by offering stand-off faceplates that bulge the gfi outward from the wall somewhat to give space behind the gfi for the extra wiring bulk. This functional solution is rarely pretty. You'd do well to measure box depth carefully and to compare to the physical requirements of a feed-through gfi before installation, especially if the outlet to be replaced is in a highly visible location. Upon completion of installation, do test as the manufacturer recommends.

Portable GFI's

Apart from plugging one of these into an outlet, there is no installation required. Portables come in several forms. The simplest is a molded case with a three-prong plug on its back. You plug it into an outlet and then plug the device you'll be using into the protected receptacle on the front of the case.

Slightly different are the extension types, in which an extension power cord plugs into an outlet at one end, while the gfi is located at the other end, protecting the receptacle feeding the device you're using. Some, like the Pass & Seymour gfi, feature well-balanced, weatherproof housings with watertight covers in a gfi design that is especially suited to use on outdoor power tools (electric lawn mowers, chain saws, tillers, and hedge trimmers), as well as the usual range of hand tools (electric drills and saws). Portables feature all the test and indicating features of built-ins, but have the great advantage of going wherever you need their protection. And that, in this very electrical world, is just about anywhere that you use something that plugs into the alternating-current power line.

GFI TESTING AND MAINTENANCE

Every gfi has a built-in test button. Its purpose is to give you a quick means of *simulating a ground-fault* so that the gfi's ability to act can be tested at regular intervals. To a generation that has grown up fairly well accustomed to trusting the authoritative action of a fuse or circuit breaker these test provisions may seem a bit strange. After all, if the gfi is to protect you against accidental electrocution from a faulty electrical product, it *should* be reliable. The truth is, however, that the very small accident currents that a gfi is designed to detect will rarely, if ever, be experienced. And so, the National Electrical Code, Canadian Standards Association, and Underwriters Laboratories have established the requirement for built-in test provisions to assure you that your gfi is capable of delivering the protection its manufacturer has promised.

By testing a gfi once every month, you will ensure that you have working protection against accidental ground fault in sensitive areas in and around your home. In the very rare number of cases where the gfi does not test out, you will likely detect a fault in its protection before it is subjected to the crucial test of detecting an actual ground fault where *you* may be part of the electrical circuit. And so, the fault-detection capabilities of the gfi will be confirmed each time you test or will be revealed as defective where a test is flunked. Either way, you win; and in the game of electrical safety, winning is everything!

As to actual maintenance, only the portable gfi requires specific care. It should be protected against physical mistreatment which may affect its internal components, and it should be guarded against the infiltration of moisture and contaminants which may affect insulation resistance. Reasonably prudent care and awareness of the sensitive character of the circuitry within a gfi will help you to avoid the mistreatment that may cause it to fail.

A FINAL WORD

Despite the best efforts of electrical product designers, users of electrical devices continue to experience fatal, or near fatal, shocks every year. No single reason can be pinpointed for this problem. If it could, it would be eliminated through conscientious effort. The simple truth is that *all* electrically powered devices require care in handling so as not to present a hazard to the user. The gfi is a useful device because it can help to mitigate against careless handling or misuse of electrical equipment and wiring. It is a means for taming the lethal power of electricity, so that even if we do something as imprudent as using a power tool outdoors, with bare feet in contact with the earth, we will not pay the consequence of loss of life for having trusted to electrical "luck." This is the strength of the gfi. It holds the same potential for improving electrical safety that fuses and circuit breakers have established in fire safety.

41

Portable AC Generators

The gasoline that powers an internal combustion engine releases energy directly in the form of *heat*. This, in turn, is converted to *mechanical energy* by the orchestrated operation of the engine's parts. That mechanical energy is put to immediate use in gas engine-powered tools that whirl, cut, chomp, and chew. But there are, by far, more *electrically powered* tools and devices in this world than those mechanical gadgets that can be directly powered by gasoline. Designed for operation from the standard 120-volt, 60-hertz (formerly called cycles) alternating current power line, everyday electrical devices include not only a host of shop and garden tools, but TV sets, radios, steam irons, hair dryers, mixers, toasters, blenders, vacuum cleaners, refrigerators, lighting, and many, many more of the household appliances that do so much to ease our daily workload and enhance our enjoyment of modern living. All, however, share an umbilical attachment to the home power outlet: You can't take 'em with you, unless you have some way to feed them the electrical power they need.

A *portable AC generator* is a positive answer to the need for powering electrical tools and devices where a power line isn't available or has failed. It can supply 120-volt, 60-hertz, alternating current power to operate standard electrical items in the backyard or on the back forty. That's why it has become such a popular item with homeowners, campers, ranchers, and farmers.

Figure 41-2. Gasoline-driven, portable AC generators provide on-the-spot electrical energy to power electrically powered tools, heaters, lights, refrigerators, TV sets, and a host of other electrically operated devices designed for operation from the standard 120-volt, 60-hertz, AC power line. GRAF-WHALEN photograph.

Figure 41-1. Portable AC generator. GRAF-WHALEN photograph.

HOW THEY WORK

The portable AC generator has its own built-in gas engine. It burns gasoline to produce heat energy, converts this to mechanical energy, and then takes it one step further by converting the mechanical energy into electrical energy. Like a tiny "power station," this compact portable serves up closely regulated electrical power that can operate any home electrical gadget in the wilderness.

In this popular design, the internal combustion engine crankshaft rotates a pair of magnets with magnetized north (N) and south (S) areas. The magnets are arranged so that their (N and S) poles always lie in opposition to each other. Between each such pair of poles is a magnetic field, and in that field, a coiled-up, wire ribbon is supported. As the magnets are rotated at high speed, the magnetic field between them "cuts" through the ribbon coil, alternately pulling and pushing the free electrons within the coil. This creates the electrical "pressure" (called *voltage*), because the field's pull-and-push creates a surplus of electrons at one terminal of the coil, while it creates a scarcity at the other. If an electrical device is connected between the two ends of the coil, current will flow through it, as the electrons attempt to flow from the side where there are too many to the side where there are too few. Because the magnets are rotating and because the coil is shaped specifically, the pull and push *alternate*, so that current flows first in one direction and then in the other. And so, this generator furnishes *alternating current*, like that available from your household power outlet. The speed of the engine is governed so that the *frequency* (rate at which the current reverses) is closely held to 60 times (or *cycles*) per second. The power output of the generator is the product of its voltage and current. And so, at 120 volts, with a maximum current of 12.5 amperes, the generator has an output rating of 1,500 watts. Because its power output rates its capacity to do work, the engine that drives it must also be doing work. This can be found by a simple relationship: *746 watts = 1 horsepower*. And so, the engine must furnish at least 2 horsepower to obtain the full, rated electrical power output from the generator. In practice, the engine will be rated at somewhat greater horsepower to account for inescapable losses in the conversion of mechanical energy (horsepower) into electrical energy (watts). Typical efficiencies range from 60 to 70 percent.

WHAT'S AVAILABLE

Portable AC generators are especially compact members of a larger family of gas-driven power plants. The distinguishing features of portables are their compactness, relatively low weight (ranging from about 60 to 130 pounds), and comparatively small engine ratings (about 3 to 7 horsepower). In this range, output electrical power ratings range from 1,500 watts for the smallest models to 3,500 watts for the huskiest models. All are compact enough to take with you in the trunk of a full-size car, to stow in a camper, or to keep handy in the garage or toolshed for those times when you need convenient power or as a backup generator to furnish essential power if commercial power goes out in a storm.

Figure 41-4. A properly located, single carrying handle provides a sure, safe grip when the heavy generator is transported. GRAF-WHALEN photograph.

NO ARMATURE, NO BRUSHES

STATOR

STATIONARY RIBBON COILS

ELECTRIC POWER GOES DIRECTLY FROM COILS TO RECEPTACLE

MAGNETIZED AREAS

CERAMIC MAGNETS ROTATE

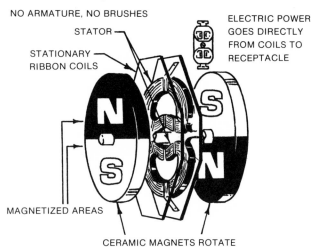

Figure 41-3. The internal combustion engine's crankshaft rotates two powerful permanent magnets at a controlled high speed, so their magnetic field "cuts" through stationary coils between them. This produces an alternating voltage between the ends of the coil that is made available at the AC outlets of the generators.

IMPORTANT FEATURES TO LOOK FOR
Size and Weight
Design and construction play an important part in determining the shape and bulk of the end product. Those that have the construction described earlier require much smaller anti-vibration mounts than other types. This reduces size. However, physical size alone should never be the single determinant of the generator you purchase.

Power Output in Watts
This is the real key to buying the right generator, and you should determine the need for the maximum power you will require well in advance of considering physical size; the table below will help. It lists the wattages consumed by various home and farm electrical devices. Look up the wattages of devices you intend to power. If more than one will be powered at a time, add their wattages

Power Requirements of Common Electrical Devices

Appliance	Average Wattage Rating	Appliance	Average Wattage Rating
Air cleaner	50	Milk pump	200 (and higher)
Air conditioner (room)	1500	Milking machine	250 (and higher)
Barn cleaner	1500 (and higher)	Mixer	125
Barn fan	125 (and higher)	Oil burner or stoker	265
Bed covering	175	Oven (microwave)	1450
Blender	390	Paint sprayer	600
Broiler	1450	Radio	70
Carving knife	120	Radio/record player	100
Clock	2	Range with oven	12,200
Clothes dryer	4850	Refrigerator	
Coffee maker	900	12 cubic feet	340
Deep fryer	1450	12 cubic feet, frostless	360
Dehumidifier	250	Refrigerator/freezer	
Dishwasher	1200	14 cubic feet	420
Drill press	700	14 cubic feet, frostless	600
Egg cooker	500	Roaster	1300
Electric brooder	100 (and higher)	Sandwich grill	1150
Electric drill	75	Sewing machine	75
Electric lawn mower	600	Soldering iron	25 (and higher)
Electric shaver	10	Steam iron	300
Fans		Sun lamp	275
Attic	370	Television	
Furnace	290	Black and white	
Window	200	Tube type	160
Feed conveyor	375 (and higher)	Solid state	55
Floor polisher	300	Color	
Food mixer	150	Tube type	300
Freezer		Solid state	200
15 cubic feet	340	Toaster	1150
15 cubic feet, frostless	440	Trash compactor	400
Frying pan	1200	Vacuum cleaner	630
Grill	1300	Waffle iron	1100
Hair dryer	1000	Washing machine	
Heater (portable)	1320	Automatic	500
Heating pad	65	Nonautomatic	280
Hot plate	1250	Waste disposer	440
Humidifier	175	Water heater	
Iron (hand)	1000	Standard	2475
Lathe	600	Quick recovery	4475
Milk cooler	500 (and higher)	Water pump	460

together. Next, add a safety factor of 20 percent to account for variations in load presented to the generator by different devices during start-up. The total wattage you sum up will be the wattage needed. Buy the generator that has the nearest, *higher* wattage rating. (That is, if you add up a need for 1,600 watts output, don't try to get by with a 1,500-watt generator. You'll shorten its life and always be unhappy with portable power, because the normal load exceeds the generator's capacity. Rather, buy a 2,000-watt generator. It will run smoother for longer, with fewer maintenance problems, because it has reserve capacity beyond the needed power.)

Noise Level
The engine that furnishes drive power to the generator will be running for prolonged periods in some cases. Choose a unit with an effective muffler system that reduces engine noise to the lowest practical level. Consider *where* and *when* you will be using your generator. If it will be running in a location that's far from earshot of you or your neighbors, noise level is not so important. But, if you will use it within 100 feet of your own location or that of your neighbors, get the quietest design you can find.

Fuel Capacity
Too small a fuel capacity means annoying stop-and-go refueling periods. At a minimum, your generator should run for at least 90 minutes at rated power output on a single fueling.

Figure 41-5. SEARS CRAFTSMAN LONG-RUN POWER PLANT® provides electricity for extended periods of time when used with its auxiliary fuel tank. This 3,000-watt model provides 120- and 240-volt, 60-hertz AC, as well as up to 8 ampere at 12-volt DC for charging vehicle batteries. GRAF-WHALEN photograph.

Interference
You may wish to power radio or TV equipment from your generator. If so, be sure that the ignition system of its engine has the latest interference-suppression devices, so that the generator does not become a source of electrical interference in the area of use.

Electrical Outlets and Extra Features
To simplify connecting of the generator to the device it will power, built-in AC outlets are provided. These are the same as standard duplex receptacles found in your home's wall outlets, in those generators designed to give 120-volt, 60-hertz, AC output. Some generators provide more than one outlet, but remember that the *total power* delivered to *all* devices plugged into these outlets must not exceed the generator's output wattage rating. For short-circuit protection, look for fuses or a circuit breaker. Also, if you need to charge batteries from time to time, you may want to consider a generator that provides 12-volt DC output, too. Some generators can provide up to 8 amps of charging power for batteries in outdoor equipment, RVs, and remote equipment. This is a real convenience where on-the-spot battery recharging is necessary in an out-of-the-way location.

TIPS FOR USING YOUR PORTABLE AC GENERATOR
A portable AC generator is a great convenience in powering outdoor tools, such as electric trimmers, electric mowers, farm machines, and for the comfort of electrical home conveniences while camping. The setup of a portable is simple: Choose a fairly level surface in the open air; fill the gas tank with clean, fresh, regular-grade gasoline; and be sure to check the engine crankcase for proper lubricant level. (Typically, SAE 30 is used in summer, while SAE 5W-20 or 5W-30 is the choice for winter operation.)

Starting
Some models have a fuel shut-off valve. This must be opened to allow fuel to reach the carburetor of the engine. (It is normally closed for safety, either when shutting off the generator engine or when the generator is in transit, to prevent fuel spillage.) For easy starting, unplug any devices from the generator's outlets or turn their power switches off. (It is very difficult to start a generator when a load is connected.) Next, close the choke (if cold starting) and operate the generator's starting mechanism (typically, a pull-rope starter). Once the engine starts, allow slight warm-up; then, gradually, ease the choke to the open position.

Running

Once the engine has come up to speed, the generator will be providing full output to the outlets. You may now plug in or turn on the electrical devices to be powered by the generator. If current drain is substantial, you may notice a variation in the engine sound at start-up, as the generator commences to supply power to the load. This should smooth out as current flow stabilizes.

Figure 41-6. The choke must be closed if you are cold-starting the generator. It is then gradually eased to an open position as the engine warms up. GRAF-WHALEN photograph.

Figure 41-7. Most portable generators include a quick-stop feature in the form of a lever that shorts the spark plug, thus depriving the engine of ignition voltage and causing it to stop. GRAF-WHALEN photograph.

Refueling

If gasoline runs out, the generator engine will stop. Cautiously refuel, remembering that the engine is still warm and will cause the flammable fuel to volatize on contact. Restart without the choke, remembering to disconnect the plug of the device being powered so as not to increase starting effort. There is danger in refueling a generator while it is running, and it is wisest to allow fuel to run out and the generator to stop before adding fuel.

Generator Stop

Most portables include a quick-stop feature to permit rapid shutoff of the generator should trouble occur. This is usually a lever that momentarily shorts the engine spark plug, thus depriving the engine of ignition voltage and causing it to stop. The preferred method of stopping is to unplug the load and allow the engine to run for a few minutes, so as to reduce its operating temperature before shutoff.

Battery Recharging

If the portable you're using includes a battery-recharge feature, proceed in the following manner: Connect the positive terminal of the battery to the positive terminal of the generator and the negative terminal of the battery to the negative terminal of the generator. Start the engine. The battery will receive an initial high charge of several amperes, reducing to a "trickle" as the battery comes up to strength over a period of time. Check charge state with a hydrometer.

RULES FOR SAFE USE

• Never operate the generator in an enclosed space; provide adequate ventilation. Gasoline engines give off deadly carbon monoxide, which can be lethal if inhaled.
• Never fill the gas tank while the engine is running or in the dark. Gasoline spillage on a hot engine can cause fire or an explosion.
• Alternators produce lethal voltages and should be treated with respect.
• Comply with laws governing the storage of gasoline.
• Maintain power cords in good condition. Bare or frayed wires can cause dangerous electrical shock.
• Check engine oil level each time you fill the gas tank.
• Never attempt to change engine speed without proper knowledge and equipment. Incorrect engine rpm is not only dangerous, but can damage the alternator or the equipment it powers.
• Study the contents of the manufacturer's manual carefully before operating your generator.

AC GENERATOR MAINTENANCE
Lubrication
Most generators require periodic engine oil change to ensure good lubrication (usually after every 25 hours of operation). Also, it will be necessary to wash the carburetor air-cleaner in gasoline to free it of airborne dirt and particles; then re-oil. The manufacturer's manual will specify the exact lubrication requirement of your generator model.

Spark Plug
About every 100 operating hours you should remove the spark plug of your generator's engine and clean it with a wire brush to remove combustion deposits. If necessary, square up the electrodes and regap (typically, to .030 inch) with a feeler gauge. Alternatively, you can replace the plug with a properly gapped new plug at 100-hour intervals to be sure of efficient ignition and full power output.

Transport
If your generator provides a fuel shut-off valve and tight-fitting gas-tank cap, you can transport your unit after taking all precautions to prevent fuel spillage. Alternatively, siphon any residual fuel from the gas tank to prevent hazardous fuel spills.

Storage
Your generator should not be stored with fuel in the tank because gas goes "stale" and releases waxy residues over prolonged storage periods. The danger is that these residues will find their way into the carburetor, causing blockage and no-start problems, necessitating messy cleanup operations. Before "mothballing" your generator, run the engine to use up any residual fuel; then sponge up any leftovers by wrapping a cloth around a stick and using this to soak up any excess in the tank. Discard the cloth safely afterward. To lubricate the engine properly during storage, remove the spark plug and pour into its hole one tablespoon of SAE 30 oil. Replace the plug and pull the starter several times to distribute an oil film over the engine cylinder and piston.

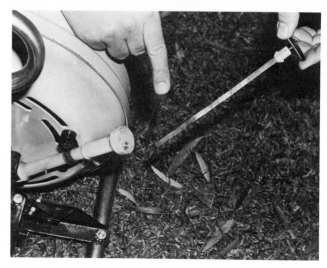

Figure 41-8. Check the oil level at regular intervals. When changing the engine oil or just "topping off," use only the proper grade of oil, as specified in the owner's manual. GRAF-WHALEN photograph.

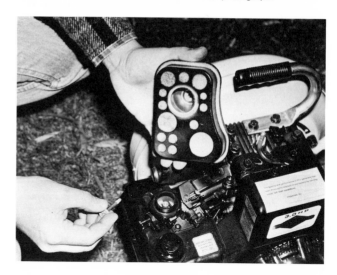

Figure 41-9. Inspect the air filter frequently. Wash it when it becomes clogged to assure a proper air-fuel mixture for efficient operation of the generator. GRAF-WHALEN photograph.

Index